THE PENGUIN CLASSICS

EDITED BY E. V. RIEU

L22

GEOFFREY CHAUCER

The Canterbury Tales

TRANSLATED
INTO MODERN ENGLISH
BY NEVILL COGHILL

PENGUIN BOOKS
BALTIMORE · MARYLAND

THIS EDITION FIRST PUBLISHED MAY 1952
REPRINTED FEBRUARY 1953
REPRINTED SEPTEMBER 1953
REPRINTED JANUARY 1954
REPRINTED JANUARY 1955
REPRINTED JULY 1955

PENGUIN BOOKS INC
3300 CLIPPER MILL ROAD, BALTIMORE 11, MARYLAND

PRINTED IN THE UNITED STATES OF AMERICA

—

... I have translated some part of his works,
only that I might perpetuate his memory,
or at least refresh it, amongst my country-
men. If I have altered him anywhere for
the better, I must at the same time acknow-
ledge, that I could have done nothing with-
out him....

JOHN DRYDEN on translating Chaucer
Preface to the Fables
1700

And such as Chaucer is, shall Dryden be.

ALEXANDER POPE
Essay on Criticism
1711

PREFACE TO THE AMERICAN EDITION

As all Chaucerians know, the great advances of the past fifty years in Chaucer scholarship owe much to the work of American scholars, too numerous to name, too distinguished to need naming. It is a pleasure to acknowledge my continual indebtedness to their learning; let no faults that may be detected in my version be laid at their door. In this edition some passages which, upon reflection, seemed to me faulty or inelegant in the first (English) edition, I have sought to improve.

I have another debt of gratitude to pay; four happy visits to America, particularly to American Universities, have made me many friends and pleasant memories. If, as I hope, American readers find pleasure in my version of Chaucer's masterpiece, I shall feel I have done something in return for many hospitalities.

N. C.

CONTENTS

7

Contents

INTRODUCTION

I

Chaucer's Life

GEOFFREY CHAUCER was born about the year 1340; the exact date is not known. His father, John, and his grandfather, Robert, had associations with the wine trade and, more tenuously, with the Court. John was Deputy Butler to the King at Southampton in 1348. Geoffrey Chaucer's mother is believed to have been Agnes de Copton, niece of an official at the Mint. They lived in London in the parish of St. Martin's-in-the-Vintry, reasonably well-to-do but in a humbler walk of life than that to be adorned so capably by their brilliant son.

It is thought that Chaucer was sent for his early schooling to St. Paul's Almonry. From there he went on to be a page in the household of the Countess of Ulster, later Duchess of Clarence, wife of Lionel the third son of Edward III. The first mention of Geoffrey Chaucer's existence is in her household accounts for 1357. She had bought him a short cloak, a pair of shoes and some parti-colored red and black breeches.

To be a page in a family of such eminence was a coveted position. His duties as a page included making beds, carrying candles and running errands. He would there have acquired the finest education in good manners, a matter of great importance not only in his career as a courtier but also in his career as a poet. No English poet has so mannerly an approach to his reader.

As a page he would wait on the greatest in the land. One of these was the Duke of Lancaster, John of Gaunt; throughout his life he was Chaucer's most faithful patron and protector.

In 1359 Chaucer was sent abroad, a soldier in the egg, on one of those intermittent forays into France that made up so large a part of the Hundred Years' War. He was taken prisoner near Rheims and ransomed in the following year; the King himself contributed towards his ransom. Well-trained and intelligent pages did not grow on every bush.

It is not known for certain when Chaucer began to write poetry, but it is reasonable to believe that it was on his return from France. The elegance of French poetry and its thrilling doctrines of *Amour Courtois** seem to have gone to his impressionable, amorous and poetical heart. He set to work to translate the gospel of that kind of love and poetry, the *Roman de la Rose*, a thirteenth-century French poem begun by Guillaume de Lorris and later completed by Jean de Meun.

Meanwhile he was promoted as a courtier. In 1367 he was attending on the King himself and was referred to as *Dilectus Valettus noster* ... our dearly beloved Valet. It was towards that year that Chaucer married. His bride was Philippa de Roet, a lady in attendance on the Queen, and sister to Catherine Swynford, third wife of John of Gaunt.

Chaucer wrote no poems to her; it was not in fashion to write poems to one's wife. It could even be debated whether love could ever have a place in marriage; the typical situation in which a 'courtly lover' found himself was to be plunged in a secret, an illicit and even an adulterous passion for some seemingly unattainable and pedestalized lady. Before his mistress a lover was prostrate, wounded to death by her beauty, killed by her disdain, obliged to an illimitable constancy, marked out for her dangerous service. A smile from her was in theory a gracious reward for twenty years of painful adoration. All Chaucer's heroes regard love when it comes upon them as the most beautiful of absolute disasters, an agony as much desired as bemoaned, ever to be pursued, never to be betrayed.

This was not in theory the attitude of a husband to his wife. It was for a husband to command, for a wife to obey. The changes that can be rung on these antitheses are to be

* For a rich account of this strange and fascinating cult I would refer the reader to *The Allegory of Love* by C. S. Lewis, O.U.P.

seen throughout *The Canterbury Tales*. If we may judge by
the *Knight's Tale* and the *Franklin's Tale* Chaucer thought
that love and marriage were perhaps compatible after all,
provided that the lover remained his wife's servant after
marriage, in private at least. If we read the *Wife of Bath's
Prologue* we shall see that she thought little of wives that
did not master their husbands. What solution to these prob-
lems was reached by Geoffrey and Philippa Chaucer he
never revealed. He only once alludes to her, or seems to do
so, when in *The House of Fame* he compares the sound of
her voice awaking him in the morning to that of an eagle.
His maturest work is increasingly ironical about women considered as wives; what the Wife of Bath and the Merchant
have to say of them is of this kind. The *Wife of Bath's Prologue* and the *Merchant's Tale* are perhaps his two most astounding performances. By the time he wrote them Philippa
had long been dead. It is in any case by no means certain
that these two characters utter Chaucer's private convictions;
they are speaking for themselves. One can only say that
Chaucer was a great enough writer to lend them unanswera-
ble thoughts and language, to think and speak on their behalf.

The King soon began to employ his beloved valet on important missions abroad. The details of most of these are not
known, but appear to have been of a civilian and commercial nature, dealing with trade relations. We can infer that
Chaucer was trustworthy and efficient.

Meanwhile Chaucer was gratifying and extending his passion for books. He was a prodigious reader and had the art
of storing what he read in an almost faultless memory. He
learned in time to read widely in Latin, French, Anglo-Nor-
man and Italian. He made himself a considerable expert in
contemporary sciences, especially in astronomy, medicine,
physics and alchemy. There is, for instance, in *The House of
Fame* a long and amusing account of the nature of sound-
waves. The *Canon's Yeoman's Tale* (one of the best) shows
an intimate knowledge of alchemical practice. In literary
and historical fields his favorites seem to have been Vergil,

Ovid, Statius, Seneca and Cicero among the ancients, and the *Roman de la Rose* and the works of Dante, Boccaccio and Petrarch among the moderns. He knew the Fathers of the Church and quotes freely and frequently from every book in the Bible and Apocrypha.

Two journeys on the King's business took Chaucer to Italy: the first in 1372 to Genoa, the second in 1378 to Milan. It has always been supposed that these missions were what first brought him in contact with that Renaissance dawn which so glorified his later poetry. While he never lost or disvalued what he had learned from French culture, he added some of the depth of Dante and much of the splendor of Boccaccio, from whom came, amongst other things, the stories of *Troilus and Criseyde* and the *Knight's Tale*. Chaucer's power to tell a story seems to have emerged at this time and to derive from Italy.

Meanwhile he was rising by steady promotions in what we should now call the Civil Service, that is in his offices as a courtier. In 1374 he became Comptroller of customs and subsidies on wools, skins and hides at the Port of London: in 1382 Comptroller of petty customs, in 1385 Justice of the Peace for the county of Kent, in 1386 Knight of the Shire. He was now in some affluence.

But in December 1386 he was suddenly deprived of all his offices. John of Gaunt had left England on a military expedition to Spain and was replaced as an influence on young King Richard II by the Duke of Gloucester. Gloucester had never been a patron of the poet, and filled his posts with his own supporters. We may be grateful to him for this, because he set Chaucer at leisure thereby. It is almost certain that the poet then began to set in order and compose *The Canterbury Tales*.

In 1389 John of Gaunt returned and Chaucer was restored to favor and office. He was put in charge of the repair of walls, ditches, sewers and bridges between Greenwich and Woolwich, and of the fabric of St. George's Chapel at Windsor. The office of Sub-Forester of North Petherton (probably a sinecure) was given him. The daily pitcher of wine allowed him by Edward III in 1374 became, under Richard II, an annual tun. Henry Bolingbroke presented him with a scarlet robe trimmed with fur. Once more he had met with that cheerful good luck which is so happily reflected in his poetry.

He felt himself to be growing old, however; he complained that the faculty of rhyming had deserted him. No one knows when he put his last touch to *The Canterbury Tales*. He never finished them.

He died on the twenty-fifth of October 1400 and was buried in Westminster Abbey. A fine tomb, erected by an admirer in the fifteenth century, marks his grave and was the first of those that are gathered into what we now know as the Poets' Corner. The Father of English Poetry lies in his family vault.*

II

Chaucer's Works

THE order in which Chaucer's works were written is not certain. Some have been lost, if we are to believe the list of them given at the end of *The Canterbury Tales,* in the 'retractions' made by the poet. His main surviving poems are:

Before 1372 part at least of a translation of the *Roman de la Rose, The Book of the Duchess,* and the *ABC of the Virgin.*

Between 1372 and 1382 *The House of Fame, The Parliament of Fowls,* and most probably a number of stories or preliminary versions of stories that were later included in *The Canterbury Tales.* Among these I incline to place the *Second Nun's Tale,* the *Clerk of Oxford's Tale,* much of the *Monk's Tale,* the *Man of Law's Tale,* the *Tale of Melibeus* and the *Knight's Tale.* These seem to indicate a phase of moral and pious interest, qualified by an intense feeling for

* For a somewhat fuller account of Chaucer's life and poetry than can here be given, reference is offered to my volume in the Home University Library series called *The Poet Chaucer.*

the romantic and by increasing touches of wit and personal observation.

The House of Fame and *The Parliament of Fowls* are longish allegorical fantasies of much humor and delicacy. They contain passages of that rich conversation in verse which it is one of Chaucer's peculiar powers to invent, and in both poems the poet himself appears in person as a plump simpleton, much as he does in *The Canterbury Tales.* It was his pose to regard himself with a mild mockery.

Between 1380 and 1385 *Troilus and Criseyde* and the translation of Boethius, *De Consolatione Philosophiae,* were completed. The latter is the main basis of most of Chaucer's philosophical speculations, especially those on tragedy and predestination, which underlie its twin, *Troilus and Criseyde.*

This poem, the most poignant love-story in English narrative poetry, is also one of the most amusing. It is his first great masterpiece, yet for all its humor can stand comparison with any tragic love-story in the world. Its psychological understanding is so subtle and its narrative line so skillfully ordered that it has been called our first novel. It appears to have given some offense to Queen Anne of Bohemia (Richard's wife) because it seemed to imply that women were more faithless than men in matters of love. Chaucer was bidden to write a retraction and so in the following year (1386) he produced a large installment of *The Legend of the Saints of Cupid* (all female), which is also known as *The Legend of Good Women.* He never finished it. His disciple Lydgate said later that it encumbered his wits to think of so many good women.

From 1386 or '87 onwards he was at work on *The Canterbury Tales.* There are some 84 MSS and early printed editions by Caxton, Pynson, Wynkyn de Worde and Thynne.

These manuscripts show that Chaucer left ten fragments of varying size of this great poem. Modern editors have arranged these in what appears to be the intended sequence, inferred from dates and places mentioned in the 'end-links,' as the colloquies of the pilgrims between tales are called.

For convenience these manuscript fragments are numbered in Groups from A to I; Group B can be subdivided into two, making ten Groups in all.

If we may trust the *Prologue*, Chaucer intended that each of some thirty pilgrims should tell two tales on the way to Canterbury and two on the way back. He never completed this immense project, and what he wrote was not finally revised even so far as it went. There are also one or two minor inconsistencies which a little revision could have rectified.

In this rendering I have followed the accepted order first worked out by Furnivall (1868) and later confirmed by Skeat (1894). It makes a reasonably continuous and consistent narrative of a pilgrimage that seems to have occupied five days (April 16 to 20) and that led to the outskirts of Canterbury. At that point Chaucer withdrew from his task with an apology for whatever might smack of sin in his work.

The idea of a collection of tales diversified in style to suit their tellers and unified in form by uniting the tellers in a common purpose is Chaucer's own. Collections of stories were common at the time, but only Chaucer hit on this simple device for securing natural probability, psychological variety and a wide range of narrative interest.

In all literature there is nothing that touches or resembles the *Prologue*. It is the concise portrait of an entire nation, high and low, old and young, male and female, lay and clerical, learned and ignorant, rogue and righteous, land and sea, town and country; but without extremes. Apart from the stunning clarity, touched with nuance, of the characters presented, the most noticeable thing about them is their normality. They are the perennial progeny of men and women. Sharply individual, together they make a party.

The tales these pilgrims tell come from all over Europe, many of them from the works of Chaucer's near contemporaries. Some come from further afield, from the ancients, from the Orient. They exemplify the whole range of contemporary European imagination, then particularly addicted to stories, especially to stories that had some sharp point and deducible maxim, moral, or idea. Almost every tale ends with a piece of proverbial or other wisdom derived from it and with a general benediction on the company.

One of the few tales believed to be his own invention is that of the Canon's Yeoman; some have imagined it to be a personal revenge taken by him upon some alchemist who had duped him; be that as it may it is one of the best of the tales. It was not considered the function of a teller of stories in the fourteenth century to invent the stories he told, but to present and embellish them with all the arts of rhetoric for the purposes of entertainment and instruction. Chaucer's choice of story ranges from what he could hear – such as tales of low life in oral circulation, like the *Miller's Tale,* that are known as fabliaux – to what he had read in Boccaccio or other classic masters or in the lives of saints. To quote Dryden once more, ' 'Tis sufficient to say, according to the proverb, that *here is God's plenty.'*

III

The Present Translation

I was brought up to hold that the classics should be the jealously guarded preserve of scholarship and that any effort to abate the rigors of the game to please a popular audience must at least lower the standards of accuracy and might well damage the reputation of the classic concerned. There is much justice in this view, but I have come to think it possible and right to try to extend the pleasures of Chaucer to a wider public without offense to serious scholarship.

Even rigorists concede a place for translations from foreign languages. The English Bible is among the chief glories of our literature. But when it comes to a translation from an earlier kind of English into a modern kind it can be argued that it is wrong, even morally wrong, for it is not only doomed to some measure of inaccuracy but is also a pandering to laziness; any Englishman who is willing to take the trouble can read Chaucer for himself in the original.

While I feel some force in this contention, I do not think it strictly true. In the first place the pressure of contemporary life seems greatly to have increased upon us and many who would be willing to take the pains to read him in the original are insufficiently at leisure to do so; secondly the original is not really so easy as all that. These, then, must be my excuses for attempting as accurately and as faithfully as I can to present Chaucer in contemporary speech, I would also plead that there is good precedent; Dryden, Pope, Wordsworth, to mention no others, have all tried their hand.

There have also been innumerable 'modernizers' whom I do not count as translators, that have presented Chaucer to the general public on the principle of retaining his actual words and word-order wherever it could be supposed that an uninstructed reader would understand them, and substituting more modern phrases here and there, or sometimes a marginal note, when Chaucer's actual words were out of currency. This method (which I began by trying) appears to me to have every disadvantage. It wrecks the verse-movement and often the rhyme, and presents Chaucer's work as a conflict of styles, partly archaic and partly modern, a language that has never been spoken by anybody. This is the highest treason to Chaucer, the natural and speech-like harmony of whose verse is one of its most distinguishing features. He wrote no 'gallimaufry or hodge-podge.' An annotated translation in semi-archaic idiom will not do. I have therefore treated his poem as any true translator would treat a classic in a foreign tongue, that is with fidelity not to the form of a word but to idiom and the wealth of meaning in a word, and also to the tone of voice or manner in which the meaning is conveyed. My first hope is that the result may be considered as a poem and not as a crib.

In the course of working I found that certain rules formed themselves for me and I hope it may be of interest if I state them in order:

(1) Always to follow Chaucer's metrical forms and rhyme-schemes exactly, with this exception that I have not always copied his occasional trick of dropping the first short syllable of a five-foot iambic line, as in his line describing the Knight:

(ᵛ) Ál | bĭsmót- | erĕd wíth | hĭs háb- | ĕrgeóun

(2) To avoid as far as possible a kind of rhyme that is no longer pleasing to an English, though it is to a French ear, such as *privity* and *honesty*. Chaucer accepts this as a rhyme, but we do not.

(3) To strive for as much meaning as would be given in an accurate, idiomatic prose-translation line for line and thought for thought, or, where the exigencies of rhyme and meter put this task beyond me, to lose as little of Chaucer's meaning as possible and to add as little as possible of my own. If at the command of rhyme or meter I have had to add some touch not actually present in the original, I have been careful that it should only be of the slightest, not indulging in the often delightful embroideries that Dryden permitted himself.

My translation is unexpurgated; the barbarous and (one is almost tempted to say) hypocritical practice of Victorian times in the matter of expurgation has lapsed in our lifetime, and what our greatest authors chose to mean and write need no longer be obscured by dashes, gaps and asterisks.

(4) To follow with an absolute fidelity what may be called 'the tone of voice' of the original, so far as it has lain in my power to hear and reproduce it. This is an aspect of the technique of translation which is peculiarly important with regard to Chaucer, and I would like to explain why.

It is at first sight tempting to say that Chaucer has many styles. But the closer you feel for it the more certainly you realize that underlying every tale and every part in it there is the same mind thinking in its own unique way, the same way of looking at things, and that is what I mean by his style. It is unchanging. I do not only mean that he is at any moment liable to pause for the pleasure of a wonderfully observed description, or of a parallel drawn from the classics, or of a sudden philosophical comment, a neat rhetorical figure, a proverb aptly placed, or a nuance of psychology. I mean an even deeper unity of manner which I can only describe by saying that his tone of voice is always felt to be exactly appropriate to the particular context, whatever it

may be. He has a perfect *tact* towards the idea he is present-
ing. This enables him to express opposite attitudes to the
same theme — such a theme, for instance, as the relations between a man and his wife — with equal sympathy and understanding. These opposite opinions are entertained and made
credible, though seeming to come in all sincerity from the
same mind, in virtue of Chaucer's variable manner or tone
of voice, varied as it were by a kind of poetical politeness of
a very wide range that is nevertheless always within the
scope of a single master style.

Now this politeness towards his subjects is related to
Chaucer's even more fundamental politeness towards his
readers, a trait in him more prominent than in any other
writer, as I have said. There was a historical reason for it:
when Chaucer was writing, the publication of a work was
effected in one of two ways. It was either copied laboriously
by a scribe in manuscript or it was read aloud to an assembled company. Very often, no doubt, the latter method
came first and led to an order for a copy. Now we know that
Chaucer used to read his poems aloud to the royal court;
there is a glorious illumination to a fifteenth-century manuscript of his *Troilus and Criseyde,* recently published as
the frontispiece to the illustrated edition of Dr. G. M. Tre-
velyan's book *English Social History,* which shows Chaucer
in a little pulpit that is placed in a garden beneath a towered palace, and surrounded by noble listeners who include
King Richard II and his Queen, Anne of Bohemia.

With an audience of a refinement such as was theirs, in a
society where good manners and fluency of good conversation were esteemed among the highest graces in social behavior, it would not be surprising if Chaucer, ever sensitive
to these things, wrote his poems with full consciousness of a
present audience, of the fact that he would soon be speaking
his verses with his own voice to a gathering of the highest in
the land, many of whom were also his personal and friendly
acquaintances, his very friends perhaps and one of them his
wife.* More than once he breaks off in a tale to address his

---

* But she died before most of *The Canterbury Tales* were
written.

hearers personally, for instance in the *Man of Law's Tale:*

> O quenes, livinge in prosperitee,
> Duchesses and ye ladies everichone,
> Haveth som routhe on hir adversitee!

These circumstances are what I think gave or encouraged in him that humane and variable tone of voice within the general scope of his style or way of thinking and taught him how to manage conversation in rhymed verse as no other English poet has ever managed it. What could be more nobly romantic and yet more like the genuine language of a dying prince than the last speech of Arcita in the *Knight's Tale?* And yet the same Arcita, on another occasion, can use a slang expression quite as naturally in the heat of argument:

> Love is a gretter lawe, by my pan,
> Than may be yeve to any erthly man.

'By my pan' is the slang expression, meaning literally 'by my brain-pan.' I have ventured to translate this couplet as follows:

> Love is a law unto itself. My hat!
> What earthly man can have more law than that?

It will be seen at once that I have faintly turned the sentence round in order to accommodate the thought to the way we speak now and to mirror that essential quality of colloquial utterance in Chaucer's poem. A crib-version could have accurately hobbled along in something like the meter with

> Love is a greater law, by my brain-pán,
> Than may be given to any earthly man.

If anyone does this translation the honor of comparing it with the original he will certainly find many examples of surface infidelity such as the above, but I hope he will find a fidelity more fundamental in compensation. If it be not too tedious I would like to offer one or two more specimens of what I mean. Chaucer often uses the historic present and the second person singular, far more often than we generally care to do today. In this translation I have taken the liberty of sometimes following him in this and sometimes not, entirely according to whether I felt that it made a given passage more readable and speakable or less. I have only used 'thee' and 'thou' in prayers and ironical apostrophes.

I have sometimes knowingly offered mistranslations; for instance there is a couplet describing the Friar in the *Prologue*.

> And certeinly he hadde a mery note;
> Wel coude he singe and pleyen on a rote.

This I have rendered:

> And certainly his voice was gay and sturdy,
> For he sang well and played the hurdy-gurdy.

Now 'rote' does not mean a hurdy-gurdy (which is a stringed instrument of the lute family played by rotating a drum under the strings with the left hand) but a 'crwth' (a stringed instrument of the fiddle family, as unintelligible to a modern reader as a rote itself). To call it a 'fiddle,' however, would have been just as misleading to a post-Stradivarius consciousness as to call it a hurdy-gurdy; and I should have lost the rhyme, the scarcity of which in English is a thing of which Chaucer himself once complained.

It is not only words that go out of date. Ideas do so too often enough, for example the Ptolemaic system of astronomy or the Code of Courtly Love, to both of which Chaucer makes frequent reference. These things will perhaps sound 'quaint' however they are worded, though Chaucer was never 'quaint' to his original hearers. He knew well enough, however, that he would seem 'quaint' to posterity:

> Ye knowe eek, that in forme of speche is chaunge
> With-inne a thousand yeer, and wordes tho
> That hadden prys, now wonder nyce and straunge
> Us thinketh hem; and yet they spake hem so,
> And spedde as wel in love as men now do:

Eek for to winne love in sondry ages,
In sondry londes, sondry ben usages.

(Troilus and Criseyde, Bk. II, Proem)

which may be translated

And then you know, the forms of language change
Within a thousand years, and long ago
Words had a value that will now seem strange
Or even quaint, and yet they spoke them so
And fared as well in love, for aught I know,
As we do now. At various times and places
Men have had various ways to win love's graces.

Finally there are to be mentioned the untranslatable words. Some are technical terms no longer in use, for instance 'limiter,' meaning a Friar whose begging activities are restricted within a certain limit. Any such words that I have been forced to incorporate in my text for want of a modern equivalent are explained in the notes at the end, where there will also be found a minimum of other notes to clarify some of Chaucer's allusions.

But the most untranslatable of all are words which were in common use in Chaucer's day and still are so but with a partially changed meaning. Two outstanding examples are the words 'gentle' and 'free.' Each of these has a variety of shades of meaning in Chaucer, but in the main 'gentle' means what you would expect of a man of good family (Latin *gens*), a certain supposedly hereditary character of kind consideration for others, including what we mean by 'gentleness,' but nearer to our 'magnanimity.' In the middle ages the Latin for a gentleman was *generosus.**

'Freedom' is one of the highest qualities of being a gentle-

---

* On at least two occasions Chaucer is careful to repudiate the idea that this nobility of soul is an hereditary quality. He asserts that it comes from the imitation of Christ, in which opinion he echoes Dante. Nevertheless it is a quality that you have a better chance of having if you are well-born, for a man of good family is accustomed to wealth and responsibility, and taught to respect the code.

man in the sense just defined. It is one of the first things loved and followed by the Knight in the *Prologue*. The nearest equivalent I can think of is 'greatness of heart.' Basically it is the opposite of a crabbed meanness or villein-like behavior. It means doing the fine thing, being open-hearted, having the impulse to give rather than to get. It is the ideal shown in the actions of Arveragus, Aurelius, and the Magician at the end of the *Franklin's Tale*.

Another such deceptive word, which looks as if it meant our 'very,' is Chaucer's 'verray.' There are indeed occasions when 'very' will do for it, but in Chaucer it often means 'true' in the fullest and noblest sense, the sense in which

> Trouthe is the hyeste thing that man may kepe

as Arveragus says in the *Franklin's Tale*. So it happens that one of the most famous lines in the *Prologue,* which anyone might think could be perfectly translated by simply modernizing the spelling, must in fact be rewritten to convey its full meaning, even at the risk of being accused of a wanton and pedantic destruction of a beautiful and familiar music.

> He was a verray parfit gentil knight.

Now 'verray' does not mean 'very,' but 'true'; nor does 'gentil' mean 'gentle' in our ordinary sense of the word. It includes that meaning but also, and more importantly, carries the sense of high breeding and good birth. Consequently it would be seriously misleading to render the line

> He was a very perfect gentle knight.

for the meaning – as near as one can get to it in a single line – is

> He was a true, a perfect gentle-knight.

A translator thus may have to hang his hope on a hyphen.

In conclusion, touching this translation, I have to explain why Chaucer's *Tale of Melibee* and the Parson's sermon on the Seven Deadly Sins appear here only in synopsis. The reason is that there is a physical limit to the length of a book published in this series. To have given an absolutely complete text would have been to go beyond this limit; something therefore had to be cut. I judged it better to cut whole tales rather than bits here and there in a number of tales; and on this assumption I chose these two prose 'tales' for sacrifice. Both are examples of Chaucer's prose at its best. But in my opinion his prose at its best is less than his verse at its least. I hope a majority will think as I do and agree that if something of Chaucer's has to go, the omission of these two tales is the least inconsiderate.

I was first moved to attempt translating Chaucer by the invitation of Mr. Stephen Potter in the autumn of 1946 to prepare part of the *Prologue* and of the *Nun's Priest's Tale* for broadcasting. This was later followed by other broadcasts from *The Canterbury Tales* and I would like here to offer my thanks to the B.B.C. and particularly to Mr. George Barnes, then Director of the Third Programme, and his successor Mr. Harman Grisewood for the opportunity that led to a work which has given me some four years of delight. The help given me in the task by the wit, sympathy and Chaucerian intuition of Mr. Potter in producing, and by many distinguished actors in reading these works of Chaucer in my rendering has been incalculable. To know, for instance, that Mr. Cecil Trouncer was going to speak a line I was struggling to write was an inspiration in crispness and warmth, two of Chaucer's great qualities, as they also are of Mr. Trouncer's.

To Dr. E. V. Rieu, the Editor of the Penguin Classics, I also owe a warm gratitude for much that I have learned from him about the art of translation, and for his long forbearance in my delays. And there are many other friends whose criticisms and suggestions have helped me to whom I here make acknowledgment without naming them.

NEVILL COGHILL

Exeter College,
Oxford.

THE CANTERBURY TALES

[GROUP A]

The Prologue

WHEN the sweet showers of April fall and shoot
        Down through the drought of March to pierce
    the root,
Bathing every vein in liquid power
From which there springs the engendering of the flower,
When also Zephyrus with his sweet breath
Exhales an air in every grove and heath
Upon the tender shoots, and the young sun
His half-course in the sign of the *Ram* has run,
And the small fowl are making melody
That sleep away the night with open eye
(So nature pricks them and their heart engages)
Then people long to go on pilgrimages
And palmers long to seek the stranger strands
Of far-off saints, hallowed in sundry lands,
And specially, from every shire's end
In England, down to Canterbury they wend
To seek the holy blissful martyr,* quick
In giving help to them when they were sick.
    It happened in that season that one day
In Southwark, at *The Tabard,* as I lay

Ready to go on pilgrimage and start
For Canterbury, most devout at heart,
At night there came into that hostelry
Some nine and twenty in a company
Of sundry folk happening then to fall
In fellowship, and they were pilgrims all
That towards Canterbury meant to ride.
The rooms and stables of the inn were wide;
They made us easy, all was of the best.
And shortly, when the sun had gone to rest,
By speaking to them all upon the trip
I was admitted to their fellowship
And promised to rise early and take the way
To Canterbury, as you heard me say.

But none the less, while I have time and space,
Before my story takes a further pace,
It seems a reasonable thing to say
What their condition was, the full array
Of each of them, as it appeared to me,
According to profession and degree,
And what apparel they were riding in;
And at a Knight I therefore will begin.

There was a *Knight,* a most distinguished man,
Who from the day on which he first began
To ride abroad had followed chivalry,
Truth, honor, greatness of heart and courtesy.
He had done nobly in his sovereign's war
And ridden into battle, no man more,
As well in christian as in heathen places,
And ever honored for his noble graces.

He saw the town of Alexandria* fall;
Often, at feasts, the highest place of all
Among the nations fell to him in Prussia.
In Lithuania he had fought, and Russia,
No christian man so often, of his rank.
And he was in Granada when they sank
The town of Algeciras, also in
North Africa, right through Benamarin;

And in Armenia he had been as well
And fought when Ayas and Attalia fell,
For all along the Mediterranean coast
He had embarked with many a noble host.
In fifteen mortal battles he had been
And jousted for our faith at Tramissene
Thrice in the lists, and always killed his man.
This same distinguished knight had led the van
Once with the Bey of Balat, doing work
For him against another heathen Turk;
He was of sovereign value in all eyes.
And though so much distinguished, he was wise
And in his bearing modest as a maid.
He never yet a boorish thing had said
In all his life to any, come what might;
He was a true, a perfect gentle-knight.

Speaking of his appearance, he possessed
Fine horses, but he was not gaily dressed.
He wore a fustian tunic stained and dark
With smudges where his armor had left mark;
Just home from service, he had joined our ranks
To do his pilgrimage and render thanks.

He had his son with him, a fine young *Squire,*
A lover and cadet, a lad of fire
With curly locks, as if they had been pressed.
He was some twenty years of age, I guessed.
In stature he was of a moderate length,
With wonderful agility and strength.
He'd seen some service with the cavalry
In Flanders and Artois and Picardy
And had done valiantly in little space
Of time, in hope to win his lady's grace.
He was embroidered like a meadow bright
And full of freshest flowers, red and white.
Singing he was, or fluting all the day;
He was as fresh as is the month of May.
Short was his gown, the sleeves were long and wide;
He knew the way to sit a horse and ride.

He could make songs and poems and recite,
Knew how to joust and dance, to draw and write.
He loved so hotly that till dawn grew pale
He slept as little as a nightingale.
Courteous he was, lowly and serviceable,
And carved to serve his father at the table.

There was a *Yeoman* with him at his side,
No other servant; so he chose to ride.
This Yeoman wore a coat and hood of green,
And peacock-feathered arrows, bright and keen
And neatly sheathed, hung at his belt the while
– For he could dress his gear in yeoman style,
His arrows never drooped their feathers low –
And in his hand he bore a mighty bow.
His head was like a nut, his face was brown.
He knew the whole of woodcraft up and down.
A saucy brace was on his arm to ward
It from the bow-string, and a shield and sword
Hung at one side, and at the other slipped
A jaunty dirk, spear-sharp and well-equipped.
A metal of St Christopher he wore
Of shining silver on his breast, and bore
A hunting-horn, well slung and burnished clean,
That dangled from a baldrick of bright green.
He was a proper forester I guess.

There also was a *Nun,* a Prioress;
Simple her way of smiling was and coy.
Her greatest oath was only 'By St Loy!'
And she was known as Madam Eglantyne.
And well she sang a service, with a fine
Intoning through her nose, as was most seemly,
And she spoke daintily in French, extremely,
After the school of Stratford-atte-Bowe;
French in the Paris style she did not know.
At meat her manners were well taught withal;
No morsel from her lips did she let fall,
Nor dipped her fingers in the sauce too deep;
But she could carry a morsel up and keep

The smallest drop from falling on her breast.
For courtliness she had a special zest.
And she would wipe her upper lip so clean
That not a trace of grease was to be seen
Upon the cup when she had drunk; to eat,
She reached a hand sedately for the meat.
She certainly was very entertaining,
Pleasant and friendly in her ways, and straining
To counterfeit a courtly kind of grace,
A stately bearing fitting to her place,
And to seem dignified in all her dealings.
As for her sympathies and tender feelings,
She was so charitably solicitous
She used to weep if she but saw a mouse
Caught in a trap, if it were dead or bleeding.
And she had little dogs she would be feeding
With roasted flesh, or milk, or fine white bread.
Sorely she wept if one of them were dead
Or someone took a stick and made it smart;
She was all sentiment and tender heart.
Her veil was gathered in a seemly way,
Her nose was elegant, her eyes glass-gray;
Her mouth was very small, but soft and red,
And certainly she had a well-shaped head,
Almost a span across the brows, I own;
She was indeed by no means undergrown.
Her cloak, I noticed, had a graceful charm.
She wore a coral trinket on her arm,
A set of beads, the gaudies tricked in green,*
Whence hung a golden brooch of brightest sheen
On which there first was graven a crowned A,
And lower, *Amor vincit omnia.*

Another *Nun*, the chaplain at her cell,
Was riding with her, and *three Priests* as well.

There was a *Monk,* a leader of the fashions;
Inspecting farms and hunting were his passions,
A manly man, to be an Abbot able,
Many the dainty horses in his stable;

His bridle, when he rode, a man might hear
Jingling in a whistling wind as clear,
Aye, and as loud as does the chapel bell
Where my lord Monk was Prior of the cell.
The Rule of good St Benet or St Maur
As old and strict he tended to ignore;
He let go by the things of yesterday
And followed the new world's more spacious way.
He did not rate that text at a plucked hen
Which says that hunters are not holy men
And that a monk uncloistered is a mere
Fish out of water, flapping on the pier,
That is to say a monk out of his cloister.
That was a text he held not worth an oyster;
And I said I agreed with his opinion;
What! Study until reason lost dominion
Poring on books in cloisters? Must he toil
As Austin bade and till the very soil?
Was he to leave the world upon the shelf?
Let Austin have his labor to himself.

This Monk was therefore a good man to horse;
Greyhounds he had, as swift as birds, to course.
Hunting a hare or riding at a fence
Was all his fun, he spared for no expense.
I saw his sleeves were garnished at the hand
With fine gray fur, the finest in the land,
And where his hood was fastened at his chin
He had a wrought-gold cunningly fashioned pin;
Into a lover's knot it seemed to pass.
His head was bald and shone as any glass,
So did his face, as if it had been greased.
He was a fat and personable priest;
His bright eyes rolled, they never seemed to settle,
And glittered like the flames beneath a kettle;
Supple his boots, his horse in fine condition.
He was a prelate fit for exhibition,
He was not pale like a tormented soul.
He liked a fat swan best, and roasted whole.

His palfrey was as brown as is a berry.
 There was a *Friar,* a wanton one and merry,
A Limiter,* a very festive fellow.
In all Four Orders* there was none so mellow
As he in flattery and dalliant speech.
He'd fixed up many a marriage, giving each
Of his young women what he could afford her.
He was a noble pillar to his Order.
Highly beloved and intimate was he
With County folk wherever he might be,
And worthy city women with possessions;
For he was qualified to hear confessions,
Or so he said, with more than priestly scope;
He had a special license from the Pope.
Sweetly he heard his penitents at shrift
With pleasant absolution, for a gift.
He was an easy man in penance-giving
Where he could hope to make a decent living;
It's a sure sign whenever gifts are given
To a poor Order that a man's well shriven,
And should he give enough he knew in verity
The penitent repented in sincerity.
For many a fellow is so hard of heart
He cannot weep, for all his inward smart.
Therefore instead of weeping and of prayer
One should give silver for a poor Friar's care.
He kept his tippet stuffed with pins for curls,
And pocket-knives, to give to pretty girls.
And certainly his voice was gay and sturdy,
For he sang well and played the hurdy-gurdy.
At sing-songs he was champion of the hour.
His neck was whiter than a lily-flower
But strong enough to butt a bruiser down.
He knew the taverns well in every town
And every innkeeper and barmaid too
Better than lepers, beggars and that crew,
For in so eminent a man as he
It was not fitting with the dignity

Of his position dealing with such scum.
It isn't decent, nothing good can come
Of having truck with slum-and-gutter dwellers,
But only with the rich and victual-sellers.
But anywhere a profit might accrue
Courteous he was and lowly of service too.
Natural gifts like his were hard to match.
He was the finest beggar of his batch,
And, for his begging-district, payed a rent;
His brethren did no poaching where he went.
For though a widow mightn't have a shoe,
So pleasant was his holy how-d'ye-do
He got his farthing from her just the same
Before he left, and so his income came
To more than he laid out. And how he romped,
Just like a puppy! He was ever prompt
To arbitrate disputes on settling days
(For a small fee) in many helpful ways,
Not then appearing as your cloistered scholar
With threadbare habit hardly worth a dollar,
But much more like a Doctor or a Pope.
Of double-worsted was the semi-cope
Upon his shoulders, and the swelling fold
About him, like a bell about its mold
When it is casting, rounded out his dress.
He lisped a little out of wantonness
To make his English sweet upon his tongue.
When he had played his harp, or having sung,
His eyes would twinkle in his head as bright
As any star upon a frosty night.
This worthy's name was Hubert, it appeared.

There was a *Merchant* with a forking beard
And motley dress; high on his horse he sat,
Upon his head a Flemish beaver hat
And on his feet daintily buckled boots.
He told of his opinions and pursuits
In solemn tones, and how he never lost.
The sea should be kept free at any cost

(He thought) upon the Harwich-Holland ranges.
He was expert at dabbling in exchanges.
This estimable Merchant so had set
His wits to work, none knew he was in debt,
He was so stately in negotiation,
Loan, bargain and commercial obligation.
He was an excellent fellow all the same;
To tell the truth I do not know his name.

There was an *Oxford Cleric* too, a student,
Long given to Logic, longer than was prudent;
The horse he had was leaner than a rake,
And he was not too fat, I undertake,
But had a hollow look, a sober air;
The thread upon his overcoat was bare.
He had found no preferment in the church
And he was too unworldly to make search.
He thought far more of having by his bed
His twenty books all bound in black and red,
Of Aristotle and philosophy
Than of gay music, fiddles or finery.
Though a philosopher, as I have told,
He had not found the stone for making gold.
Whatever money from his friends he took
He spent on learning or another book
And prayed for them most earnestly, returning
Thanks to them thus for paying for his learning.
His only care was study, and indeed
He never spoke a word more than was need,
Formal at that, respectful in the extreme,
Short, to the point, and lofty in his theme.
The thought of moral virtue filled his speech
And he would gladly learn, and gladly teach.

A Sergeant at the Law who paid his calls,
Wary and wise, for clients at St Paul's*
There also was, of noted excellence.
Discreet he was, a man to reverence,
Or so he seemed, his sayings were so wise.
He often had been Justice of Assize

By letters patent, and in full commission.
His fame and learning and his high position
Had won him many a robe and many a fee.
There was no such conveyancer as he;
All was fee-simple to his strong digestion,
Not one conveyance could be called in question.
Though there was none so busy as was he
He was less busy than he seemed to be.
He knew of every judgment, case and crime
Recorded ever since King William's time.
He could dictate defenses or draft deeds;
No one could pinch a comma from his screeds,
And he knew every statute off by rote.
He wore a homely parti-colored coat
Girt with a silken belt of pin-stripe stuff;
Of his appearance I have said enough.

A land-owner, a *Franklin*,* had appeared;
White as a daisy-petal was his beard.
A sanguine man, high-colored and benign,
He loved a morning sop of cake in wine.
He lived for pleasure and had always done,
For he was Epicurus' very son,
In whose opinion sensual delight
Was the one true felicity in sight.
As noted as St Julian was for bounty
He made his household free to all the County.
His bread, his ale were finest of the fine
And no one had a better stock of wine.
His house was never short of bake-meat pies,
Of fish and flesh, and these in such supplies
It positively snowed with meat and drink
And all the dainties that a man could think.
According to the seasons of the year
Changes of dish were ordered to appear.
He kept fat partridges in coops, beyond,
Many a bream and pike were in his pond.
Woe to the cook whose sauces had no sting
Or who was unprepared in anything!

And in his hall a table stood arrayed
And ready all day long, with places laid.
As Justice at the Sessions none stood higher;
He often had been Member for the Shire.
A dagger and a little purse of silk
Hung at his girdle, white as morning milk.
As Sheriff he checked audit, every entry.
He was a model among landed gentry.

A *Haberdasher*, a *Dyer*, a *Carpenter*,
A *Weaver* and a *Carpet-maker* were
Among our ranks, all in the livery
Of one impressive guild-fraternity.
They were so trim and fresh their gear would pass
For new. Their knives were not tricked out with brass
But wrought with purest silver, which avouches
A like display on girdles and on pouches.
Each seemed a worthy burgess, fit to grace
A guild-hall with a seat upon the dais.
Their wisdom would have justified a plan
To make each one of them an alderman;
They had the capital and revenue,
Besides their wives declared it was their due.
And if they did not think so, then they ought;
To be called '*Madam*' is a glorious thought,
And so is going to church and being seen
Having your mantle carried like a queen.

They had a *Cook* with them who stood alone
For boiling chicken with a marrow-bone,
Sharp flavoring-powder and a spice for savor.
He could distinguish London ale by flavor,
And he could roast and seethe and broil and fry,
Make good thick soup and bake a tasty pie.
But a great pity, as it seemed to me,
Was that he had an ulcer on his knee.
As for blancmange, he made it with the best.

There was a *Skipper* hailing from far west;
He came from Dartmouth, so I understood.
He rode a farmer's horse as best he could,

In a woolen gown that reached his knee.
A dagger on a lanyard falling free
Hung from his neck under his arm and down.
The summer heat had tanned his color brown,
And certainly he was an excellent fellow.
Many a draught of vintage, red and yellow,
He'd drawn at Bordeaux, while the vintner slept.
Few were the rules his tender conscience kept.
If, when he fought, the enemy vessel sank,
He sent his prisoners home; they walked the plank.
As for his skill in reckoning his tides,
Currents and many another risk besides,
Moons, harbors, pilots, he had such dispatch
That none from Hull to Carthage was his match.
Hardy he was, prudent in undertaking;
His beard in many a tempest had its shaking,
And he knew all the havens as they were
From Gottland to the Cape of Finisterre,
And every creek in Brittany and Spain;
The barge he owned was called *The Maudelayne.*

    A *Doctor* too emerged as we proceeded;
No one alive could talk as well as he did
On points of medicine and of surgery,
For, being grounded in astronomy,
He watched his patient's favorable star
And, by his Natural Magic, knew what are
The lucky hours and planetary degrees
For making charms and magic effigies.
The cause of every malady you'd got
He knew, and whether dry, cold, moist or hot;*
He knew their seat, their humor and condition.
He was a perfect practicing physician.
These causes being known for what they were,
He gave the man his medicine then and there.
All his apothecaries in a tribe
Were ready with the drugs he would prescribe,
And each made money from the other's guile;
They had been friendly for a goodish while.

He was well-versed in Esculapius* too
And what Hippocrates and Rufus knew
And Dioscorides, now dead and gone,
Galen and Rhazes, Hali, Serapion,
Averroes, Avicenna, Constantine,
Scotch Bernard, John of Gaddesden, Gilbertine.
In his own diet he observed some measure;
There were no superfluities for pleasure,
Only digestives, nutritives and such.
He did not read the Bible very much.
In blood-red garments, slashed with bluish-gray
And lined with taffeta, he rode his way;
Yet he was rather close as to expenses
And kept the gold he won in pestilences.
Gold stimulates the heart, or so we're told.
He therefore had a special love of gold.

A worthy *woman* from beside *Bath* city
Was with us, somewhat deaf, which was a pity.
In making cloth she showed so great a bent
She bettered those of Ypres and of Ghent.
In all the parish not a dame dared stir
Towards the altar steps in front of her,
And if indeed they did, so wrath was she
As to be quite put out of charity.
Her kerchiefs were of finely woven ground;
I dared have sworn they weighed a good ten pound,
The ones she wore on Sunday, on her head.
Her hose were of the finest scarlet red
And gartered tight; her shoes were soft and new.
Bold was her face, handsome, and red in hue.
A worthy woman all her life, what's more
She'd have five husbands, all at the church door,
Apart from other company in youth;
No need just now to speak of that, forsooth.
And she had thrice been to Jerusalem,
Seen many strange rivers and passed over them;
She'd been to Rome and also to Boulogne,
St James of Compostella and Cologne,

And she was skilled in wandering by the way.
She had gap-teeth, set widely, truth to say.
Easily on an ambling horse she sat
Well wimpled up, and on her head a hat
As broad as is a buckler or a shield;
She had a flowing mantle that concealed
Large hips, her heels spurred sharply under that.
In company she liked to laugh and chat
And knew the remedies for love's mischances,
An art in which she knew the oldest dances.

    A holy-minded man of good renown
There was, and poor, the *Parson* to a town,
Yet he was rich in holy thought and work.
He also was a learned man, a clerk,
Who truly knew Christ's gospel and would preach it
Devoutly to parishioners, and teach it.
Benign and wonderfully diligent,
And patient when adversity was sent
(For so he proved in great adversity)
He much disliked extorting tithe or fee,
Nay rather he preferred beyond a doubt
Giving to poor parishioners round about
From his own goods and Easter offerings.
He found sufficiency in little things.
Wide was his parish, with houses far asunder,
Yet he neglected not in rain or thunder,
In sickness or in grief, to pay a call
On the remotest whether great or small
Upon his feet, and in his hand a stave.
This noble example to his sheep he gave,
First following the word before he taught it,
And it was from the gospel he had caught it.
This little proverb he would add thereto
That if gold rust, what then will iron do?
For if a priest be foul in whom we trust
No wonder that a common man should rust;
And shame it is to see – let priests take stock –
A shitten shepherd and a snowy flock.

The true example that a priest should give
Is one of cleanness, how the sheep should live.
He did not set his benefice to hire
And leave his sheep encumbered in the mire
Or run to London to earn easy bread
By singing masses for the wealthy dead,
Or find some Brotherhood and get enrolled.
He stayed at home and watched over his fold
So that no wolf should make the sheep miscarry.
He was a shepherd and no mercenary.
Holy and virtuous he was, but then
Never contemptuous of sinful men,
Never disdainful, never too proud or fine,
But was discreet in teaching and benign.
His business was to show a fair behavior
And draw men thus to Heaven and their Saviour,
Unless indeed a man were obstinate;
And such, whether of high or low estate,
He put to sharp rebuke to say the least.
 I think there never was a better priest.
He sought no pomp or glory in his dealings,
No scrupulosity had spiced his feelings.
Christ and His Twelve Apostles and their lore
He taught, but followed it himself before.
 There was a *Plowman* with him there, his brother.
Many a load of dung one time or other
He must have carted through the morning dew.
He was an honest worker, good and true,
Living in peace and perfect charity,
And, as the gospel bade him, so did he,
Loving God best with all his heart and mind
And then his neighbor as himself, repined
At no misfortune, slacked for no content,
For steadily about his work he went
To thrash his corn, to dig or to manure
Or make a ditch; and he would help the poor
For love of Christ and never take a penny
If he could help it, and, as prompt as any,

He paid his tithes in full when they were due
On what he owned, and on his earnings too.
He wore a tabard smock and rode a mare.

There was a *Reeve,* also a *Miller,* there,
A College *Manciple* from the Inns of Court,
A papal *Pardoner* and, in close consort,
A Church-Court *Summoner,* riding at a trot,
And finally myself – that was the lot.

The *Miller* was a chap of sixteen stone,
A great stout fellow big in brawn and bone.
He did well out of them, for he could go
And win the ram at any wrestling show.
Broad, knotty and short-shouldered, he would boast
He could heave any door off hinge and post,
Or take a run and break it with his head.
His beard, like any sow or fox, was red
And broad as well, as though it were a spade;
And, at its very tip, his nose displayed
A wart on which there stood a tuft of hair
Red as the bristles in an old sow's ear.
His nostrils were as black as they were wide,
He had a sword and buckler at his side,
His mighty mouth was like a furnace door.
A wrangler and buffoon, he had a store
Of tavern stories, filthy in the main.
His was a master-hand at stealing grain.
He felt it with his thumb and thus he knew
Its quality and took three times his due –
A thumb of gold, by God, to gauge an oat!
He wore a hood of blue and a white coat.
He liked to play his bagpipes up and down
And that was how he brought us out of town.

The *Manciple* came from the Inner Temple;
All caterers might follow his example
In buying victuals; he was never rash
Whether he bought on credit or paid cash.
He used to watch the market most precisely
And got in first, and so he did quite nicely.

Now isn't it a marvel of God's grace
That an illiterate fellow can outpace
The wisdom of a heap of learned men?
His masters – he had more than thirty then –
All versed in the abstrusest legal knowledge,
Could have produced a dozen from their College
Fit to be stewards in land and rents and game
To any Peer in England you could name,
And show him how to live on what he had
Debt-free (unless of course the Peer were mad)
Or be as frugal as he might desire,
And they were fit to help about the Shire
In any legal case there was to try;
And yet this Manciple could wipe their eye.

    The *Reeve** was old and choleric and thin;
His beard was shaven closely to the skin,
His shorn hair came abruptly to a stop
Above his ears, and he was docked on top
Just like a priest in front; his legs were lean,
Like sticks they were, no calf was to be seen.
He kept his bins and garners very trim;
No auditor could gain a point on him.
And he could judge by watching drought and rain
The yield he might expect from seed and grain.
His master's sheep, his animals and hens,
Pigs, horses, dairies, stores and cattle-pens
Were wholly trusted to his government.
And he was under contract to present
The accounts, right from his master's earliest years.
No one had ever caught him in arrears.
No bailiff, serf or herdsman dared to kick,
He knew their dodges, knew their every trick;
Feared like the plague he was, by those beneath.
He had a lovely dwelling on a heath,
Shadowed in green by trees above the sward.
A better hand at bargains than his lord,
He had grown rich and had a store of treasure
Well tucked away, yet out it came to pleasure

His lord with subtle loans or gifts of goods,
To earn his thanks and even coats and hoods.
When young he'd learnt a useful trade and still
He was a carpenter of first-rate skill.
The stallion-cob he rode at a slow trot
Was dapple-gray and bore the name of Scot.
He wore an overcoat of bluish shade
And rather long; he had a rusty blade
Slung at his side. He came, as I heard tell,
From Norfolk, near a place called Baldeswell.
His coat was tucked under his belt and splayed.
He rode the hindmost of our cavalcade.

There was a *Summoner** with us in the place
Who had a fire-red cherubinny face,*
For he had carbuncles. His eyes were narrow,
He was as hot and lecherous as a sparrow.
Black, scabby brows he had, and a thin beard.
Children were afraid when he appeared.
No quicksilver, lead ointments, tartar creams,
Boracic, no, nor brimstone, so it seems,
Could make a salve that had the power to bite,
Clean up or cure his whelks of knobby white
Or purge the pimples sitting on his cheeks.
Garlic he loved, and onions too, and leeks,
And drinking strong red wine till all was hazy.
Then he would shout and jabber as if crazy,
And wouldn't speak a word except in Latin
When he was drunk, such tags as he was pat in;
He only had a few, say two or three
That he had mugged up out of some decree;
No wonder, for he heard them every day.
And, as you know, a man can teach a jay
To call out 'Walter' better than the Pope.
But had you tried to test his wits and grope
For more, you'd have found nothing in the bag.
Then *'Questio quid juris'* was his tag.*
He was a gentle varlet and a kind one,
No better fellow if you went to find one.

He would allow – just for a quart of wine –
Any good lad to keep a concubine
A twelvemonth, and dispense it altogether!
Yet he could pluck a finch to leave no feather;
And if he found some rascal with a maid
He would instruct him not to be afraid
In such a case of the Archdeacon's curse
(Unless the rascal's soul were in his purse)
For in his purse the punishment should be.
'Purse is the good Archdeacon's Hell,' said he.
But well I know he lied in what he said;
A curse should put a guilty man in dread,
For curses kill, as shriving brings, salvation.
We should beware of excommunication.
Thus, by mere threat, this fellow could possess
The boys and girls of all the Diocese,
He knew their secrets and they went in dread.
He wore a garland set upon his head
Large as the holly-bush upon a stake
Outside an ale-house, and he had a cake,
A round one, which it was his joke to wield
As if it were intended for a shield.

He and a gentle *Pardoner** rode together,
A bird from Charing Cross of the same feather,
Just back from visiting the Court of Rome.
He loudly sang *'Come hither, love, come home!'*
The Summoner sang deep seconds to this song,
No trumpet ever sounded half so strong.
This Pardoner had hair as yellow as wax
Hanging down smoothly like a hank of flax.
In driblets fell his locks behind his head
Down to his shoulders which they overspread;
Thinly they fell, like rat-tails, one by one.
He wore no hood upon his head, for fun;
The hood inside his wallet had been stowed,
He aimed at riding in the latest mode;
But for a little cap his head was bare
And he had bulging eye-balls, like a hare.

He'd sowed a holy relic on his cap;
His wallet lay before him on his lap,
Brimful of pardons come from Rome all hot.
He had the same small voice a goat has got.
His chin no beard had harbored, nor would harbor,
Smoother than ever chin was left by barber.
I judge he was a gelding, or a mare.
As to his trade, from Berwick down to Ware
There was no pardoner of equal grace,
For in his trunk he had a pillow-case
Which he asserted was Our Lady's veil.
He said he had a gobbet of the sail
Saint Peter had the time when he made bold
To walk the waves, till Jesu Christ took hold.
He had a cross of metal set with stones
And, in a glass, a rubble of pigs' bones.
And with these relics, any time he found
Some poor up-country parson to astound,
On one short day, in money down, he drew
More than the parson in a month or two,
And by his flatteries and prevarication
Made monkeys of the priest and congregation.
But still to do him justice first and last
In church he was a noble ecclesiast.
How well he read a lesson or told a story!
But best of all he sang an Offertory,
For well he knew that when that song was sung
He'd have to preach and tune his honey-tongue
And (well he could) win silver from the crowd.
That's why he sang so merrily and loud.

Now I have told you shortly, in a clause,
The rank, the array, the number and the cause
Of our assembly in this company
In Southwark, at that high-class hostelry
Known as *The Tabard*, close beside *The Bell*.
And now the time has come for me to tell
How we behaved that evening; I'll begin
After we had alighted at the Inn.

Then I'll report our journey, stage by stage,
All the remainder of our pilgrimage.
But first I beg of you, in courtesy,
Not to condemn me as unmannerly
If I speak plainly and with no concealings
And give account of all their words and dealings,
Using their very phrases as they fell.
For certainly, as you all know so well,
He who repeats a tale after a man
Is bound to say, as nearly as he can,
Each single word, if he remembers it,
However rudely spoken or unfit,
Or else the tale he tells will be untrue,
The things invented and the phrases new.
He may not flinch although it were his brother,
If he says one word he must say the other.
And Christ Himself spoke broad in Holy Writ,
And as you know there's nothing there unfit,
And Plato says, for those with power to read,
'The word should be as cousin to the deed.'
Further I beg you to forgive it me
If I neglect the order and degree
And what is due to rank in what I've planned.
I'm short of wit as you will understand.

Our *Host* gave us great welcome; everyone
Was given a place and supper was begun.
He served the finest victuals you could think,
The wine was strong and we were glad to drink.
A very striking man our Host withal,
And fit to be a marshal in a hall.
His eyes were bright, his girth a little wide;
There is no finer burgess in Cheapside.
Bold in his speech, yet wise and full of tact,
There was no manly attribute he lacked,
What's more he was a merry-hearted man.
After our meal he jokingly began
To talk of sport, and, among other things
After we'd settled up our reckonings,

45

He said as follows: 'Truly, gentlemen,
You're very welcome and I can't think when
– Upon my word I'm telling you no lie –
I've seen a gathering here that looked so spry,
No, not this year, as in this tavern now.
I'd think you up some fun if I knew how.
And, as it happens, a thought has just occurred
And it will cost you nothing, on my word.
You're off to Canterbury – well, God speed!
Blessed St Thomas answer to your need!
And I don't doubt, before the journey's done
You mean to while the time in tales and fun.
Indeed, there's little pleasure for your bones
Riding along and all as dumb as stones.
So let me then propose for your enjoyment,
Just as I said, a suitable employment.
And if my notion suits and you agree
And promise to submit yourselves to me
Playing your parts exactly as I say
Tomorrow as you ride along the way,
Then by my father's soul (and he is dead)
If you don't like it you can have my head!
Hold up your hands, and not another word.'

    Well, our consent of course was not deferred,
It seemed not worth a serious debate;
We all agreed to it at any rate
And bade him issue what commands he would.
'My lords,' he said, 'now listen for your good,
And please don't treat my notion with disdain.
This is the point, to make it short and plain.
Each one of you shall help to make things slip
By telling two stories on the outward trip
To Canterbury, that's what I intend,
And, on the homeward way to journey's end
Another two, tales from the days of old;
And then the man whose story is best told,
That is to say who gives the fullest measure
Of good morality and general pleasure,

He shall be given a supper, paid by all,
Here in this tavern, in this very hall,
When we come back again from Canterbury.
And in the hope to keep you bright and merry
I'll go along with you myself and ride
All at my own expense and serve as guide.
I'll be the judge, and those who won't obey
Shall pay for what we spend upon the way.
Now if you all agree to what you've heard
Tell me at once without another word,
And I will make arrangements early for it.'

Of course we all agreed, in fact we swore it
Delightedly, and made entreaty too
That he should act as he proposed to do,
Become our Governor in short, and be
Judge of our tales and general referee,
And set the supper at a certain price.
We promised to be ruled by his advice
Come high, come low; unanimously thus
We set him up in judgment over us.
More wine was fetched, the business being done;
We drank it off and up went everyone
To bed without a moment of delay.

Early next morning at the spring of day
Up rose our Host and roused us like a cock,
Gathering us together in a flock,
And off we rode, at slightly faster pace
Than walking, to St Thomas' watering-place;
And there our Host drew up, began to ease
His horse, and said, 'Now, listen if you please,
My lords! Remember what you promised me.
If evensong and matins will agree
Let's see who shall be first to tell a tale.
And as I hope to drink good wine and ale
I'll be your judge. The rebel who disobeys,
However much the journey costs, he pays.
Now draw for cut and then we can depart;
The man who draws the shortest cut shall start.

My Lord the Knight,' he said, 'step up to me
And draw your cut, for that is my decree.
And come you near, my Lady Prioress,
And you, Sir Cleric, drop your shamefastness,
No studying now! A hand from every man!'
Immediately the draw for lots began
And to tell shortly how the matter went,
Whether by chance or fate or accident,
The truth is this, the cut fell to the Knight,
Which everybody greeted with delight.
And tell his tale he must, as reason was
Because of our agreement and because
He too had sworn. What more is there to say?
For when the good man saw how matters lay,
Being by wisdom and obedience driven
To keep a promise he had freely given,
He said, 'Since it's for me to start the game,
Why, welcome be the cut in God's good name!
Now let us ride, and listen to what I say.'
And at the word we started on our way
And in a cheerful style he then began
At once to tell his tale, and thus it ran.

The Knight's Tale

PART I

STORIES of old have made it known to us
That there was once a Duke called Theseus,
Ruler of Athens, Lord and Governor,
And in his time so great a conqueror
There was none mightier beneath the sun.
Many and rich the countries he had won,
What with his wisdom and his troops of horse.
He had subdued the Amazons by force

48

And all their realm once known as Scythia
But then called Femeny. Hippolyta
Their queen he took to wife, and, says the story,
He brought her home in solemn pomp and glory,
Also her younger sister, Emily.
And thus victorious and with minstrelsy
I leave this noble Duke for Athens bound
With all his host of men-at-arms around.

    And were it not too long to tell again
I would have fully pictured the campaign
In which his men-at-arms and he had won
Those territories from the Amazon
And the great battle that was given then
Between those women and the Athenian men,
Or told you how Hippolyta had been
Besieged and taken, fair courageous queen,
And what a feast there was when they were married,
And of the violence of the storm that harried
Their home-coming. I pass these over now
Having, God knows, a larger field to plow.
Weak are my oxen for such mighty stuff;
What I have yet to tell is long enough.
I won't delay the others of our rout,
Let every fellow tell his tale about
And see who wins the supper at the Inn.
Where I left off, let me again begin.

    This Duke I mentioned, ere alighting down
And on the very outskirts of the town
In all felicity and height of pride
Became aware, casting an eye aside,
That kneeling on the highway, two by two,
A company of ladies were in view
All clothed in black, each pair in proper station
Behind the other. And such lamentation
And cries they uttered, it was past conceiving
The world had ever heard such noise of grieving,
Nor did they hold their misery in check
Till they grasped bridle at his horse's neck.

'Who may you be that, at my coming, so
Perturb my festival with cries of woe?'
Said Theseus. 'Do you grudge the celebration
Of these my honors with your lamentation?
Who can have injured you or who offended?
And tell me if the matter may be mended
And why it is that you are clothed in black?'

The eldest of these ladies answered back,
Fainting a little in such deadly fashion
That but to see and hear her stirred compassion,
And said, 'O Sir, whom Fortune has made glorious
In conquest and is sending home victorious,
We do not grudge your glory in our grief
But rather beg your mercy and relief.
Have pity on our sorrowful distress!
Some drop of pity, in your nobleness,
On us unhappy women let there fall!
For sure there is not one among us all
That was not once a duchess or a queen,
Though wretches now, as may be truly seen,
Thanks be to Fortune and her treacherous wheel
That suffers no estate on earth to feel
Secure a moment. Be assured that we,
Here at the shrine of Goddess Clemency,
Have watched a fortnight for this very hour.
Help us, my Lord, it lies within your power.
I, wretched Queen, that weep aloud my woe,
Was wife to King Capaneus long ago
That died at Thebes, accursed be the day!
And we in our disconsolate array
That make this sorrowful appeal to pity
Lost each her husband in that fatal city
During the siege, for so it came to pass.
Now old King Creon – O alas, alas! –
The Lord of Thebes, grown cruel in his age
And filled with foul iniquity and rage,
For tyranny and spite as I have said
Does outrage on the bodies of our dead,

On all our husbands, for when they were killed
Their bodies were dragged out – so Creon willed –
Into a heap and there, as we have learnt,
They neither may have burial nor be burnt,
But he makes dogs devour them, in scorn.'

  At that they all at once began to mourn,
And every woman fell upon her face
And cried, 'Have pity, Lord, on our disgrace
And let our sorrow sink into your heart.'

  The Duke, who felt a pang of pity start
At what they spoke, dismounted from his steed;
He felt his heart about to break indeed,
Seeing how piteous and disconsolate
They were, that once had been of high estate!
He raised them in his arms and sought to fill
Their hearts with comfort and with kind good will,
And swore an oath that as he was true knight,
So far as it should lie within his might,
He would take vengeance on this tyrant King,
This Creon, till the land of Greece should ring
With how he had encountered him and served
The monster with the death he had deserved.
Instantly then and with no more delay,
He turned and with his banners in display
Made off for Thebes with all his host beside,
For not a step to Athens would he ride
Nor take his ease so much as half a day,
But marched into the night upon his way.
But yet he sent Hippolyta the Queen
And Emily her sister the serene
On into Athens, where they were to dwell,
And off he rode; there is no more to tell.

  The figure of red Mars with spear and targe
So shone upon his banners white and large,
That all the meadows glittered up and down,
And close by them his pennon of renown
Shone rich with gold, emblazoned with that feat,
His slaying of the Minotaur in Crete.

Thus rode this Duke, thus rode this conqueror
And led his flower of chivalry to war,
Until he came to Thebes, there to alight
In splendor on a chosen field to fight.
And, to speak briefly of so great a thing,
He conquered Creon there, the Theban king,
And slew him manfully, as became a knight,
In open battle, put his troops to flight,
And by assault captured the city after
And rent it, roof and wall and spar and rafter;
And to the ladies he restored again
The bones belonging to their husbands slain,
To do, as custom was, their obsequies.

But it were all too long to speak of these
Or of the clamorous complaint and yearning
These ladies uttered at the place of burning
The bodies, or of all the courtesy
That Theseus, noble in his victory,
Showed to the ladies when they went their way;
I would be brief in what I have to say.

Now when Duke Theseus worthily had done
Justice on Creon and when Thebes was won,
That night, camped in the field, he took his rest,
Having disposed the land as he thought best.

Crawling for ransack among heaps of slain
And stripping their accoutrements for gain,
The pillagers went busily about
After the battle on the field of rout.
And so befell among the heaps they found
Thrust through with bloody wounds upon the ground
Two pale young knights there, lying side by side,
Wearing the self-same arms in blazoned pride.
Of these Arcita was the name of one,
That of the other knight was Palamon;
And they were neither fully quick nor dead.
By coat of arms and crest upon the head
The heralds knew, for all the filth and mud,
That they were Princes of the Royal Blood;

Two sisters of the House of Thebes had borne them.
Out of the heap these pillagers have torn them
And gently carried them to Theseus' tent.
And he decreed they should at once be sent
To Athens, and gave order they be kept
Perpetual prisoners – he would accept
No ransom for them. This was done, and then
The noble Duke turned homeward with his men
Crowned with the laurel of his victory,
And there in honor and felicity
He lived his life; what more is there to say?
And in a tower, in grief and anguish lay
Arcite and Palamon, beyond all doubt
Forever, for no gold could buy them out.

Year after year went by, day after day,
Until one morning in the month of May
Young Emily, that fairer was of mien
Than is the lily on its stalk of green,
And fresher in her coloring that strove
With early roses in a May-time grove
– I know not which was fairer of the two –
Ere it was day, as she was wont to do,
Rose and arrayed her beauty as was right,
For May will have no sluggardry at night,
Season that pricks in every gentle heart,
Awaking it from sleep, and bids it start,
Saying, 'Arise! Do thine observance due!'
And this made Emily recall anew
The honor due to May and she arose,
Her beauties freshly clad. To speak of those,
Her yellow hair was braided in a tress
Behind her back, a yard in length, I guess,
And in the garden at the sun's uprising
Hither and thither at her own devising
She wandered gathering flowers, white and red,
To make a subtle garland for her head,
And like an angel sang a heavenly song.

The great, grim tower-keep, so thick and strong,

Principal dungeon at the castle's core
Where the two knights, of whom I spoke before
And shall again, were shut, if you recall,
Was close-adjoining to the garden wall
Where Emily chose her pleasures and adornings.
Bright was the sun this loveliest of mornings
And the sad prisoner Palamon had risen
With license from the jailer of the prison
As was his wont and roamed a chamber high
Above the city, whence he could descry
The noble buildings and the branching green
Where Emily the radiant and serene
Went pausing in her walk and roaming on.

This sorrowful prisoner, this Palamon,
Was pacing round his chamber to and fro
Lamenting to himself in all his woe.
'Alas,' he said, 'that ever I was born!'
And so it happened on this May day morn,
Through a deep window set with many bars
Of mighty iron squared with massive spars,
He chanced on Emily to cast his eye
And, as he did, he blenched and gave a cry
As though he had been stung unto the heart.
And, at the cry, Arcita gave a start
And said, 'My cousin Palamon, what ails you?
How deadly pale you look! Your color fails you!
Why did you cry? Who can have given offense?
For God's love, take things patiently, have sense,
Think! We are prisoners and shall always be.
Fortune has given us this adversity,
Some wicked planetary dispensation,
Some Saturn's trick or evil constellation
Has given us this, and Heaven, though we had sworn
The contrary, so stood when we were born.
We must endure it, that's the long and short.'
And Palamon in answer made retort,
'Cousin, believe me, your opinion springs
From ignorance and vain imaginings.

Imprisonment was not what made me cry.
I have been hurt this moment through the eye,
Into my heart. It will be death to me.
The fairness of the lady that I see
Roaming the garden yonder to and fro
Is the whole cause that made me cry my woe.
Woman or Goddess, which is she? Who knows?
Not I. But it is Venus, I suppose.'
He fell upon his knees before the sill
And prayed: 'O Venus, if it be thy will
Here in this garden to transfigure thee
Before a sorrow-stricken wretch like me,
Lend thine assistance that we may escape!
Yet if my destiny have evil shape
By some eternal word, and I must pine
In prison, have compassion on our line
And kindred, humbled under tyrant law!'

  Now, as he uttered this, Arcita saw
This lady at her roaming to and fro,
And at the sight her beauty hurt him so
That if his cousin had a wound before
Arcite was hurt as much as he, or more,
And with a deep and piteous sigh he said:
'The freshness of her beauty strikes me dead,
Hers that I see, roaming in yonder place!
Unless I gain the mercy of her grace,
Unless at least I see her day by day,
I am but dead. There is no more to say.'

  On hearing this young Palamon looked grim
And in contempt and anger answered him,
'Do you speak this in earnest or in jest?'
'No, in good earnest,' said Arcite, 'the best!
So help me God, I mean no jesting now.'

  Then Palamon began to knit his brow:
'It's no great honor, then,' he said, 'to you
To prove so false, to be a traitor too
To me, that am your cousin and your brother
Both deeply sworn and bound to one another,

Though we should die in torture for it, never
To loose the bond that only death can sever,
And when in love neither to hinder other,
Nor in what else soever, dearest brother.
Rather to further me in all, and do
As much in furthering me as I for you.
This was our oath and nothing can untie it,
And well I know you dare not now deny it.
You are my trusted friend, as none can doubt,
Yet you would treacherously go about
To love my lady, whom I love and serve
And ever shall, till death cut my heart's nerve.
No, no, you shall not, false Arcita! no,
I loved her first (O grief!) and told you so
As to the brother and the friend that swore
To further me, as I have said before,
So you are bound in honor as a knight
To help me, should it lie within your might;
Else you are false, I say, your honor vain!'
Arcita proudly answered back again:
'You shall be judged as false,' he said, 'not me;
And false you are, I tell you, utterly!
I loved her as a woman before you.
What can you say? Just now you hardly knew
If she were girl or goddess from above!
Yours is a holy, spiritual love,
And mine is love as to a human being
And so I told you at the moment, seeing
You were my cousin and sworn friend. At worst
What do I care? Suppose you loved her first,
Haven't you heard the old proverbial saw
"Who ever bound a lover by a law?"
Love is a law unto itself. My hat!
What earthly man can have more law than that?
All man-made law, all positive injunction
Is broken every day without compunction
For love. A man must love, for all his wit;
There's no escape though he should die for it,

Be she a maid, a widow or a wife.
   'Yet you are little likely, all your life,
To stand in grace with her; no more shall I.
You know yourself, too well, that here we lie
Condemned to prison both of us, no doubt
Perpetually. No ransom buys us out.
We're like two dogs in battle on their own;
They fought all day but neither got the bone,
There came a kite above them, nothing loth,
And while they fought he took it from them both.
And so it is in politics, dear brother,
Each for himself alone, there is no other.
Love if you want to; I shall love her too,
And that is all there is to say or do.
We're prisoners and must endure it, man,
And each of us must take what chance he can.'
   Great was the strife for many a long spell
Between them had I but the time to tell,
But to the point. It happened that one day,
To tell it you as briefly as I may,
A certain famous Duke, Perotheus,
Friend and companion of Duke Theseus
Since they were little children, came to spend
A holiday in Athens with his friend,
Visiting him for pleasure as of yore,
For there was no one living he loved more.
His feelings were as tenderly returned;
Indeed they were so fond, as I have learned,
That when one died (so ancient authors tell)
The other went to seek him down in Hell;
But that's a tale I have no time to treat.
Now this Perotheus knew and loved Arcite
In Theban days of old for many years,
And so, at his entreaty, it appears,
Arcita was awarded his release
Without a ransom; he could go in peace
And was left free to wander where he would
On one condition, be it understood,

As I shall tell you; the condition thus
Imposed upon Arcite by Theseus
Was that if ever he again were found
By day or night on any land or ground
Ruled by Duke Theseus, even for an hour,
And caught, the Duke should exercise his power;
It was agreed the knight should lose his head,
No remedy. What more could there be said?

Off went Arcite upon the homeward trek.
Let him beware! For he has pawned his neck.
What misery it cost him to depart!
He felt the stroke of death upon his heart,
He wept, he wailed. How piteously he cried
And secretly he thought of suicide.
He said, 'Alas the day that gave me birth!
Worse than my prison is the endless earth,
Now I am doomed eternally to dwell
No more in Purgatory but in Hell.
Alas that ever I knew Perotheus!
For else I had remained with Theseus.
Fettered in prison and without relief
I still had been in bliss and not in grief.
Only to see her whom I love and serve,
Though it were never granted to deserve
Her favor, would have been enough for me.
O my dear cousin Palamon,' said he,
'Yours is the victory in this adventure.
How blissfully you serve your long indenture
In prison – prison? No, in Paradise!
How happily has Fortune cast her dice
For you! You have her presence, I the loss.
For it is possible, since your paths may cross
And you're a knight, a worthy one, and able,
That by some chance – for Fortune is unstable –
You may attain to your desire at last.
But I, that am an exile and outcast,
Barren of grace and in such deep despair
That neither earth nor water, fire nor air,

Nor any creature that is made of these
Can ever bring me help, or do me ease,
I must despair and die in my distress.
Farewell my life, my joy, my happiness!
    'Alas, why is it people so dispraise
God's providence or Fortune and her ways,
That can so often give in many a guise
Far better things than ever they devise?
One man desires to have abundant wealth,
Which brings about his murder or ill-health;
Another, freed from prison as he'd willed,
Comes home, his servants catch him, and he's killed.
Infinite are the harms that come this way;
We little know the things for which we pray.
Our ways are drunkard ways – drunk as a mouse;
A drunkard knows quite well he has a house
But what he doesn't know is the way thither,
And for a drunk the way is slip and slither.
Such is our world indeed, and such are we.
How eagerly we seek felicity
Yet are so often wrong in what we try!
Yes, we can all say that, and so can I,
In whom the foolish notion had arisen
That if I only could escape from prison
I should be well, in pure beatitude,
Whereas I am an exile from my good,
For since I may not see you, Emily,
I am but dead and there's no remedy.'
    Now, on the other hand, poor Palamon,
When it was told him that Arcite had gone,
Fell in such grief, the tower where he was kept
Resounded to his yowling as he wept.
The very fetters on his mighty shins
Shine with his bitter tears as he begins,
'Alas, Arcite, dear cousin! In our dispute
And rivalry God knows you have the fruit.
I see you now in Thebes our native city
As free as air, with never a thought of pity

For me! You, an astute, determined man
Can soon assemble all our folk and clan
For war on Athens, make a sharp advance,
And by some treaty or perhaps by chance
Your lady may be won to be your wife
For whom, needs must, I here shall lose my life.
For, in the way of possibility,
As you're a prisoner no more, but free,
A Prince, you have the advantage to engage
In your affair. I perish in a cage,
For I must weep and suffer while I live
In all the anguish that a cell can give
And all the torment of my love, O care
That doubles all my suffering and despair.'

With that he felt the fire of jealousy start,
Flame in his breast and catch him by the heart
So madly that he seemed to fade and fail,
Cold as dead ashes, or as box-wood pale.
He cried, 'O cruel Gods, whose government
Binds all the world to your eternal bent,
And writes upon an adamantine table
All that your conclave has decreed as stable,
What more is man to you than to behold
A flock of sheep that cower in the fold?
For men are slain as much as other cattle,
Arrested, thrust in prison, killed in battle,
In sickness often and mischance, and fall
In innocency, for no guilt at all.
Where is your rule if prescience can determine
To doom the innocent of heart as vermin?
Yet there is more, for added to my load,
I am to pay the duties that are owed
To God, for Him I am to curb my will
In all the lusts that cattle may fulfill.
A dead beast has no punishment or pain,
But after death a man must weep again
That living has endured uncounted woe;
I have no doubt that it may well be so.

I leave the answer for divines to tell,
But that there's pain on earth I know too well.

    'I have seen many a serpent, many a thief
Bring down the innocent of heart to grief,
Yet be at large and take what turn they will.
But I lie languishing in prison still.
Juno and Saturn in their jealous rage
Have almost quelled our Theban lineage;
Thebes stands in waste, her walls are broken wide.
And Venus slays me on the other side
With jealous fears of what Arcite is doing.'

    Now I will turn a little from pursuing
Palamon's thoughts, and leave him in his cell,
For I have something of Arcite to tell.

    The summer passes, and long winter nights
Double the miseries and appetites
Of lover in jail and lover free as air.
I cannot tell you which had most to bear.
To put it shortly, Palamon the pale
Lies there condemned to a perpetual jail,
Chained up in fetters till his dying breath;
Arcita is exiled on pain of death
Forever from the long-desired shore
Where lives the lady he will see no more.

    You lovers, here's a question I would offer,
Arcite or Palamon, which had most to suffer?
The one can see his lady day by day,
But he must dwell in prison, locked away.
The other's free, the world lies all before,
But never shall he see his lady more.
Judge as you please between them, you that can,
For I'll tell on my tale as I began.

PART II

Now when Arcita got to Thebes again
Daylong he languished, crying out in pain

'Alas!' for never could he hope to see
His lady more. To sum his misery,
There never was a man so woe-begone,
Nor is, nor shall be while the world goes on
Meat, drink and sleep – he lay of all bereft,
Thin as a shaft, as dry, with nothing left.
He pined away, his eyes were sunk and old,
Fallow his face, like ashes dead and cold,
And he went solitary, all alone,
And wailed away the night in many a moan;
And if the sound of music touched his ears
He wept, unable to refrain his tears.
So feeble were his spirits and so low,
So changed his very being, none could know
His voice, his very accents were in doubt;
And so for all the world he went about
Not merely like a lover on the rack
Of Eros, but more like a maniac
In melancholy madness, under strain
Of fantasy – those cells that front the brain.
Briefly, his love had turned him upside-down
In looks and disposition, toe to crown,
This poor distracted lover, Prince Arcite.

But I shall take all day if I repeat
All that he suffered for the first two years
In cruel torment and in painful tears
At Thebes, in his home-country, as I said.

Now as he lay one night asleep in bed
Mercury, so he thought, whose feet are clad
With wings, stood there and bade him to be glad.
His sleep-imbuing wand he held in air,
He wore a hat upon his golden hair,
Arrayed (Arcita noticed) in the guise
He wore when closing up the hundred eyes·
Of Argus, and he said, 'You are to go
To Athens. There shall be an end to woe.'
And, on the word, Arcita with a start
Woke up and cried, 'However keen the smart,

I'll go Athens, now. The Gods have sent me,
Nor shall the fear of death itself prevent me
From seeing my lady. Though I were to die,
What should I care if she were standing by?'
    He rose and snatched a mirror from its place
And saw what change had come upon his face,
The color gone, the features redesigned,
And instantly it came into his mind
That being so disfigured and so wan
From the long sickness he had undergone,
He might, if he assumed a humble tone,
Live out his life in Athens unbeknown
And see his lady almost every day.
So, on the spot, he doffed his lord's array,
And dressed as a poor laborer seeking hire.
Then all alone, except for a young squire
Who knew the secret of his misery
And was disguised as wretchedly as he,
He went to Athens by the shortest way
And came to Court. And on the following day
Arcita proffered at the gate for hire
To do what drudgery they might require
And briefly (there is little to explain)
He fell in service with a chamberlain
Who had his dwelling there with Emily.
The man was cunning and was quick to see
What work the servants did and which were good.
Arcite could carry water or hew wood,
For he was young and powerfully grown,
A tall young fellow too, and big of bone,
Fit to do any work that was ordained.
    Thus, for a year or two, Arcite remained
With Emily the bright, her page-of-state,
And gave it out his name was Philostrate.
And half so well beloved a man as he
There never was at Court, of his degree.
He was so much a gentleman by breed
He grew quite famous through the Court indeed,

And it would be a charitable notion
(They said) if Theseus offered him promotion
And put him to a service less despised
In which his virtues might be exercised.
Thus in a little while his fame had sprung
Both for good deeds and for a courteous tongue,
And Theseus took him and advanced him higher,
Made him his personal and chamber-squire,
And gave him money to maintain his station.
There came, moreover, men of his own nation
Secretly, year by year, and brought his dues.
He spent them cunningly, these revenues,
But honestly; none wondered at his wealth.
Three years went by in happiness and health;
He bore himself so well in peace and war
That there was no one Theseus valued more.
I leave him there in bliss, though bliss is brittle,
And turn to speak of Palamon a little.

In darkness horrible and prison tears
Poor Palamon has sat for seven years,
Pining away in sorrow and distress.
Who feels a two-fold grief and heaviness
But Palamon the love-constrained? He sits
As one that woe has sundered from his wits.
On top of that he was in prison, due
To stay there ever, not a year or two.

Who could make rhymes in English fit to vie
With martyrdom like that? Indeed, not I.
Let me pass lightly over it and say
It happened in the seventh year, in May,
The third of May (my ancient sources give
This detail in their fuller narrative),
Whether by accident or destiny,
For as events are shaped they have to be,
Soon after midnight, ere the sun had risen,
Helped by a friend, Palamon broke from prison
And fled the town as fast as he could go.
A drink had proved his jailer's overthrow,

A kind of honeyed claret he had fixed
With Theban opium and narcotics mixed.
The jailer slept all night; had he been shaken
He would have been impossible to waken.
So off runs Palamon as best he may.
The night was short and it was nearly day,
So it was necessary he should hide.
Into a grove that flanked the city's side
Palamon stalked with terror-stricken feet.
Here was, in his opinion, a retreat
In which he could conceal himself all day
And whence at nightfall he could make his way
On towards Thebes and rally at his back
A host of friends all eager to attack
Duke Theseus. He would either lose his life
Or conquer and win Emily to wife.
That was his whole intention, fair and plain.

    I turn my story to Arcite again.
He little knew how close he was to care
Till Fortune brought him back into the snare.

    The busy lark, the messenger of day,
Sings salutation to the morning gray,
And fiery Phoebus rising up so bright
Sets all the Orient laughing with the light,
And with his streams he dries the dewy sheaves
And silver droplets hanging on the leaves.
And now Arcita, at the royal court,
Principal squire to Theseus, seeking sport
Has risen from bed and greets the merry day.
Thinking to do observances to May,
And musing on the point of his desires
He rode a courser full of flickering fires
Into the fields for pleasure and in play
A mile or two from where the palace lay,
And to the very grove you heard me mention
He chanced to hold his course, with the intention
To make himself a garland. There he weaves
A hawthorn-spray and honeysuckle leaves

And sings aloud against the sunny sheen
'O Month of May, with all thy flowers and green,
Welcome be thou, O fairest, freshest May,
Give me thy green in hope of happy day!'
  Quickly dismounting from his horse, he started
To thrust his way into the grove, light-hearted,
And roamed along the pathway on and on,
Until he came by chance where Palamon
Crouched in a bush, scarce daring to draw breath
Lest he be seen, in deadly fear of death.
He little thought Arcite had come in view,
God knows he could not have believed it true.
There is a proverb, older than the years,
That tells us 'Fields have eyes and woods have ears.'
It's good to keep one's poise and be protected,
Since all day long we meet the unexpected.
  Little indeed Arcita, truth to say,
Thought Palamon was listening to his lay
Crouched in a bush and keeping very still.
Presently, when Arcite had roamed his fill
And sung his roundel, he began to brood
And fell at once into a somber mood,
As do these lovers in their quaint desires,
Now on the spray, now down among the briars,
Now up, now down, like buckets in a well,
Just like a Friday morning, truth to tell,
Shining one moment and then raining fast.
So changey Venus loves to overcast
The hearts of all her folk; she, like her day,
Friday, is changeable. And so are they.
Seldom is Friday like the rest of the week.
  When he had sung Arcite began to speak,
Sighingly, sinking down as one forlorn.
'Alas,' he said, 'the day that I was born!
How long, O Juno, in thy cruelty
Wilt thou be harrying Thebes with misery?
Thou hast confounded those that played the lion,
The royal blood of Cadmus and Amphion!

Cadmus, the first of men to win renown
By building Thebes, or first in laying down
Her strong foundations, first to be crowned her king;
And I that share his lineage, I that spring
By right descent out of the royal stock,
Have fallen captive and am made a mock,
Slave to my mortal enemy, no higher
Than a contemptible, a menial squire!
Yet Juno does me even greater shame;
I dare no more acknowledge my own name.
Time was Arcita was my name by right;
Now I'm called Philostrate, not worth a mite!
Alas, fell Mars! Ah, Juno, stern of face,
You have destroyed our kin without a trace
Save for myself and Palamon, who dwells
In martyrdom, poor wretch, in Theseus' cells.
On top of this, to slay me utterly.
The fiery dart of love so burningly
Thrusts through my faithful heart with deadly hurt!
My death was shaped for me before my shirt.
You kill me with your eyes, my Emily,
You are the cause that brings my death on me!
All the remainder of my cares and needs
I'd rate no higher than a mound of weeds
Could I but please or earn a grateful glance!'
    And on the word he fell into a trance
A long, long time, then woke and moved apart.
    Palamon felt a cleaving in his heart
As of a cold sword suddenly gliding through.
He quaked with anger; hiding would not do
Now that he'd listened to Arcita's tale,
And with a madman's face, extinct and pale,
He started up out of his bushy thicket
And cried, 'Arcita! Traitor! False and wicked,
Now you are caught that love my lady so,
For whom I suffer all this pain and woe,
And are my blood – sworn friend – for so we swore
As I have told you many times before,

And you have cheated Theseus with this game,
False as you are, of a pretended name!
Let it be death for you or death for me.
You shall not love my lady Emily.
I, no one else, will love her! Look and know
That I am Palamon your mortal foe.
And though I have no weapon in this place,
Having escaped from prison by God's grace,
I doubt it not you shall be slain by me
Or else yield up the love of Emily.
You shan't escape me, therefore choose your part!'
     Arcite, however, full of scorn at heart,
Knowing his face and hearing what he said,
Fierce as a lion drew his sword instead
And answered him, 'By God that sits above,
Were you not sick, and lunatic for love,
And weaponless moreover in this place,
You never should so much as take a pace
Beyond this grove, but perish at my hand.
And I denounce all covenants that stand
Or are alleged, as between you and me.
Fool that you are, remember love is free
And I will love her! I defy your might.
Yet, as you are an honorable knight
Willing by battle to decide your claim,
Tomorrow, by the honor of my name
I will not fail you, nor will make it known
To anyone. Tomorrow, here, alone
You'll find me as a knight, and on my oath
I shall bring arms and harness for us both;
And you shall have the right of choosing first,
Taking the best and leaving me the worst.
I'll bring you meat and drink, let that be said,
Enough for you, and clothes to make your bed.
As for my lady, should you chance to win
And kill me in this thicket we are in,
Then you can have your lady as for me.'
And Palamon gave answer, 'I agree.'

68

And thus they parted at the coppice-edge
Until the morning. Each had given pledge.
　O Cupid, Cupid, lost to charity!
O realm that brooks no fellow-king in thee!
Well is it said that neither love nor power
Admit a rival, even for an hour.
Arcite and Palamon had found that out.
　So back to town Arcite turned about,
And the next morning, ere the day was light,
He filched two suits of armor by a sleight,
Fully sufficient for the work in hand,
The battle in the fields, as they had planned.
Alone as at his birth Arcita rode
And carried all the armor in a load.
There in the grove where time and place were set
These two, Arcite and Palamon, are met.
　Then slowly changed the color in each face
Just as when hunters in the realm of Thrace
That standing in the gap will poise a spear
And wait for bear or lion to appear,
Then hear him coming, breaking through the branches,
And hear the swish of leaves upon his haunches,
And think, 'Here comes my mortal enemy!
It's either death for him or death for me.
For either I must slay him at this gap
Or he slay me, if I should have mishap.'
Just so these knights changed color when they met,
Knowing each other and the purpose set.
　There was no salutation, no 'Good day,'
But without word or prelude straight away
Each of them gave his help to arm the other
As friendly as a brother to his brother;
And after that with spears of sharpened strength
They fought each other at amazing length.
You would have thought, seeing Palamon engage,
He was a lion fighting-mad with rage,
Arcite a cruel tiger, as they beat
And smote each other, or as boars that meet

And froth as white as foam upon the flood.
They fought till they were ankle-deep in blood.
And in this rage I leave them fighting thus
And turn once more to speak of Theseus.

Now Destiny, that Minister-General
Who executes on earth and over all
That providence which God has long foreseen,
Has so much power that though the world might ween
The contrary, swearing by Yea and Nay,
It still would happen on a certain day,
Though never again within a thousand years.
And certainly our appetites and fears,
Whether in war or peace, in hate or love,
Are governed by a providence above.

This must explain why mighty Theseus found
A sudden wish to hunt with horse and hound,
Especially the hart in early May.
About his bed there never dawned a day
But he was up and ready dressed to ride
With horn and hound and hunter at his side.
Hunting to him was such a keen delight
It was his ruling joy and appetite
To be a stag's destroyer, for the stars
Ruled he should serve Diana after Mars.

Clear was the day, as I have told ere this,
And Theseus, bathed in happiness and bliss,
With fair Hippolyta, his lovely Queen,
And Emily, who was arrayed in green,
Rode out to hunt; it was a royal band.
And to the coppice lying near at hand
In which a hart – or so they told him – lay,
He led his gathering by the shortest way.
And pressing on towards a glade in sight
Down which the hart most often took to flight
Over a brook and off and out of view,
The Duke had hopes to try a course or two
With certain hounds that he had singled out;
And when he reached the glade he looked about.

Glancing towards the sun he thereupon
Beheld Arcita fighting Palamon.
They fought like boars in bravery. There go
The shining swords in circle, to and fro,
So hideously that with their lightest stroke
It seemed as if they would have felled an oak.
What they could be he did not know, of course,
But he clapped spur at once into his horse
And, at a bound, he parted blow from blow,
And pulling out his sword he shouted, 'Ho!
No more on pain of death! Upon your head!
By mighty Mars the next to strike is dead,
The next to make a movement that I see!
Tell me, what sort of fellows may you be
That have the impudence to combat here
Without a judge or other overseer,
Yet as if jousting at a royal tilt?'

Palamon answered quickly and in guilt,
'O Sir, what need of further word or breath?
Both of us have deserved to die the death,
Two wretched men, your captives, met in strife,
And each of them encumbered with his life.
And as you are a righteous judge and lord
Give neither of us refuge, and accord
No grace.... Yet kill me first, in charity!
But kill my fellow too, as well as me.
Or kill him first, for little though you know,
This is Arcita and your mortal foe,
Banished by you on forfeit of his head,
For which alone he merits to be dead.
This is the man that waited at your gate
And told you that his name was Philostrate.
This is the man that mocked you many a year,
And you have made him chief equerry here.
This is the man who dares love Emily.
Now, since my day of death has come to me,
I will make full confession and go on
To say I am that woeful Palamon

That broke out of your jail feloniously.
And it is I, your mortal enemy,
That am in love with Emily the Bright
And glad to die this moment in her sight.
And so I ask for judgment and for death;
But slay my fellow in the self-same breath,
Since we have both deserved that we be slain!'

And noble Theseus answered back again,
'This is a short conclusion. It shall stand.
Your own confession damns you out of hand.
I shall record your sentence as it stood;
There needs no torturing to make it good.
Death you shall have, by mighty Mars the Red!'

On hearing this, the Queen began to shed
Her womanly tears, and so did Emily
And all the ladies in the company.
It seemed so very piteous to them all
That ever such misfortune should befall
Two gentlemen, that were of high estate,
And love the only cause of their debate.
They saw their bloody gashes gaping wide
And, from the greatest to the least, they cried,
'Have mercy, Lord, upon us women all!'
Down on their knees they then began to fall,
Ready to kiss his feet as there he stood.

Abated in the end his angry mood;
Pity runs swiftly in a noble heart.
Though he had quaked with anger at the start
He had reflected, having time to pause,
Upon their trespass and upon its cause,
And what his anger at their guilt refused
In way of pardon, reason now excused;
For thus he argued: almost any man
Will help himself to love, if so he can,
And anyone will try to break from prison;
And then compassion in his heart had risen
Seeing these ladies weeping there together,
And in his noble heart he wondered whether

He should not show his clemency, and 'Fie,'
He thought, 'on lords who show no mercy! Why,
To be a lion both in word and deed
Towards a penitent is not to heed
His change of heart; it equals him with one
Proudly persisting in an evil done.
A lord will lack discretion among his graces
Who does not make distinction in such cases,
But weighs humility and pride as one.'
And, to be brief, his anger being done,
His eyes began to sparkle and uncloud
And having taken thought he said aloud:
'The God of Love! Ah, *Benedicite!*
How mighty and how great a lord is he!
No obstacles for him make any odds;
His miracles proclaim his power a God's.
Cupid can make of every heart and soul
Just what he pleases, such is his control.
Look at Arcita here and Palamon!
Both had escaped scot-free and could have gone
To Thebes and lived there royally; they know
That I have ever been their mortal foe;
Their lives are mine, they can make no defense;
Yet Cupid in the teeth of common sense
Has brought them here to die in melancholy!
Consider, is it not the height of folly?
What is so foolish as a man in love?
Look at them both! By God that sits above
See how they bleed! Are they not well arrayed?
Thus has their lord, the God of Love, repaid
Their services; these are his fees and wages!
And yet, in spite of that, they pose as sages,
These devotees of Love, as I recall.
But still this is the finest stroke of all,
That she, the cause of all these jolly pranks,
Has no more reason to return them thanks
Than I, and knows no more of this affair
By God, than does a cuckoo or a hare!

Well, well, try anything once, come hot, come cold.
If we're not foolish young, we're foolish old.
I long have known myself what Love can do,
For, in my time, I was a lover too.
And therefore, knowing something of love's pain,
How violently it puts a man to strain,
As one so often caught in the same snare,
I readily forgive the whole affair,
Both at the Queen's request, that on her knees
Petitions, and my sister Emily's.
But you shall swear to me, and give your hands
Upon it, never to attack my lands,
Or levy war on me by night or day,
But be my friends in everything you may.
I pardon you your fault. You are forgiven.'

    They swore as he had asked, and, having striven
To gain his patronage and further grace,
Were satisfied, and Theseus summed the case:
    'So far as riches go, and nobleness,
Were she a queen in question, or princess,
You would be worthy when the moment came,
Either of you, to marry. All the same,
Speaking as for my sister Emily,
The cause of all your strife and jealousy,
You are aware yourselves that she can never
Wed both at once, though you should fight forever,
And one of you, come joy to him or grief,
Must go pipe tunes upon an ivy-leaf;
That is to say she cannot have you both
However jealous you may be or loth.
And so, to put the matter in good order,
Let Destiny herself be your recorder
And shape your fortune. Listen to the close,
For here is the solution I propose.

    'My will is this, to make a flat conclusion
And end all counterpleading and confusion,
(And you will please to take it for the best)
That each shall take his freedom, east or west,

And without ransom or the threat of war;
And, a year later, neither less nor more,
Each shall return, bringing a hundred knights,
Armed for the lists and everything to rights,
Ready by battle to decide his claim
To Emily. To this I give my name,
My faith and honor, as I am a knight.
Whichever of you proves of greater might,
Or, more precisely, whether you or he,
Backed by the hundred knights allowed by me,
Can drive his foe to stake, or take his life,
To him I shall give Emily to wife,
To whom kind Fortune gives so fair a grace.
I'll build the lists upon this very place,
And God in wisdom deal my soul its due
As I shall prove an even judge and true.
There is no other way, let that be plain;
One of you must be taken or else slain.
And if this seems to you to be well said,
Think yourselves lucky, sirs, and nod your head.
That's the conclusion I've decided on.'

    Who looks delighted now but Palamon?
And who springs up rejoicing but Arcite?
And who could tell, what poetry repeat
The joy of all those present in the place
That Theseus had vouchsafed so fair a grace?
Down on their knees went everyone in sight
Returning thanks with all their heart and might,
Especially the Thebans, time on time.
Thus in good hope, with beating heart a-climb,
Each took his leave, and they began to ride
To Thebes and to her ancient walls and wide.

PART III

I JUDGE it would be held for negligence
If I forgot to tell of the dispense

Of money by the Duke who set about
To make the lists a royal show throughout.
A theater more noble in its plan
I dare well say was never seen by man.
It had a circuit of a mile about,
Well walled with stone; there was a ditch without.
Shaped like a circle, there it stood complete
In tier on tier, the height of sixty feet,
So that a man set in a given row
Did not obstruct his neighbor from below.

Eastward there stood a gate of marble white,
And westward such another rose to sight;
Briefly, there never was upon the face
Of earth so much within so small a space.
No craftsmen in the land that had the trick
Of pure geometry, arithmetic,
Portraiture, carving and erecting stages
But Theseus found him and supplied his wages
To build this theater and carve devices.
And, to observe due rights and sacrifices,
Eastward he built upon the gate, above,
An oratory to the Queen of Love,
To Venus and her worship, and he dressed
An altar there; and like it, to the west,
In reverence to Mars he built a second;
The cost in gold was hardly to be reckoned.
Yet, northward, in a turret on the wall
He built a third, an oratory tall
And rich, of whitest alabaster, set
With crimson coral, to discharge the debt
Of worship to Diana of Chastity.
And it was thus that Theseus built these three
Temples in great magnificence of style.

But yet I have forgotten all this while
To tell you of the portraits that there were,
The shapes, the carvings and the figures there
To grace these temples high above the green.

First, in the temple of Venus, you had seen

Wrought on the wall, and piteous to behold,
The broken sleeps and sighings manifold,
The sacred tears and the lamenting songs
And every fiery passion that belongs
To those that suffer love the long-endured,
Their taken oaths, their covenants assured,
Pleasure and hope, desire, foolhardiness,
Beauty and youth, lasciviousness, largesse,
Philters and force, false tales and flattery,
Extravagance, intrigue, and jealousy
Gold-garlanded with many a yellow twist,
That had a cuckoo sitting on her wrist.
Stringed instruments, and carols, feasts and dances,
Joy and display, and all the circumstances
Of love, as I have told you and shall tell,
Were in due order painted there as well,
And more than I can mention or recount.
Truly the whole of Citherea's Mount,
Where Venus has her dwelling above all
Her other playgrounds, figured on the wall
With all her garden in its joyful dress.
Nor was forgotten her porter, Idleness,
Nor yet Narcissus, beauty's paragon
In times gone by, nor doting Solomon,
Nor the unmastered strength of Hercules.
Medea and her enchantments next to these,
And Circe's too, and Turnus fierce and brave,
And rich King Croesus, captive and a slave,
That men might see that neither wit nor wealth,
Beauty or cunning, bravery or health
Can challenge Venus or advance their worth
Against that goddess who controls the earth.
And all these people captured in her noose
Cried out, 'Alas!' but it was little use.
Suffice these few examples, but the score
Could well be reckoned many thousands more.
    Her statue, glorious in majesty,
Stood naked, floating on a vasty sea,

And from the navel down there were a mass
Of green and glittering waves as bright as glass.
In her right hand a cithern carried she,
And on her head, most beautiful to see,
A garland of fresh roses, while above
There circled round her many a flickering dove.

Cupid her son was standing to behold her
Fronting her statue, winged on either shoulder,
And he was blind, as it is often seen;
He bore a bow with arrows bright and keen.

Why should I not go on to tell you all
The portraiture depicted on the wall
Within the Temple of Mighty Mars the Red?
The walls were painted round and overhead
Like the recesses of that grisly place
Known as the Temple of Great Mars in Thrace,
That frosty region under chilling stars
Where stands the sovereign mansion of King Mars.

First on the walls a forest with no plan
Inhabited by neither beast nor man
Was painted – tree-trunks, knotted, gnarled and old,
Jagged and barren, hideous to behold,
Through which there ran a rumble and a soughing
As though a storm should break the branches bowing
Before it. Downwards from a hill there went
A slope; the Temple of Omnipotent
Mars was erected there in steel, and burnished.
The Gateway, narrow and forbidding, furnished
A ghastly sight, and such a rushing quake
Raged from within, the portals seemed to shake.
In at the doors a northern glimmer shone
Onto the walls, for windows there were none;
One scarce discerned a light, it was so scant.
The doors were of eternal adamant,
And vertically clenched, and clenched across
For greater strength with many an iron boss,
And every pillar to support the shrine
Weighed a full ton of iron, bright and fine.

And there I saw the dark imaginings
Of felony, the stratagems of kings,
And cruel wrath that glowed an ember-red,
The pick-purse and the coward pale with dread,
The smiler with the knife beneath his cloak,
The out-houses that burnt with blackened smoke;
Treason was there, a murder on a bed,
And open war, with wounds that gaped and bled;
Dispute, with bloody knife and snarling threat;
A screaming made the place more dreadful yet.
The slayer of himself, I saw him there
With all his heart's blood matted in his hair;
The driven nail that made the forehead crack,
And death stone-cold and gaping on his back.

And in the middle of the shrine mischance
Stood comfortless with sorry countenance.
There I saw madness cackling his distress,
Armed insurrection, outcry, fierce excess,
The carrion in the undergrowth slit-throated
And thousands violently slain. I noted
The raping tyrant with his prey o'ertaken,
The leveled city, gutted and forsaken,
The ships on fire dancingly entangled,
The luckless hunter that wild bears had strangled,
The sow devouring children in the cradle,
The scalded cook who had too short a ladle —
Nothing forgotten of the unhappy art
Of Mars: the carter crushed beneath his cart,
Flung to the earth and pinned beneath the wheel;
Those also on whom Mars has set his seal,
The barber and the butcher and the smith
Who forges things a man may murder with.
And high above, depicted in a tower,
Sat Conquest, robed in majesty and power,
Under a sword that swung above his head,
Sharp-edged and hanging by a subtle thread.

And Caesar's slaughter stood in effigy
And that of Nero and Mark Antony;

Though to be sure they were as yet unborn.
Their deaths were there prefigured to adorn
This Temple with the menaces of Mars,
As it is also painted in the stars
Who shall be murdered, who shall die for love;
Such were the portraits on the walls above.
Let these examples from the past hold good,
For all I cannot reckon, though I would.

    Mars in a chariot was carved, and clad
In armor, grim and staring, like the mad,
Above his head there shone with blazing looks
Two starry figures, named in ancient books,
Puella one, the other Rubeus.
The God of Battles was encompassed thus:
There stood a wolf before him at his feet,
His eyes glowed red, he had a man to eat.
Subtle the pencil was that told this story
Picturing Mars in terror and in glory.

    The Temple of Diana now, the Chaste,
Let me describe, and I shall use such haste
And brevity in that I now recall
As possible. The paintings on the wall
Were scenes of hunting and of chastity.
There I perceived the sad Callisto, she
Whom in her rage Diana did not spare,
But changed her from a woman to a bear,
Then to a star, and she was painted so
(She is the lode-star, that is all I know;
Her son, too, is a star, as one can see).
There I saw Dana, turned into a tree*
(No, not Diana, she was not the same,
But Penneus' daughter, Dana was her name).
I saw Actaeon turned into a stag;
This was Diana's vengeance, lest he brag
Of having seen her naked. There they show him
Caught and devoured – his own hounds did not know him.
Close by there was a painting furthermore
Of Atalanta hunting a wild boar,

And Meleager; there were others too
Diana chose to harry and undo,
And many other wonders on the wall
Were painted, that I need not now recall.

   High on a stag the Goddess held her seat,
And there were little hounds about her feet;
Below her feet there was a sickle moon,
Waxing it seemed, but would be waning soon.
Her statue bore a mantle of bright green,
Her hand a bow with arrows cased and keen;
Her eyes were lowered, gazing, as she rode,
Down to where Pluto has his dark abode.
A woman in her travail lay before her,
Her child unborn; she ceased not to implore her
To be delivered and with piteous call
Cried, 'Help, Lucina, thou the best of all!'
It was a lively painting, every shade
Had cost the painter many a florin paid.

   And now the lists were made, and Theseus
Who, at huge cost, had bidden them produce
These temples in a theater so stately,
Saw it was finished, and it pleased him greatly.
No more of Theseus now; I must pass on
To speak of Arcite and of Palamon.

   The day approached for trial of their rights
When each should bring with him a hundred knights
To settle all by battle, as I said;
So, back to Athens each of them had led
His hundred knights, all helmeted and spurred
And armed for war. They meant to keep their word.
And it was said indeed by many a man
That never since the day the world began
In all God's earth, wide seas and reach of land,
Had so few men made such a noble band
As in respect of knighthood and degree.
Everyone with a taste for chivalry
And eager, of course, to win a glorious name
Had begged to be allowed to join the game.

Lucky for those selected, so I say!
If such a thing should happen here to-day,
As you can well imagine, every knight
Who loves a lady and is game to fight,
Whether in England here, or anywhere,
Would certainly feel eager to be there.
Fight for a lady? *Benedicite!*
That would be something for a man to see.

And that was just the case with Palamon.
His knights had come and had been taken on;
Some were in coat of mail and others wore
A breastplate and a tunic, little more.
Some carried heavy plating, front and back,
And some a Prussian shield to ward attack;
Some cased their legs in armor, thigh to heel,
Some bore an ax and some a mace of steel
– There's never a new fashion but it's old –
And so they armed themselves as I have told,
Each man according to his own opinion.

You might have seen arrive from his dominion
Mighty Lycurgus, famous King of Thrace;
Black was his beard and manly was his face.
To see the circling eye-balls of the fellow
Set in his head and glowing red and yellow!
And like a gryphon he would stare and rouse
The shaggy hair upon his beetling brows.
Huge were his limbs, his muscles hard and strong,
His back was broad, his bulging arms were long.
True to his country's custom from of old
He towered in a chariot of gold
And four white bulls were harnessed in the traces.
Over his armor, which in many places
Was studded with bright nails of yellow gold,
He wore a coal-black bear-skin, fold on fold,
Blackened with age; and down behind his back
His fell of hair was combed and shone as black
As raven's feather, and a golden wreath,
Thick as your arm, weighted the head beneath.

It was immensely heavy, and was bright
With many precious stones of fiery light,
With finest rubies and with diamonds.
About his chariot, white enormous hounds,
Twenty and more, each larger than a steer,
And trained to hunt the lion and the deer,
Went following him. Their muzzles were fast bound;
Their collars were of gold with rings set round.
He had a hundred nobles in his rout
Armed to the teeth; their hearts were stern and stout.

   And with Arcita, so the poets sing,
Went great Emetrius the Indian king
On a bay steed, whose trappings were of steel,
Covered in cloth of gold from haunch to heel,
Fretted with diaper. Like Mars to see,
His surcoat was in cloth of Tartary,
Studded with great white pearls; beneath its fold
A saddle of new-beaten burnished gold.
He had a mantle hanging from his shoulders
Which, crammed with rubies, dazzled all beholders.
His hair was crisped in ringlets, as if spun
In yellow, and it glittered like the sun.
Aquiline nose and eyes with lemon light
And rounded lips he had, his color bright,
With a few freckles sprinkled here and there,
Some yellow and some black. He bore an air
As of a lion when he cast a glance.
He was some twenty-five years old, to chance
A guess at it; a healthy beard was springing.
His voice resounded like a trumpet ringing.
He had a wreath of laurel on his head
For he was freshly, greenly garlanded.
And on his hand he bore for his delight
An eagle; it was tame and lily-white.
He had a hundred lords beside him there,
In all their armor (though their heads were bare)
And sumptuously decked with furnishings.
For take my word for it that dukes and kings

Were gathered in this noble company
For love and for the spread of chivalry.
Many a lion tame and spotted pard
Gamboled about this king of stern regard,
And in this manner in their fine adorning
These lords came to the city on Sunday morning,
Round about nine o'clock, and lighted down.

The noble Theseus led them through his town
(So it became him as a duke and knight),
And housed them each according to his right.
He feasted them and took great pains to please,
To honor and to set them all at ease,
And to this day it's said no human wit
However lofty could have bettered it.

What minstrelsy, what service at the feast,
What gifts bestowed on greatest as on least,
How richly decked the palace, what the place
Ordained for first and last upon the dais,
What ladies loveliest in the dancing throng,
And which most exquisite in dance and song
And which to speak most feelingly of love,
Or what the falcons that were perched above,
And what the hounds that couched upon the floor —
Of all such questions I shall say no more
Than the result of it; I will not tease you,
Here comes the point, so listen if it please you.

That Sunday night ere day began to spring
There was a lark which Palamon heard sing
(Although two hours before the day came on
Yet the lark sang, and so did Palamon).
With holy heart and in a lofty mood
He rose on pilgrimage and he pursued
His path to Citherea, the benign
And blissful Venus, to her honored shrine.
And in her hour, among the early mists,
He stepped towards her Temple in the lists
And down he knelt in humbleness and fear
With aching heart, and said as you shall hear:

'Fairest of Fair, O Venus, Lady mine,
Consort of Vulcan, Daughter of Jove Divine,
Giver of joy upon the heights above
The Mount of Citherea, by that love
Thou gavest to Adonis, heal my smart
And take my humble prayer into thy heart.
Alas! I have no language that can tell
The ravages and torments of my hell,
Which heart is all unable to bewray,
And I am so confused I cannot say
More than: "O Lady bright, that art aware
Of all my thought and seest my despair,
Consider this, have pity on my pain
As I shall ever struggle to maintain
Thy service, in so far as it shall be
Within my power to combat chastity."
There is my vow if you will tend my harms.
I am not one to brag of deeds of arms,
Nor do I ask for victory to-morrow,
Nor for renown; I neither seek nor borrow
Vainglorious praises or the proud profession
Of prowess, but would fully have possession
Of Emily, and die thy worshiper.
Choose Thou the means for this, administer
The ways, I care not how, whether it be
By my defeat of them, or theirs of me,
So that I have my lady in my arms.
Though Mars be god of battles and alarms
Thy power is so great in Heaven above
That if thou please I well may have my love.
And I will worship at thy shrine forever;
Ride where I may, to thee my whole endeavor
Shall be in sacrifice and kindling fires
Upon thy altars. Yet if my desires,
Sweet lady, cannot please thee, end my sorrow
With death upon Arcita's spear to-morrow.
I shall not care when I have lost my life,
Though he should win my Emily to wife.

This is the sum and purpose of my prayer,
Give me my love, sweet Goddess ever fair!'
    When Palamon had done his orison
He then did sacrifice with woe-begone
Devotion and with ceremonial rite
More than I now have leisure to recite.
And in the end the statue of Venus shook
And made a sign; and by that sign he took
His prayer had been accepted on that day,
For though the sign had hinted a delay
He knew for certain that his boon was granted,
And home he went at once, his soul enchanted.

    In the third hour after Palamon
Had sought out Venus for his orison,
Up rose the sun, and up rose Emily
And hastened to Diana's sanctuary,
Taking such maidens as she might require
And they were ready furnished with the fire,
The incense and the vestments and a throng
Of other necessaries that belong
To sacrifices, horns of brimming mead,
As was the custom, all that they could need.
The Temple smoked and the adornments there
Glittered in beauty. Emily the fair
Joyfully washed her body in a well,
But how she did her rite I dare not tell
Save in a general way, though I for one
Think that to hear the detail would be fun.
If one means well why bother to feel queasy?
It's good for people to be free and easy.
Her shining hair untressed upon her cloak
They combed, and set a crown of cerrial oak
Green on her golden head, with fitting grace.
Two fires she kindled in the proper place
And did her rites, as he will find who looks
In Statius' *Book of Thebes* and other books,
And when the fires were kindled she drew near
With piteous heart, and prayed as you shall hear:

'O Goddess Chaste of all the woodlands green,
That seest earth and heaven and sea, O Queen
Of Pluto's kingdom, dark and deep below,
Goddess of virgins, that from long ago
Hast known my heart, and knowest my desire,
As I may shun the vengeance of thine ire
Such as upon Actaeon once was spent,
Thou knowest well, O chaste omnipotent,
That I would be a virgin all my life
And would be neither mistress, no, nor wife.
I am, thou knowest, of thy company,
A huntress, still in my virginity,
And only ask to walk the woodlands wild,
And not to be a wife or go with child,
Nor would I know the company of man.
O help me, Goddess, for none other can,
By the three Forms that ever dwell in thee,*
And as for Palamon who longs for me
And for Arcita's passion, I implore
This favor of thy grace and nothing more;
Set them in amity and let them be
At peace, and turn their hearts away from me.
Let all their violent loves and hot desires,
Their ceaseless torments and consuming fires,
Be quenched, or turned towards another place.
Yet if thou wilt not do me so much grace,
Or if my destiny ordains it so
That one shall have me whether I will or no,
Then send me him that shall desire me most.
Clean Goddess of the chaste and virgin host,
Look down upon the bitter tears that fall
Upon my cheeks, O keeper of us all,
Keep thou my maidhood, prosper my endeavor,
And while I live a maid I'll serve thee ever.'

The fires flamed up upon the altar fair
And clear while Emily was thus in prayer;
But all at once she saw a curious sight,
For suddenly one fire quenched its light

And then rekindled; as she gazed in doubt
The other fire as suddenly went right out;
As it was quenched it made a whistling sound
As of wet branches burning on the ground.
Then, from the faggot's tip, there ran a flood
Of many drops that had the look of blood.

Now at the sight she was so terrified
It almost drove her from her wits; she cried,
Not knowing what it was to signify,
For it was fear alone that made her cry,
She wept and it was pitful to hear.
And then began Diana to appear,
With bow in hand, garbed as a Hunteress,
And said, 'My daughter, cease your heaviness.
For thee the Gods on high have set their term,
And, by eternal word and writ, confirm
That thou shalt be espoused to one of those
That have for thee endured so many woes.
But unto which of them I may not tell
Longer I cannot tarry, fare thee well.
And yet the fires of sacrifice that glow
Upon my altar shall, before thou go,
Make plain thy destiny in this forever.'

And on the word the arrows in her quiver
Clattered together and began to ring
And forth she went and made a vanishing.

Wholly amazed at what had come to pass,
Emily thought, 'What can this mean? Alas!
O take me, take me under thy protection,
Diana, for I yield to thy direction!'
Then she went homeward by the shortest way
And that was all, there is no more to say.

Now in the hour of Mars next after this
Arcite rose up and sought the edifice
Of fiery Mars, to do beneath his banner
His sacrifice, as was the pagan manner,
In high devotion with a piteous heart,
And thus he said his orison apart:

'O thou strong God of War that art adored
In the cold realms of Thrace and held for Lord;
That hast of every monarchy and land
Of warlike men the bridle in thine hand,
And dealest them their fortunes by thy choice,
Accept my sacrifice and hear my voice.
And if my youth be such as to deserve
Thy favor, if my strength be fit to serve
Thy godhead, if I may be one of thine,
I pray thee then, pity this pain of mine.

'By that same suffering and burning fire
That long ago consumed thee with desire,
Having in use the incomparable flesh
Of fair free-hearted Venus, young and fresh,
Holding her in thine arms and at thy will,
– Albeit that once the time was chosen ill,
Seeing that Vulcan caught thee in his net
And found thee lying with his wife – but yet
By all the pain and passion of thy heart
Pity me too that suffer the same smart!
Thou knowest I am ignorant and young,
And, as I think, more passionately stung
By love than any creature dead or living;
Little she thinks, in all the grief she's giving,
Of me, or cares whether I swim or sink,
And well I know ere she can learn to think
Kindly of me that force must have its place,
And well I know without thy help or grace
The little strength I have is all too slight;
Then help me, Lord, to-morrow in the fight,
Not only for the flames that burnt in thee
But for the fire that now is burning me.
Grant victory to-morrow to my sword!
Mine be the labor, thine the glory, Lord;
Thy sovereign temple I will honor above
All other places, it shall be my love
To work for thy delight, to use thy arts,
And hang my banner, yea, my heart of hearts

Above thy altar. All my Company
Shall do the same forever, there shall be
Eternal fires burning at thy Shrine,
Nay, further to this binding vow of mine,
My beard and hair, whose length and excellence
Has never suffered yet from the offense
Of razor or of shear, to Thee I give,
And will be thy true servant while I live.
Now, Lord, have pity on a heart so sore;
And give me victory, I ask no more.'

   His prayer was over, and the rings that hung
Upon the portals of the Temple swung;
So did the doors and clattered far and near,
At which Arcita felt the touch of fear.
The fires blazed, the altar glistened bright,
So that the Temple was suffused with light,
A scented air rose upward from the ground.
Arcita lifted up his hand and found
More incense and he cast it on the flame
With other rituals. At last the frame
Of mighty Mars began to shake and ring
Its hauberk, and he heard a murmuring,
Low-voiced and dim, that answered *'Victory';*
And giving thanks and glorifying he,
Filed with the joyful hope that he would win,
Returned at once and went to seek his inn,
As happy as a bird is of the sun.

   Immediately an uproar was begun
Over this granted boon in Heaven above,
As between Venus, fairest Queen of Love,
And the armipotent Mars; it did not cease,
Though Jupiter was busy making peace,
Until their father Saturn, pale and cold,
Who knew so many stratagems of old,
Searched his experience and found an art
To please the disputants on either part.
Age has a great advantage over youth
In wisdom and by custom, that's the truth.

The old may be out-run but not out-reasoned.
And Saturn stopped their argument and seasoned
Their fears, although it's not his nature to,
And found a remedy for this to-do.

   'My dearest daughter Venus,' said old Saturn,
'My heavenly orbit marks so wide a pattern
It has more power than anyone can know;
In the wan sea I drown and overthrow,
Mine is the prisoner in the darkling pit,
Mine are both neck and noose that strangles it,
Mine the rebellion of the serfs astir,
The murmurings, the privy poisoner;
And I do vengeance, I send punishment,
And when I am in *Leo* it is sent.
Mine is the ruin of the lofty hall,
The falling down of tower and of wall
On carpenter and mason, I their killer.
'Twas I slew Samson when he shook the pillar;
Mine are the maladies that kill with cold,
The dark deceits, the stratagems of old;
A look from me will father pestilence.
Then weep no more, for by my diligence
This Palamon, your dedicated knight,
Shall have his lady, as you swore he might.
Though Mars should help his champion, none the less
Peace must be made between you soon, I guess,
Although you do not share the same complexions;
That is what brings these daily insurrections.
I am your grandfather and, as before,
I'll do my best to please you; weep no more.'

   Now I shall cease to speak of Gods above,
Of angry Mars and Venus Queen of Love,
And tell you all, as plainly as I can,
The grand result for which I first began.

PART IV

GREAT was the festival they held that day
In Athens, and the lusty time of May
Put everyone so well in countenance
They spent all Monday at a joust and dance
And the high services of Venus. Yet
Because they knew that up they'd have to get,
And early too, to witness the great fight,
They went to bed betimes on Monday night.

Next morning when the day began to spring
Clattering horse and noise of harnessing
Echoed through all the hostelries about.
Up to the palace cantered rout on rout
Of lords on palfreys, stallions, many a steed;
And what device of harness too indeed,
So rich and so outlandish, what a deal
Of goldsmith work, embroidery and steel!
Bright shields and trophies, headpieces and charms,
Great golden helmets, hauberks, coats of arms,
Lords on appareled coursers, squires too
And knights belonging to their retinue,
Spears being nailed and helmets buckled strong,
Strapping of shields and lacing up of thong,
The work was urgent, not a man was idle.
The foamy steeds gnawing the golden bridle,
The armorers up and down and round about
Racing with file and hammer through the rout,
Yeomen on foot and commonalty come
With pipe and clarion, trump and kettle-drum,
Armed with short sticks and making such a rattle
It sounded like the blast of bloody battle.
The palace full of people up and down,
Here three, there ten, in all the talk of town
And making bets about the Theban knights.
Says one, 'He'll win'; another, 'Not by rights';
Some backed the man whose beard was black and squared,
Some backed the bald and some the shaggy-haired;

Said one, 'There's a grim fellow, I'll be bound,
He has a battle-ax weighs twenty pound!'
And prophecy went seething round the hall
Long after day had sprung upon them all.

Great Theseus was awoken out of sleep
By minstrelsy and noise about the keep,
But kept his chamber – such a splendid room –
Till the two Theban knights, to both of whom
An equal honor was done, were brought in presence.

Throned in a window giving on a pleasance
Sat Theseus like a god in panoply,
And all the people crowded there to see
The Duke and offer him their reverence
And hear what orders he might issue thence.
A herald on a scaffold shouted 'Ho!'
Till all the noise was quieted below;
Seeing at last the people hushed and still
He thus declared the mighty Theseus' will:

'Our Lord the Duke has in his high discretion
Considered the destruction and suppression
Of gentle blood, were he to jeopardize
The lives of those engaging under guise
Of mortal battle. Wishing none to die,
His Grace now purposes to modify
His ordinance. On forfeit of your lives
No sort of dart, no poleaxes or knives
May pass into the lists or be conveyed
Thither, no stabbing-sword with pointed blade
Be drawn or even carried at the side.
Further, no pair of combatants shall ride
More than one course with spears, descending thence
To thrust on foot only in self-defense.
If any man be injured, none shall take
His life; he shall be carried to the stake
That is to be ordained on either side,
And there conveyed by force he shall abide.
And should the principal of either faction
Be taken to the stake, or killed in action,

All fighting shall determine thereupon.
God speed you all, go forward and lay on!
With mace and long-sword you may fight your fill.
Now go your ways. This is his Grace's will.'

The people rifted heaven with a shout
Of merriest good humor, crying out,
'God bless our Duke for doing what he can
To save the blood of many a gentleman!'

Up go the trumpets and the melody,
Forth to the lists canter the company,
As they were bidden, to the city verge;
The streets were hung in cloth-of-gold, not serge.

And like a lord the Duke began to ride
With these two Theban knights on either side.
Behind them rode the Queen and Emily,
And behind them another company
Of one or other according to their rank,
Threading through the city with the clank
Of hoof and armor, to the lists that lay
Beyond. It was not fully prime of day
When Theseus took his seat in majesty.
Hippolyta the Queen and Emily
Were with him, other ladies ranked about,
And round the scaffoldage a seething rout.

And westward, look! Under the Martian Gate
Arcita and his hundred knights await,
And now, under a banner of red, march on.
And at the self-same moment Palamon
Enters by Venus' Gate and takes his place
Under a banner of white, with cheerful face.
You had not found, though you had searched the earth,
Two companies so equal in their worth.
Never were two so splendidly arrayed
And there was none so wise as to have weighed
Which of them had advantage of his foe
In valiance, age, degree or strength of show;
They were so equal one could only guess.

In two formations they began to dress

And when the roll was called that all might see
Their number was not swelled by treachery,
The gates were shut, and then the herald cried:
'Young knights, now do your duty, show your pride!'
   The heralds then withdrew, their work was done;
Out blared the trumpet and the clarion.
There is no more to say, but east and west
All couch their spears and eager for the test
Clap spur to horse. Not difficult to tell
Which of the champions rode and jousted well;
There the shafts shiver on the shields so thick;
One through his breast-bone feels the thrust and prick.
Up spring the spears to twenty foot in height,
Out go the long-swords flashing silver-bright,
Hewing the helmets as they shear and shred;
Out bursts the blood in streams of sternest red,
The mighty maces swing, the bones are bashed,
One thrusting through the thickest throng has crashed,
There the strong steeds have stumbled, down goes all,
Man under foot and rolling like a ball.
Another on his feet with truncheon pound
Hurtles a rider and his horse to ground,
Another is wounded, whom the marshals take
In spite of all and bear him to the stake
As was ordained, and there he has to stay;
A third is carried off the other way.
From time to time the Duke decrees a rest
That all may drink and freshen up their zest.
   Many a time our Thebans in the flow
Of battle met, exchanging blow for blow,
And each unhorsed the other. There could be
No tiger in the vale of Galgophy
Raging in search after a stolen cub
So cruel as Arcite with spear and club
For jealousy of heart to Palamon.
No lion is so fierce to look upon
In all Benamarin, and none so savage
In quest for blood, so hunger-mad in ravage

95

As Palamon to slay his foe Arcite.
The blows upon their helmets bite and beat
And the red blood runs out on man and steed.

There comes at last an end to every deed,
And ere into the west the sun had gone
Strong King Emetrius took Palamon
As he was fighting with Arcite, still fresh,
And made his sword bite deeply in his flesh;
It took the strength of twenty men to take
The yet-unyielded Palamon to stake.
Seeking a rescue, King Lycurgus coursed
Towards Palamon but was himself unhorsed,
And King Emetrius for all his strength
Was flung out of the saddle a sword's length
By Palamon's last stroke in sweeping rake.
But all for nought, they brought him to the stake;
Nothing could help, however hard he fought,
His hardy heart must stay there, he was caught
By force and by the rules decided on.

Who clamors now in grief but Palamon
Who may no more go in again and fight?
And when the noble Theseus saw this sight
He rose and thundered forth to every one,
'Ho! Stop the fight! No more, for it is done!
I will be true judge and no partisan.
The Theban Prince Arcita is the man
And shall have Emily, won by Fortune's grace.'

A tumult of rejoicing filled all space
From every throat in such a caterwaul
It seemed as if the very lists would fall.

What now can lovely Venus do above?
What is she saying, hapless Queen of Love?
Wanting her will her eyes were filled with mists
And shining tears fell down upon the lists.

She cried, 'I am disgraced and put to shame!'
But Saturn said, 'Peace, daughter, watch the game.
Mars has his will, his knight has had his boon,
But, by my head, it shall be your turn soon.'

The trumpeters with loudest minstrelsy
And the shrill heralds shouting frenziedly
Were in high joy for honor of Arcite.
But listen now and don't give way to heat,
See what a miracle happened thereupon!

The fierce Arcita, with no helmet on,
Riding his courser round to show his face
Cantered the whole length of the jousting-place,
Fixing his eye on Emily aloft;
And her returning gaze was sweet and soft,
For women, speaking generally, are prone
To follow Fortune's favors, once they're known.
She was his whole delight, his joy of heart.

Out of the ground behold a fury start,
By Pluto sent at the request of Saturn.
Arcita's horse in terror danced a pattern
And leapt aside and foundered as he leapt,
And ere he was aware Arcite was swept
Out of the saddle and pitched upon his head
Onto the ground, and there he lay for dead;
His breast was shattered by the saddle-bow.
As black he lay as any coal or crow
For all the blood had run into his face.
Immediately they bore him from the place
Sadly to Theseus' palace. What avail
Though he was carved out of his coat of mail
And put to bed with every care and skill?
Yet he was still alive, and conscious still,
And calling ceaselessly for Emily.

Theseus, attended by his company,
Came slowly home to Athens in full state
Of joyous festival, no less elate
For this misfortune, wishing not to cast
A gloom upon the town for what had passed.
Besides it was not thought Arcite would die,
He would recover from his injury.
And then there was another thing that filled
All hearts with pleasure, no one had been killed,

Though some were badly hurt among the rest,
Especially the man with stoven breast.
As for the other wounds and broken arms
Some produced salves and some relied on charms
And herbal pharmacy to make them trim;
They drank them off, hoping to save a limb.

For such as these Duke Theseus did his best,
He comforted and honored every guest
And ordered revelry to last the night
For all the foreign princes, as was right.
There was no sorrowing or discontent;
It was a jousting, just a tournament,
In fact there was no hardship worth the name,
A fall or two are all part of the game.
There is no shame in being borne by force,
Unyielded, to the stake by twenty horse,
If you have been cut off. It must be so,
Harried away by arm and foot and toe,
And on a horse maddened by sticks and noise
By men on foot, by yeomen and their boys.
There's nothing despicable in all this;
No one could ever call it cowardice.
And therefore Theseus made proclamation
To stop all rancor, grudge and emulation,
That each side was as valorous as the other
And both as like as brother is to brother.
He gave them gifts, to each in his degree,
And for three days they held festivity.
Then he conveyed the Kings in solemn state
Out of his city, far beyond the gate,
And home went everyone by various ways
With no more than 'Good-by!' and 'Happy days!'

The battle done with, I may now go on
To speak of poor Arcite and Palamon.
Up swells Arcita's breast, the grievous sore
About his heart increases more and more;
The clotting blood, for all the doctor's skill,
Corrupts and festers in his body still

That neither cupping, bleeding at a vein
Or herbal drink can make him well again.
The expulsive forces known as 'animal'
Had lost their power to cleanse the 'natural'
Of poison, and it could not be expelled.*
His lungs began to choke, the vessels swelled;
Clotted was every muscle of his chest
By poison and corruption in his breast.
Nor could he profit, in his will to live,
By upward vomit or by laxative.
All, all was shattered and beyond repair,
Nature no longer had dominion there,
And sure wherever nature cannot work,
Physic, farewell! Go, bear the man to kirk!
This is the sum of all, Arcite must die.

And so he sent for Emily to be by,
And Palamon, the cousin of his heart,
And thus he spoke, preparing to depart:
'Nothing of all the sorrows in my breast
Can now declare itself or be expressed
To you, O lady that I love the most;
But I bequeath the service of my ghost
To you, above all creatures in the world,
Now that my life is done, and banner furled.
Alas the woe! Alas the pain, so strong,
That I have suffered for you, and so long!
Alas, O Death! Alas, my Emily!
Alas the parting of our company!
Alas, my heart's own queen, alas, my wife,
O lady of my heart that ends my life!
What is this world? What is it man would have?
Now with his love, now in his cold, cold grave
Lying alone, with none for company!
Farewell, my sweetest foe, my Emily!
O softly take me in your arms, I pray,
For love of God, and hearken what I say.
'I have here, with my cousin Palamon,
Had strife and rancor many a day now gone

99

For love of you, and for my jealousy.
And may Jove's wisdom touch the soul in me,
To speak of love and what its service means
Through all the circumstances and the scenes
Of life, namely good faith and knightly deed,
Wisdom, humility and noble breed,
Honor and truth and openness of heart,
For, as I hope my soul may have its part
With Jove, in all the world I know of none
So worthy to be loved as Palamon,
Who serves you and will serve you all his life.
And should you ever choose to be a wife,
Forget not Palamon that great-hearted man.'

   Speech failed in him, the cold of death began
Its upward creeping from his feet to numb
The breast, and he was slowly overcome;
Slowly moreover from his arms there went
The vital power, all was lost and spent;
Only the intellect – there was nothing more –
That dwelt within his being sick and sore,
Began to fail him, as his heart felt death.
Dusked his two eyes at last and failed his breath.
And yet he gazed at her while he could see
And his last word was 'Mercy ... Emily!'
His spirit changed its house and went away
To where I never came – I cannot say
Where, so am silent. I am no divine;
Souls are not mentioned in this tale of mine,
I offer no opinion where they dwell,
Though there are some who claim that they can tell.
Arcite is cold. Mars guide him on his way!
Something of Emily I have to say.

   Palamon howls and Emily is shrieking,
And Theseus leads away his sister, seeking
To bear her from the corpse; she faints away.
What use in tarrying on the tears that day
Or telling how she wept both eve and morrow?
For in these cases women feel such sorrow,

When it befalls their husbands to be taken,
The greater part seem utterly forsaken
And fall into a sickness so extreme
That many of them perish, it would seem.

Infinite were the sorrows and the tears
Of older folk and those of tender years
Throughout the town, all for this Theban's death.
Wept man and boy, and sure a wilder breath
Of lamentation never had been heard
Since Hector, freshly slaughtered, was interred
In Troy. Alas to see the mourning there,
The scrabbled faces, the disheveled hair!
'Must you have died?' the women wailed. 'For, see,
Had you not gold enough – and Emily?'

No one could lighten Theseus of his care
Except his father, old Aegeus, there.
He knew the transmutations of the world
And he had seen its changes as it whirled
Bliss upon sorrow, sorrow upon bliss;
He gave his son instruction upon this:

'Just as there never died a man,' said he,
'But had in life some station or degree,
Just so there never lived a man,' he said,
'In all the world but in the end was dead.
This world is but a thoroughfare of woe
And we are pilgrims passing to and fro.
Death is the end of every worldly sore.'
On top of this he said a great deal more
To this effect, with wisest exhortation,
Heartening the people in their tribulation.

In time the thoughts of Theseus were astir
To find a site and build a sepulcher
For good Arcite, and how it best might be
Ordained to fit his honor and degree.
And in the end the place decided on
Was where Arcite first met with Palamon
In battle for their love, and there between
The branches in that very grove of green

Where he had sung his amorous desires
In sad complaint; and, as his love had fires,
He planned a fire for the funeral games
And all should be accomplished in its flames.
So he commanded them to hack and fell
The ancient oak-trees and to lay them well
In rows and bundles, faggoted to burn.

Forth ride his officers and soon return
On swiftest foot with his commandments done.
And after this, Theseus appointed one
To fetch a bier and had it fitly clad
In cloth-of-gold, the finest that he had.
And in the self-same cloth he clad Arcite
And on his hands white gauntlets, as was meet,
He placed, and on his head a laurel crown
And in his hand the sword of his renown.
He laid him, bare his face, upon the bier,
And wept upon him, pity was to hear.
And, that his body might be seen by all,
When it was day he bore him to the hall
That roared with mourning sounds in unison.

Then came that woeful Theban, Palamon,
With fluttering beard and ash-besprinkled hair,
In sable garments stained with many a tear.
Yet, passing all in weeping, Emily
Was the most sorrowful of the company.
And that the service to be held might be
The nobler, and more fitting his degree,
Duke Theseus commanded them to bring
Three steeds, all trapped in steel and glittering,
And mantled with the arms of Prince Arcite.
Upon these huge white steeds that paced the street
First there rode one who bore Arcita's shield,
A second bore the spear he used to wield;
His Turkish bow and quiver of burnished gold
Was given to the third of them to hold;
Slowly they paced, their countenances drear,
Towards the destined grove, as you shall hear.

Upon the shoulders of the noblest men
Among the Greeks there came the coffin then.
Their eyes were red with tears, their slackened feet
Paced through the city by the master-street;
The way was spread with black, and far on high
Black draperies hung downwards from the sky.

The old Aegeus to the right was placed
With Theseus on his left, and so they paced
Bearing gold vessels of a rare design
Brimming with honey and milk, with blood and wine;
And then came Palamon with his company,
And after that the woeful Emily
With fire in her hand, the custom then
Used in the obsequies of famous men.

The solemn work of building up the pyre
Was done in splendor and they laid a fire
That reached to heaven in a cone of green.
The arms were twenty fathom broad – I mean
The boughs and branches heaped upon the ground –
And straw in piles had first been loaded round.

But how they made the funeral fires flame,
Or what the trees by number or by name
– Oak, fir-tree, birch, aspen and poplar too,
Ilex and alder, willow, elm and yew,
Box, chestnut, plane, ash, laurel, thorn and lime,
Beech, hazel, whipple-tree – I lack the time
To tell you, or who felled them, nor can tell
How their poor gods ran up and down the dell
All disinherited of habitation,
Robbed of their quiet and in desolation,
The nymph and dryad of the forest lawn,
The hamadryad and the subtle faun,
These I pass over, birds and beasts as well
That fled in terror when the forest fell,
Nor shall I say how in the sudden light
Of the unwonted sun the dell took fright,
Nor how the fire first was couched in straw,
Then in dry sticks thrice severed with a saw,

Then in green wood with spice among the stems
And then in cloth-of-gold with precious gems
And many a flower-garland in the stir
Of breathing incense and the scent of myrrh;
Nor how Arcita lay among it all,
Nor of the wealth and splendor of his pall
Nor yet how Emily thrust in the fire,
As custom was, and lit the funeral pyre,
Nor how she fainted when they fed the flame,
Nor what she said or thought; and I shall name
None of the jewels that they took and cast
Into the fire when it flamed at last,
Nor shall I tell how some threw shield and spear,
Or what their garments by the burning bier,
Nor of the cups of wine and milk and blood
That others poured upon the fiery flood,
Nor tell you how the Greeks in mighty rout
Left-handedly went thrice and thrice about
The flaming pyre, and shouted as they drove,
And thrice they clashed their spears about the grove;
Nor yet relate how thrice the ladies wept
Nor who supported Emily and kept
Pace with her homeward, nor shall it be told
How Prince Arcita burnt to ashes cold;
Nor how the wake was held in the delight
Of funeral games, that lasted all the night.
What naked wrestler, glistening with oil,
Made the best showing in his dangerous toil
I will not say, nor say how one by one
They all went home after the games were done;
But shortly to the point; for I intend
To bring my long narration to an end.

In course of time, and after certain years,
Mourning had been accomplished and their tears
Were shed no more, by general consent.
And then it seems they held a parliament
At Athens touching certain points and cases;
And among these they dealt with certain places

With which to form alliances abroad,
To keep the Thebans fully overawed;
And noble Theseus ordered thereupon
That summons should be sent for Palamon.

Not knowing for what reason ordered back,
And still in melancholy suit of black,
Palamon came on this authority
In haste. Then Theseus sent for Emily.

When all were seated there and hushed the place,
The noble Duke kept silent for a space
And ere he chose to let his wisdom fall
His eyes ranged slowly round about the hall.
Then with a sober visage and the still
Sound of a sigh, he thus expressed his will:

'The first Great Cause and Mover of all above
When first He made that fairest chain of love,
Great was the consequence and high the intent.
He well knew why He did, and what He meant.
For in that fairest chain of love He bound
Fire and air and water and the ground
Of earth in certain limits they may not flee.
And that same Prince and Mover then,' said he,
'Established this poor world, appointing ways,
Seasons, durations, certain length of days,
To all that is engendered here below,
Past which predestined hour none may go,
Though we have power to abridge our days.
I need not quote authority or raise
More proof than what experience can show,
But give opinion here from what I know.

'Since we discern this order, we are able
To know that Prince is infinite and stable,
And any but a fool knows in his soul
That every part derives from this great whole.
For nature cannot be supposed to start
From some particular portion or mere part,
But from a whole and undisturbed perfection
Descending thence to what is in subjection

To change, and will corrupt. And therefore He,
In wise foreknowledge, stablished the decree
That species of all things and the progression
Of seasons shall have being by succession,
And not immutably. This is no lie,
As any man can see who has an eye.

'Look at the oak; how slow a tree to nourish
From when it springs until it comes to flourish!
It has so long a life, and yet we see
That in the end it falls, a wasted tree.

'Consider too how hard the stone we tread
Under our feet! That very rock and bed
On which we walk is wasting as it lies.
Time will be when the broadest river dries
And the great cities wane and last descend
Into the dust, for all things have an end.

'For man and woman we can plainly see
Two terms appointed; so it needs must be
— That is to say, the terms of youth and age.
For every man will perish, king and page,
Some in their beds and some in the deep sea,
And some upon the battle-field, maybe.
There is no help for it, all take the track,
For all must die and there is none comes back.

'Who orders this but Jupiter the King,
The Prince and Cause of all and everything,
Converting all things back into the source
From which they were derived, to which they course?
And against this no creature here alive
Whatever his degree may hope to strive.

'Then hold it wise, for so it seems to me,
To make a virtue of necessity,
Take in good part what we may not eschew,
Especially the things that are our due.
It is the folly of a rebel soul
To murmur against Him who guides the whole;
And it is honor to a man whose hour
Strikes in his day of excellence and flower,

When he is certain of his own good name
And never known in any act of shame
To friend or foe; we should be glad of death
Where there is honor in the yielded breath,
Gladder than for a name by age made stale,
And all forgotten the heroic tale.
Then is the time, if you would win a name,
To die, upon the moment of your fame.

'The contrary of this is willfulness;
Why do we grumble? Where is the distress
If good Arcite, the flower of chivalry,
Departed in all honor, stainlessly
Set free from the foul prison of this life?
Shall those he loved, his cousin and his wife,
Murmur against his welfare, or suppose
He can return them thanks? Not he, God knows.
Offending so against him, they offend
Themselves, and are no better in the end.

'So what conclusion can I draw from this
Except that after grief there should be bliss,
And praise to Jupiter for all his grace?
So, ere we make departure from this place,
I rule that of two sorrows we endeavor
To make one perfect joy, to last forever.
Then let us look, and where we find herein
The greatest grief, let happiness begin.

'Sister,' he said, 'it has my full assent,
And is confirmed by this my parliament,
That gentle Palamon, your own true knight,
Who loves and serves you, heart and soul and might,
And always has since first he saw your face,
Shall move you to feel pity, gain your grace
And so become your husband and your lord.
Give me your hand, for this is our award.
Let us now see your womanly compassion.
By God, he's a king's nephew! Were his fashion
No more than that of a knight-bachelor,
What with the years he served and suffered for

Your love (unless his sufferings deceive me)
He would be worth considering, believe me;
For mercy is a greater thing than right.'
　And then he said to Palamon the knight,
'I think there needs but little sermoning
To gain your own assent to such a thing.
Come near, and take your lady by the hand.'
And they were joined together by the band
That is called matrimony, also marriage,
By counsel of the Duke and all his peerage.
　And thus with every bliss and melody
Palamon was espoused to Emily,
And God that all this wide, wide world has wrought,
Send them his love, for it was dearly bought!
Now Palamon's in joy, amid a wealth
Of bliss and splendor, happiness and health.
She gave him tenderest love with constancy,
And he, her knight and servant, faithfully
Requited it; no jealous word was spoken
Ever between them in a love unbroken.
Thus ended Palamon and Emily,
And God save all this happy company!
Amen.

The Miller's Tale

Words between the Host and the Miller

WHEN we had heard the tale the Knight had told,
　Not one among the pilgrims, young or old,
But said it was indeed a noble story
Worthy to be remembered for its glory,
And it especially pleased the gentlefolk.
Our Host began to laugh, and swore in joke:

'It's going well, we've opened up the bale;
Now, let me see. Who'll tell another tale?
Upon my soul the game was well begun!
Come on, Sir Monk, and show what can be done;
Repay the Knight a little for his tale!'

The Miller, very drunk and rather pale,
Was straddled on his horse, half-on half-off,
And in no mood for manners, or to doff
His hood or hat, or wait on any man,
But in a voice like Pilate's he began*
To huff and swear. 'By blood and bones and belly,
I've got a noble story I can tell 'ee;
I'll pay the Knight his wages, not the Monk.'

Our Host perceived at once that he was drunk
And said, 'Now hold on, Robin, dear old brother;
We'll get some better man to tell another;
You wait a bit. Let's have some common sense.'
'God's soul, I won't!' said he. 'At all events
I mean to talk, or else I'll go my way.'
Our Host replied, 'Well, blast you then, you may.
You're just a fool; your wits are overcome.'

'Now listen,' said the Miller, 'all and some,
To what I have to say. But first I'm bound
To say I'm drunk, I know it by my sound.
And if the words get muddled in my tale
Just put it down to too much Southwark ale.
I've got a story: it's about the life
Of an old carpenter, and of his wife,
And how a student came and set his cap ...'

The Reeve looked up and shouted, 'Shut your trap!
Give over with your drunken harlotry.
A sin it is and folly, seems to me,
To slander any man or bring a scandal
On wives in general. Why can't you handle
Some other tale? There's other things beside.'

To this the drunken Miller then replied,
'My dear old brother Oswald, such is life.
A man's no cuckold if he has no wife.

For all that, I'm not saying you are one;
There's many virtuous wives, all said and done,
Ever a thousand good for one that's bad,
As well you know yourself, unless you're mad.
What's biting you? Can't I tell stories too?
I've got a wife, Lord knows, as well as you,
Yet for the oxen in my plow indeed
I wouldn't take it on me, more than need,
To think myself a cuckold, just because.
I'm pretty sure I'm not, and never was.
One shouldn't be too inquisitive in life
Either about God's secrets or one's wife.
You'll find God's plenty all you could desire;
Of the remainder, better not inquire.'
   What can I add? The Miller had begun,
He would not hold his peace for anyone,
But told his churl's tale his own way, I fear.
And yet it seems I should repeat it here,
And so I beg of all who are refined,
For God's love not to think me ill-inclined
Or evil in my purpose. I rehearse
Their tales as told, for better or for worse,
For else I should be false to what occurred.
So if this tale had better not be heard,
Just turn the page and choose another sort;
You'll find them here in plenty, long and short;
Many historical, that will profess
Morality, good breeding, saintliness.
Do not blame me if you should choose amiss.
The Miller was a churl, I've told you this,
So was the Reeve, and other some as well,
And harlotry was all they had to tell.
Consider then, and hold me free of blame;
And why be serious about a game?

The Miller's Tale

SOME time ago there was a rich old codger
Who lived in Oxford and who took a lodger.
The fellow was a carpenter by trade,
His lodger a poor student who had made
Some studies in the arts, but all his fancy
Turned to astrology and geomancy,
And he could deal with certain propositions,
And make a forecast under some conditions
About the likelihood of drought or showers
For those who asked at favorable hours,
Or put a question how their luck would fall
In this or that, I can't describe them all.

    This lad was known as Nicholas the Spark.
He was a dab at love, but kept it dark,
For he was sly and secret and he took
Advantage of his meek and girlish look.
He rented a small chamber in the kip,
All by himself without companionship.
He decked it charmingly with herbs and fruit,
And he himself was sweeter than the root
Of licorice or any fragrant herb.
His astronomic text-books were superb,
He had an astrolabe to match his art
And calculating counters, laid apart
On handy shelves that stood above his bed.
His press was curtained coarsely and in red;
Above there lay a gallant harp in sight
On which he played melodiously at night
With such a touch that all the chamber rang;
It was *The Virgin's Angelus* he sang,
And after that he sang *King William's Note,*
And people often blessed his merry throat.
And that was how this charming scholar spent
His time and money, which his friends had sent.

This carpenter had married a young wife
Not long before, and loved her more than life.
She was a girl of eighteen years of age.
Jealous he was and kept her in the cage,
For he was old and she was wild and young;
He thought himself quite likely to be stung.

He might have known, were Cato on his shelf,
A man should marry someone like himself;
A man should pick an equal for his mate.
Youth and old age are often in debate.
His wits were dull, he'd fallen in the snare
And had to bear his cross, as others bear.

She was a pretty creature, fair and tender,
And had a weasel's body, softly slender.
She used to wear a girdle of striped silk,
Her apron was as white as morning milk
To deck her loins, all gusseted and pleated.
Her smock was white; embroidery repeated
Its pattern on the collar front and back,
Inside and out; it was of silk, and black.
And all the ribbons on her milky mutch
Were made to match her collar, even such.
She wore a broad silk fillet rather high,
And certainly she had a lecherous eye.
And she had plucked her eyebrows into bows,
Slenderly arched they were, and black as sloes.
And a more truly blissful sight to see
She was than blossom on a cherry-tree,
And softer than the wool upon a wether.
And by her girdle hung a purse of leather,
Tasseled in silk, with metal droplets, pearled.
If you went seeking up and down the world,
The wisest man you met would have to wrench
His fancy to imagine such a wench.
She had a shining color, gaily tinted,
And brighter than a florin newly minted,
And when she sang it was as loud and quick
As any swallow perched above a rick.

And she would skip or play some game or other
Like any kid or calf behind its mother.
Her mouth was sweet as mead or honey – say
A hoard of apples lying in the hay.
Skittish she was, and jolly as a colt,
Tall as a mast and upright as a bolt
Out of a bow. Her collaret revealed
A brooch as big as boss upon a shield.
High shoes she wore, and laced them to the top.
She was a daisy, O a lollypop
For any nobleman to take to bed,
Or some good man of yeoman stock to wed.

   Now, gentlemen, young Nicholas the Spark,
So things fell out, one day began to lark
With this young woman, and to romp about
Taking a chance, her husband being out.
Students are sly, and giving way to whim
He made a grab and caught her by the quim
And said, 'O God, I love you! Can't you see
If I don't have you it's the end of me?'
Then held her haunches hard and gave a cry
'O love-me-all-at-once or I shall die!'

   She gave a spring, just like a skittish colt
Boxed in a frame for shoeing, and with a jolt
Managed in time to wrench her head away,
And said, 'Give over, Nicholas, I say!
No, I won't kiss you! Stop it! Let me go
Or I shall scream! I'll let the neighbors know!
Where are your manners? Take away your paws!'

   Then Nicholas began to plead his cause
And spoke so fair in proffering what he could
That in the end she promised him she would,
Swearing she'd love him, with a solemn promise
To be at his disposal by St Thomas,
When she could spy an opportunity.
'My husband is so full of jealousy,
Unless you watch your step and hold your breath
I know for certain it will be my death,'

She said, 'So keep it well under your hat.'
'Oh, never mind about a thing like that,'
Said he; 'A scholar doesn't have to stir
His wits so much to trick a carpenter.'

And so they both agreed to it, and swore
To watch their chance, as I have said before.
When things were settled thus as they thought fit,
And Nicholas had stroked her loins a bit
And kissed her sweetly, he took down his harp
And played away, a merry tune and sharp.

It happened later she went off to church,
This worthy wife, one holiday, to search
Her conscience and to do the works of Christ.
She put her work aside and she enticed
The color to her face, to make her mark;
Her forehead shone. There was a parish clerk
Serving the church whose name was Absalon.
His hair was all in golden curls and shone;
Just like a fan it strutted outwards, starting
To left and right from an accomplished parting.
Ruddy his face, his eyes as gray as goose,
His shoes cut out in tracery, as in use
In old St Paul's. The hose upon his feet
Showed scarlet through, and all his clothes were neat
And proper. In a jacket of light blue,
Flounced at the waist and tagged with laces too,
He went, and wore a surplice just as gay
And white as any blossom on the spray.
God bless my soul, he was a merry knave!
He knew how to let blood, cut hair and shave,
And draw up legal deeds; at other whiles
He used to dance in twenty different styles
(After the current school at Oxford though,
Casting his legs about him to and fro).
He played a two-stringed fiddle, did it proud,
And sang a high falsetto rather loud;
And he was just as good on the guitar.
There was no public-house in town or bar

He didn't visit with his merry face,
If there were saucy barmaids round the place.
He was a little squeamish in the matter
Of farting, and satirical in chatter.

This Absalon, so jolly in his ways,
Would bear the censer round on holy days
And cense the parish women. He would cast
Many a love-lorn look before he passed,
Especially at this carpenter's young wife;
Looking at her would make a happy life
He thought, so neat, so sweet, so lecherous.
And I dare say if she had been a mouse
And he a cat, she'd have been pounced upon.

In taking the collection Absalon
Would find his heart was set in such a whirl
Of love, he would take nothing from a girl,
For courtesy, he said, it wasn't right.

That evening, when the moon was shining bright,
He ups with his guitar and off he starts
Doing his rounds and looking out for tarts.
Larky and amorous, away he strode
Until he reached the carpenter's abode
A little after cock-crow, took his stand
Beside the casement window close at hand
(It was set low upon the cottage-face)
And started singing softly and with grace,
   'Now dearest lady, if thy pleasure be
   In thoughts of love, think tenderly of me!'
On his guitar he plucked a tuneful string.

This carpenter awoke and heard him sing
And turning to his wife said, 'Alison!
Wife! Do you hear him? There goes Absalon
Chanting away under our chamber wall.'
And she replied, 'Yes, John, I hear it all.'
If she thought more of it she didn't tell.

So things went on. What's better than 'All's well'?
From day to day this jolly Absalon
Wooing away became quite woe-begone;

He lay awake all night, and all the day
Combed his thick locks and tried to pass for gay,
Wooed her by go-between and wooed by proxy,
Swore to be page and servant to his doxy,
Trilled and rouladed like a nightingale,
Sent her sweet wine and mead and spicy ale,
And wafers piping hot and jars of honey,
And, as she lived in town, he offered money.*
For there are some a money-bag provokes
And some are won by kindness, some by strokes.

Once, in the hope his talent might engage,
He played the part of Herod on the stage.
What was the good? Were he as bold as brass,
She was in love with dandy Nicholas;
However Absalon might blow his horn
His labor won him nothing but her scorn.
She looked upon him as her private ape
And held his earnest wooing all a jape.

There is a proverb – and it is no lie –
You'll often hear repeated: *'Nigh and Sly
Wins against Fair and Square who isn't there.'*
For much as Absalon might tear his hair
And rage at being seldom in her sight,
Nicholas, nigh and sly, stood in his light.
Now show your paces, Nicholas the Spark,
And leave lamenting to the parish clerk.

And so it happened that one Saturday,
When the old carpenter was safe away
At Osney, Nicholas and Alison
Agreed at last in what was to be done.
Nicholas was to exercise his wits
On her suspicious husband's foolish fits,
And if so be the trick worked out all right
She then would sleep with Nicholas all night,
For such was his desire and hers as well;
And even quicker than it takes to tell,
Young Nicholas, who simply couldn't wait,
Went to his room on tip-toe with a plate

Of food and drink, enough to last a day
Or two, and Alison was told to say,
In case her husband asked for Nicholas,
That she had no idea where he was,
And that she hadn't set eyes on him all day
And thought he must be ill, she couldn't say;
And more than once the maid had given a call
And shouted but no answer came at all.

So things went on the whole of Saturday
Without a sound from Nicholas, who lay
Upstairs, and ate or slept as pleased him best
Till Sunday when the sun went down to rest.

This foolish carpenter was lost in wonder
At Nicholas; what could have got him under?
He said, 'I can't help thinking, by the Mass,
Things can't be going right with Nicholas.
What if he took and died? God guard his ways!
A ticklish place the world is, nowadays.
I saw a corpse this morning borne to kirk
That only Monday last I saw at work.
Run up,' he told the serving-lad, 'be quick,
Shout at his door, or knock it with a brick.
Take a good look and tell me how he fares.'

The serving-boy went sturdily upstairs,
Stopped at the door and, standing there, the lad
Shouted away and, hammering like mad,
Cried, 'Ho! What's up? Hi! Master Nicholay!
How can you lie up there asleep all day?'

But all for nought, he didn't hear a soul.
He found a broken panel with a hole
Right at the bottom, useful to the cat
For creeping in; he took a look through that,
And so at last by peering through the crack
He saw this scholar gaping on his back,
As if he'd caught a glimpse of the new moon.
Down went the boy and told his master soon
About the state in which he found the man.

On hearing this the carpenter began

To cross himself and said, 'St Frideswide bless us!
We little know what's coming to distress us.
The man has fallen, with this here astromy,
Into a fit, or lunacy maybe.
I always thought that was how it would go.
God has some secrets that we shouldn't know.
How blessed are the simple, aye, indeed,
That only know enough to say their creed!
Happened just so with such another student
Of astromy, and he was so imprudent
As to stare upwards while he crossed a field
Busy foreseeing what the stars revealed;
And what should happen but he fell down flat
Into a marl-pit. No foreseeing that!
But by the Saints we've reached a sorry pass;
I can't help worrying for Nicholas.
He shall be scolded for his studying
If I know how to scold, by Christ the King!
Get me a staff to prize against the floor.
Robin, you put your shoulder to the door.
We'll shake the study out of him, I guess!'
　　The pair of them began to heave and press
Against the door. Happened the lad was strong
And so it didn't take them very long
To heave it off its hinges; down it came.
Still as a stone lay Nicholas, with the same
Expression, gaping upwards into air.
The carpenter supposed it was despair
And shook him by the shoulders with a stout
And purposeful attack, and gave a shout:
'What, Nicholas! Hey! Look down! Is that a fashion
To act? Wake up and think upon Christ's passion!
I sign you with the cross from elves and sprites!'
And he began the spell for use at nights
In all four corners of the room, and out
Across the threshold too, and round about:
　　Jesu Christ and Benedict Sainted
　　Bless this house from creature tainted,

Drive away night-hags, white Pater-noster,
Where did you go St Peter's soster?
And in the end the dandy Nicholas
Began to sigh, 'And must it come to pass?'
He said, 'Must all the world be cast away?'
The carpenter replied, 'What's that you say?
Put trust in God as we do, working men.'

Nicholas answered, 'Fetch some liquor then,
And afterwards, in strictest secrecy,
I'll speak of something touching you and me,
But not another soul must know, that's plain.'

This carpenter went down and came again
Bringing some powerful ale – a largish quart.
When each had had his share of this support
Young Nicholas got up and shut the door
And, sitting down beside him on the floor,
Said to the carpenter, 'Now, John, my dear,
My excellent host, swear on your honor here
Not to repeat a syllable I say,
For here are Christ's intentions, to betray
Which to a soul puts you among the lost,
And vengeance for it at a bitter cost
Shall fall upon you. You'll be driven mad!'
'Christ and His holy blood forbid it, lad!'
The silly fellow answered. 'I'm no blab,
Though I should say it. I'm not given to gab.
Say what you like, for I shall never tell
Man, woman or child, by Him that harrowed Hell!'*

'Now, John,' said Nicholas, 'believe you me,
I have found out by my astrology,
And looking at the moon when it was bright,
That Monday next, a quarter way through night,
Rain is to fall in torrents, such a scud
It will be twice as bad as Noah's Flood.
This world,' he said, 'in just about an hour,
Shall all be drowned, it's such a hideous shower,
And all mankind, with total loss of life.'
The carpenter exclaimed, 'Alas, my wife!

My little Alison! Is she to drown?'
And in his grief he very near fell down.
'Is there no remedy,' he said, 'for this?'
'Thanks be to God,' said Nicholas, 'there is,
If you will do exactly what I say
And don't start thinking up some other way.
In wise old Solomon you'll find the verse
"Who takes advice shall never fare the worse,"
And so if good advice is to prevail
I undertake with neither mast nor sail
To save her yet, and save myself and you.
Haven't you heard how Noah was saved too
When God forewarned him and his sons and daughters
That all the world should sink beneath the waters?'
'Yes,' said the carpenter, 'a long time back.'
'Haven't you heard,' said Nicholas, 'what a black
Business it was, when Noah tried to whip
His wife (who wouldn't come) on board the ship?
He'd have been better pleased, I'll undertake,
With all that weather just about to break,
If she had had a vessel of her own.
Now, what are we to do? We can't postpone
The thing; it's coming soon, as I was saying,
It calls for haste, not preaching or delaying.

   'I want you, now at once, to hurry off
And fetch a shallow tub or kneading-trough
For each of us, but see that they are large
And such as we can float in, like a barge.
And have them loaded with sufficient victual
To last a day – we only need a little.
The waters will abate and flow away
Round nine o'clock upon the following day.
Robin the lad mayn't know of this, poor knave,
Nor Jill the maid, those two I cannot save.
Don't ask me why; and even if you do
I can't disclose God's privity to you.
You should be satisfied, unless you're mad,
To find as great a grace as Noah had.

The Miller's Tale

And I shall save your wife, you needn't doubt it,
Now off you go, and hurry up about it.

'And when the tubs have been collected, three,
That's one for her and for yourself and me,
Then hang them in the roof below the thatching,
That no one may discover what we're hatching.
When you have finished doing what I said
And stowed the victuals in them overhead,
Also an ax to hack the ropes apart,
So, when the water rises, we can start,
And, lastly, when you've broken out the gable,
The garden one that's just above the stable,
So that we may cast free without delay
After the mighty shower has gone away,
You'll float as merrily, I undertake,
As any lily-white duck behind her drake.
And I'll call out, "Hey, Alison! Hey, John!
Cheer yourselves up! The flood will soon be gone."
And you'll shout back, "Hail, Master Nicholay!
Good morning! I can see you well. It's day!"
We shall be lords for all the rest of life
Of all the world, like Noah and his wife.

'One thing I warn you of; it's only right.
We must be very careful on the night,
Once we have safely managed to embark,
To hold our tongues, to utter no remark,
No cry or call, for we must fall to prayer.
This is the Lord's dear will, so have a care.

'Your wife and you must hang some way apart,
For there must be no sin before we start,
No more in longing looks than in the deed.
Those are your orders. Off with you! God speed!
To-morrow night when everyone's asleep
We'll all go quietly upstairs and creep
Into our tubs, awaiting Heaven's grace.
And now be off. No time to put the case
At greater length, no time to sermonize;
The proverb says, "Say nothing, send the wise."

You're wise enough, I do not have to teach you.
Go, save our lives for us, as I beseech you.'
    This silly carpenter then went his way
Muttering to himself, 'Alas the day!'
And told his wife in strictest secrecy.
She was aware, far more indeed than he,
What this quaint stratagem might have in sight,
But she pretended to be dead with fright.
'Alas!' she said. 'Whatever it may cost,
Hurry and help, or we shall all be lost.
I am your honest, true and wedded wife,
Go, dearest husband, help to save my life!'
    How fancy throws us into perturbation!
People can die of mere imagination,
So deep is the impression one can take.
This silly carpenter began to quake,
Before his eyes there verily seemed to be
The floods of Noah wallowing like the sea
And drowning Alison, his honey-pet.
He wept and wailed, his features were all set
In grief, he sighed with many a doleful grunt.
He went and got a tub, began to hunt
For kneading-troughs, found two, and had them sent
Home to his house in secret; then he went
And, unbeknowns, he hung them from a rafter.
With his own hands he made three ladders after,
Uprights and rungs, to help them in their scheme
Of climbing where they hung upon the beam.
He victualed tub and trough, and made all snug
With bread and cheese, and ale in a large jug,
Enough for three of them to last the day,
And, just before completing this array,
Packed off the maid and his apprentice too
To London on a job they had to do.
And on the Monday, when it drew to night,
He shut his door and dowsed the candle-light
And made quite sure all was as it should be.
And shortly, up they clambered, all the three,

Silent and separate. They began to pray
And '*Pater Noster* mum,' said Nicholay,
And 'mum' said John, and 'mum' said Alison.
The carpenter's devotions being done
He sat quite still, then fell to prayer again
And waited anxiously to hear the rain.

The carpenter, with all the work he'd seen,
Fell dead asleep – round curfew, must have been,
Maybe a little later on the whole.
He groaned in sleep for travail of his soul
And snored because his head was turned awry.

Down by their ladders, stalking from on high
Came Nicholas and Alison, and sped
Softly downstairs without a word to bed,
And where this carpenter was wont to be
The revels started and the melody.
And thus lay Nicholas and Alison
At busy play in eager quest of fun,
Until the bell for lauds had started ringing
And in the chancel Friars began their singing.

This parish clerk, this amorous Absalon,
Love-stricken still and very woe-begone,
Upon the Monday was in company
At Osney with his friends for jollity,
And chanced to ask a resident cloisterer
What had become of John the carpenter.
The fellow drew him out of church to say,
'Don't know; not been at work since Saturday.
I can't say where he is; I think he went
To fetch the Abbot timber. He is sent
Often enough for timber, has to go
Out to the Grange and stop a day or so;
If not he's certainly at home to-day,
But where he is I can't exactly say.'

Absalon was a jolly lad and light
Of heart; he thought, 'I'll stay awake to-night;
I'm certain that I haven't seen him stirring
About his door since dawn; it's safe inferring

That he's away. As I'm alive I'll go
And tap his window softly at the crow
Of cock – the sill is low-set on the wall.
I shall see Alison and tell her all
My love-longing, and I can hardly miss
Some favor from her, at the least a kiss.
I'll get some satisfaction anyway;
There's been an itching in my mouth all day
And that's a sign of kissing at the least.
And all last night I dreamt about a feast.
I think I'll go and sleep an hour or two,
Then wake and have some fun, that's what I'll do.'
  The first cock crew at last, and thereupon
Up rose this jolly lover Absalon
In gayest clothes, garnished with that and this;
But first he chewed a grain of licorice
To charm his breath before he combed his hair.
Under his tongue the comfit nestling there
Would make him gracious. He began to roam
To where old John and Alison kept home
And by the casement window took his stand.
Breast-high it stood, no higher than his hand.
He gave a cough, no more than half a sound:
'Alison, honey-comb, are you around?
Sweet cinnamon, my little pretty bird,
Sweetheart, wake up and say a little word!
You seldom think of me in all my woe,
I sweat for love of you wherever I go!
No wonder if I do, I pine and bleat
As any lambkin hungering for the teat,
Believe me, darling, I'm so deep in love
I croon with longing like a turtle-dove,
I eat as little as a girl at school.'
'You go away,' she answered, 'you Tom-fool!
There's no come-up-and-kiss-me here for you.
I love another and why shouldn't I too?
Better than you, by Jesu, Absalon!
Take yourself off or I shall throw a stone.

I want to get some sleep. You go to Hell!'
'Alas!' said Absalon. 'I knew it well;
True love is always mocked and girded at;
So kiss me, if you can't do more than that,
For Jesu's love and for the love of me!'
'And if I do, will you be off?' said she.
'Promise you, darling,' answered Absalon.
'Get ready then; wait, I'll put something on,'
She said, and then she added under breath
To Nicholas, 'Hush ... we shall laugh to death!'

This Absalon went down upon his knees;
'I am a lord at least, and by degrees
I hope,' he said, 'there may be more to come.
Mercy, my pretty bird, ah, drop a crumb!'

She flung the window open then in haste
And said, 'Have done, come on, no time to waste,
The neighbors here are always on the spy.'

Absalon started wiping his mouth dry.
Dark was the night as pitch, as black as coal,
And at the window out she put her hole,
And Absalon, so fortune framed the farce,
Put up his mouth and kissed her naked arse,
Most savorously, before he knew of this.

And back he started. Something was amiss;
He knew quite well a woman has no beard,
Yet something rough and hairy had appeared.
'What have I done?' he said. 'Can that be you?'
'Teehee!' she cried and clapped the window to.
Off went poor Absalon sadly through the dark.
'A beard! a beard!' cried Nicholas the Spark.
'God's body, that was something like a joke!'
And Absalon, overhearing what he spoke,
Bit on his lips and nearly threw a fit
In rage, and thought, 'I'll pay you back for it!'

Who's busy rubbing, scraping at his lips
With dust, with sand, with straw, with cloth, with chips,
But Absalon? He thought, 'I'll bring him down!
I wouldn't let this go for all the town.

I'd take my soul and sell it to the Devil
To be revenged upon him! I'll get level.
O God, why did I let myself be fooled?'

The fiery heat of love by now had cooled,
For from the time he kissed her hinder parts
He didn't give a tinker's curse for tarts;
His malady was cured by this endeavor
And he defied all paramours whatever.

So, weeping like a child that has been whipped,
He turned away; across the road he slipped
And called on Gervase. Gervase was a smith;
His forge was full of things for plowing with
And he was busy sharpening a share.

Absalon knocked, and with an easy air
Called, 'Gervase! Open up the door, come on!'
'What's that? Who's there?' 'It's me, it's Absalon.'
'What, Absalon? By Jesu's blessed tree
You're early up! Hey, *benedicite*,
What's wrong? Some jolly girl as like as not
Has coaxed you out and set you on the trot.
Blessed St Neot! You know the thing I mean.'

But Absalon, who didn't give a bean
For all his joking, offered no debate.
He had a good deal more upon his plate
Than Gervase knew, and said, 'Would it be fair
To borrow that coulter in the chimney there,
The hot one, see it? I've a job to do;
It won't take long, I'll bring it back to you.'
Gervase replied, 'Why, if you asked for gold,
A bag of sovereigns or for wealth untold,
It should be yours, as I'm an honest smith.
But, Christ, why borrow that to do it with?'
'Let that,' said Absalon, 'be as it may;
You'll hear about it all some other day.'

He caught the coulter up – the haft was cool –
And left the smithy softly with the tool,
Crept to the little window in the wall
And coughed. He knocked and gave a little call

126

Under the window as he had before.
  Alison said, 'There's someone at the door.
Who's knocking there? I'll warrant it's a thief.'
'Why, no,' said he, 'my little flower-leaf,
It's your own Absalon, my sweety-thing!
Look what I've brought you – it's a golden ring
My mother gave me, as I may be saved.
It's very fine, and prettily engraved;
I'll give it to you, darling, for a kiss.'
  Now Nicholas had risen for a piss,
And thought he could improve upon the jape
And make him kiss his arse ere he escape,
And opening the window with a jerk,
Stuck out his arse, a handsome piece of work,
Buttocks and all, as far as to the haunch.
  Said Absalon, all set to make a launch,
'Speak, pretty bird, I know not where thou art!'
This Nicholas at once let fly a fart
As loud as if it were a thunder-clap.
He was near blinded by the blast, poor chap,
But his hot iron was ready; with a thump
He smote him in the middle of the rump.
  Off went the skin a hand's-breadth round about
Where the hot coulter struck and burnt it out.
Such was the pain, he thought he must be dying
And, mad with agony, he started crying,
'Help! Water! Water! Help! For Heaven's love!'
  The carpenter, startled from sleep above,
And hearing shouts for water and a thud,
Thought, 'Heaven help us! Here comes Nowel's Flood!'
And up he sat and with no more ado
He took his ax and smote the ropes in two
And down went everything. He didn't stop
To sell his bread and ale, but came down flop
Upon the floor and fainted right away.
  Up started Alison and Nicholay
And shouted, 'Help!' and 'Murder!' in the street.
The neighbors all came running up in heat

And stood there staring at the wretched man.
He lay there fainting, pale beneath his tan;
His arm in falling had been broken double.
But still he was obliged to face his trouble,
For when he spoke he was at once borne down
By Nicholas and his wife. They told the town
That he was mad, there'd got into his blood
Some sort of nonsense about 'Nowel's Flood,'
That vain imaginings and fantasy
Had made him buy the kneading-tubs, that he
Had hung them in the rafters up above
And that he'd begged them both for heaven's love
To sit up in the roof for company.

    All started laughing at this lunacy
And streamed upstairs to gape and pry and poke,
And treated all his sufferings as a joke.
No matter what the carpenter asserted
It went for nothing, no one was converted;
With powerful oaths they swore the fellow down
And he was held for mad by all the town;
Even the learned said to one another,
'The fellow must be crazy, my dear brother.'
So to a general laughter he succumbed.

    That's how the carpenter's young wife was plumbed
For all the tricks his jealousy could try,
And Absalon has kissed her nether eye
And Nicholas is branded on the bum.
And God bring all of us to Kingdom Come.

The Reeve's Tale

The Reeve's Prologue

WHEN all had laughed at the preposterous lark
Of Absalon and Nicholas the Spark,
Various folk made various comment after;
But the majority dissolved in laughter,
Nor did I see a soul it seemed to grieve
Unless it might be Oswald, the old Reeve,
For, as he was a carpenter by trade,
He was a little angry still, and made
Grumbling remarks and scolded for a bit.
'As I'm a man I'd pay you back for it,'
He said, 'with how they bleared a Miller's eye,
If I liked dirt and wished to argufy.
But I am old. Dirt doesn't go with doddering,
Grass-time is done and I'm for winter foddering.
My hoary top-knot writes me down for old;
Same as my hair, my heart is full of mold,
Unless I be like them there medlar-fruit,
Them that gets rottener as they ripen to't,
Till they be rotted down in straw and dung.
That's how we get to be, no longer young.
Till we be rotten we can never ripe.
We hop along, as long as world will pipe;
Our will is always catching on the nail,
Wanting a hoary head and a green tail,
Like leeks have got; the strength to play that game
Is gone, though we love foolishness the same.
What we can't do no more we talk about
And rake the ashes when the fire is out.

'Yet we have four live coals, as I can show;
Lies, boasting, greed and rage will always glow.

Those are the sparks among the ancient embers
Though we be nigh unwelded in our members.
Desire never fails, and that's the truth,
For even now I have a coltish tooth,
Many as be the years now dead and done
Before my tap of life began to run.
Certain, when I was born, so long ago,
Death drew the tap of life and let it flow;
And ever since the tap has done its task,
And now there's little but an empty cask.
My stream of life's but drops upon the rim.
An old fool's tongue will run away with him
To chime and chatter of monkey-tricks that's past.
There's nothing left but dotage at the last!'

    Our Host, on hearing all this sermoning,
Began to speak as lordly as a king,
And said, 'What does it come to, all this wit?
What! Spend the morning talking Holy Writ?
The devil that makes a preacher of a Reeve
Turns cobblers into doctors, I believe.
Give us your story, if you've one in stock.
Why, look! Here's Deptford and it's nine o'clock!
And Greenwich too, with many a blackguard in it.
High time to tell your story, so begin it.'

    'Now, gentlemen,' Oswald the Reeve replied,
'I hope as none will be dissatisfied
Though I should tweak the Miller by the cap,
For lawful 'tis to give him tap for tap.

    'This drunken Miller we've had so much drool of,
Told how a carpenter was made a fool of,
Maybe to score off me, for I am one.
By y'r leave, I'll pay him back before I've done
In his own filthy words, you may expec'.
I hope to God he breaks his bloody neck.
He sees the mote in my eye, if there is un,
But cannot see the beam there is in his'n.'

The Reeve's Tale

A<small>T</small> Trumpington, not far from Cambridge town,
A bridge goes over where the brook runs down
And by that brook there stands a mill as well.
And it's God's truth that I am going to tell.

There was a miller lived there many a day
As proud as any peacock and as gay;
He could play bag-pipes too, fish, mend his gear,
And turn a lathe, and wrestle, and poach deer.
And at his belt he carried a long blade,
Trenchant it was as any sword that's made,
And in his pouch a jolly little knife.
No one dared touch him, peril of his life.
He had a Sheffield dagger in his hose.
Round was his face and puggish was his nose;
His head on top was bald, just like an ape.
He was a market bully in such shape
None dared lay hand on him or come too near
Without him swearing that they'd buy it dear.

He was a thief as well of corn and meal,
And sly at that; his habit was to steal.
Simpkin the Swagger he was called all round.
He had a wife whose breeding was renowned.
Town-clergyman, no less, her father was;
Gave her fine brass for dowery, because
He wanted to have Simpkin his relation.
The nuns had given her an education.
Simpkin would take no woman, so he said,
Unless she were a virgin and well-bred,
To save the honor of his yeoman stock;
And she was proud, pert as a magpie cock.

It was a proper sight to see the pair
On holidays, what with him strutting there
In front of her, his hood about his head,
And she behind him all decked out in red,

Like Simpkin's hose, for scarlet-red he had 'em.
No one dared call her anything but 'Madam,'
And there was no one bold enough to try
A bit of fun with her or wink an eye.
It would have been as much as ask old Swagger
To murder you with cutlass, knife or dagger,
For jealous folk are dangerous, you know,
At least they want their wives to think them so.
And then her birth was smirched to say the least;
Being the daughter of a celibate priest
She must maintain her dignity, of which
She had as much as water in a ditch.
She was a sneering woman and she thought
That ladies should respect her, so they ought,
What with her well-connected family,
And education in a nunnery.

They had a daughter too between them both.
She was a girl of twenty summers' growth;
But that was all except a child they had
Still in the cradle, but a proper lad.
The wench was plump, well-grown enough to pass,
With a snub nose and eyes as gray as glass;
Her rump was broad, her breasts were round and high;
She'd very pretty hair, I will not lie.

Now the town-clergyman, as she was fair,
Intended to appoint the girl as heir
To all his property in house and land,
And he was stiff with suitors to her hand.
He purposed to bestow her, if he could,
Where blood and ancient lineage made it good.
For Holy Church's goods should be expended
On Holy Church's blood, so well-descended,
And holy blood should have what's proper to it
Though Holy Church should be devoured to do it.

This miller levied toll beyond a doubt
On wheat and malt from all the land about,
Particularly from a large-sized College
In Cambridge, Solar Hall.* 'Twas common knowledge

They sent their wheat and malt to him to grind it.
Happened one day the man who ought to mind it,
The college manciple, lay sick in bed,
And some reported him as good as dead.
On hearing which the miller robbed him more
A hundred times than he had robbed before;
For up till then he'd only robbed politely,
But now he stole outrageously, forthrightly.
   The Warden scolded hard and made a scene,
But there! The miller didn't give a bean,
Blustered it out and swore it wasn't so.
   Two poor young Bible-clerks or students, though,
Lived in this College (that of which I spoke).
Headstrong they were and eager for a joke
And simply for the chance of sport and play
They went and plagued the Warden night and day
Just for a little leave, to spend the morn
Watching the miller grind their meal and corn,
And each was ready to engage his neck
The miller couldn't rob them half a peck
Of corn by trickery, nor yet by force;
And in the end he gave them leave of course.
   One was called John and Alan was the other,
Both born in the same village, name of Strother,
Far in the north, can't say exactly where.
   Alan collected all his gear with care,
Loaded his corn upon a horse he had,
And off he went with John, the other lad,
Each with his sword and buckler by his side.
John knew the way – he didn't need a guide –
Reaches the mill and down the sack he flings.
   Alan spoke first: 'Well, Simon, lad, how's things?
And how's your canny daughter* and your wife?'
Says Simpkin, 'Welcome, Alan! Odds my life,
It's John as well! What are you up to here?'
'By God,' said John. 'Needs-must has got no peer,
And it behoves a man that has nae servant
To work, as say the learned and observant.

Wor Manciple is like enough to dee,
Such aches and torments in his teeth has he;
So Alan here and I have brought wor sack
Of corn for grinding and to bring it back.
Help us get home as quickly as ye can.'
'It shall be done,' said he, 'as I'm a man.
What'll you do while I've the job in hand?'
'By God,' said John, 'I have a mind to stand
Right by the hopper here and watch the corn
As it gans in. Never since I was born
Saw I a hopper wagging to and fro.'
    Alan spoke up: 'Eh, John, and will ye so?
Then I shall stand below a short way off
And watch the meal come down into the trough;
I need no more than that by way of sport,
For John, in faith, I'm one of the same sort
And diven't knaa nowt of milling, same as ye.'
    The miller smiled at their simplicity
And thought, 'It's just a trick, what they're about.
They think that nobody can catch them out,
But by the Lord I'll blear their eyes a bit,
For all their fine philosophy and wit.
The more they try to do me on the deal,
When the time comes, the more I mean to steal.
Instead of flour they shall be given bran.
"The greatest scholar is not the wisest man,"
As the wolf said in answer to the mare.
Them and their precious learning! Much I care.'
    And when he saw his chance he sidled out
Into the yard behind, and looked about
Without their noticing, until at last
He found their horse where they had made him fast,
Under an arbor just behind the mill.
    Up to the horse he goes with quiet skill
And strips the bridle off him there and then.
And when the horse was loose, off to the fen
Through thick and thin, and whinneying 'Weeheel'
He raced to join the wild mares running free.

The miller then went back, and did not say
A word of this, but passed the time of day
With John and Alan till their corn was ground;
And when the meal was fairly sacked and bound
Young John went out and found the horse away
And started shouting, 'Help! Alack the day!
Wor horse is lost, Alan! The devil's in it!
God's bones, man, use your legs! Come out this minute!
Lord save us all, the Warden's palfrey's lost.'
Alan forgot his meal and corn and cost,
Abandoning frugality and care.
'What's that?' he shouted. 'Palfrey? Which way? Where?'
The miller's wife ran clucking like a hen
Towards them, saying, 'Gone off to the fen
To the wild mares, as fast as he can go.
Curse on the clumsy hand that tied him so!
Should have known better how to knit the reins.'
John said, 'Bad luck to it. Alan, for Christ's pains,
Put down your sword, man; so will I; let's gan!
We'll rin him like a roe together, man!
God's precious heart! He cannot scape us all!
Why didn't you put the palfrey in the stall?
You must be daft, bad luck to you! Haway!'
And off ran John and Alan in dismay,
Towards the fen as fast as they could go.
And when the miller saw that this was so,
A good half-bushel of their flour he took
And gave it over to his wife to cook.
'I think,' he said, 'these lads have had a fright.
I'll pluck their beards. Yes, let 'em read and write,
But none the less a miller is their match.
Look at them now! Like children playing catch.
Won't be an easy job to get him, though!'
These foolish Bible-clerks ran to and fro
And shouted, 'Woa, lad, stand! ... Look out behind
Whistle him up ... I've got him ... watch it ... *mind!*'
But to be brief, it wasn't until night
They caught the palfrey, hunt him as they might

Over the fens, he ran away so fast;
But in a ditch they captured him at last.
  Weary and wet, like cattle in the rain,
Came foolish John and Alan back again.
Said John, 'Alas the day that I was born!
We've earned nowt here but mockery and scorn.
Wor corn is stolen and they'll call us fools,
Warden and all wor meäts in the Schools,
And most of all the miller. What a day!'
  So back they went, John grousing all the way,
Towards the mill and put the horse in byre.
They found the miller sitting by the fire,
For it was night, too late for going home,
And, for the love of God, they begged a room
For shelter and they proffered him their penny.
'A room?' the miller said. 'There isn't any.
There's this, such as it is; we'll share it then.
My house is small, but you are learned men
And by your arguments can make a place
Twenty foot broad as infinite as space.
Take a look round and see if it will do,
Or make it bigger with your parley-voo.'
'Ah, Simon, you must have your little joke
And, by St Cuthbert, that was fairly spoke!
Well, people have a proverb to remind them
To bring their own, or take things as they find them,'
Said John. 'Dear host, do get us out the cup;
A little meat and drink would cheer us up.
We'll give ye the full payment, on my word.
No empty-handed man can catch a bird;
See, here's the silver, ready to be spent.'
  Down into Trumpington the daughter went
For bread and ale; the miller cooked a goose,
And tied their horse up lest it should get loose
Again, and in his chamber made a bed
With clean white sheets and blankets fairly spread,
Ten foot from his, upon a sort of shelf.
His daughter had a bed all by herself

Quite close in the same room; they were to lie
All side by side, no help for it, and why?
Because there was no other in the house.

They supped and talked and had a fine carouse
And drank a lot of ale, the very best.
Midnight or thereabout they went to rest.

Properly pasted was this miller's head,
Pale-drunk he was, he'd passed the stage of red;
Hiccuping through his nose, he talked and trolled
As if he'd asthma, or a heavy cold.
To bed he goes, his wife and he together;
She was as jolly as a jay in feather,
Having well wet her whistle from the ladle.
And by her bed she planted down the cradle,
To rock the baby or to give it sup.

When what was in the crock had been drunk up
To bed went daughter too, and thereupon
To bed went Alan and to bed went John.
That was the lot; no sleeping-draught was needed.
The miller had taken so much booze unheeded
He snorted like a cart-horse in his sleep,
And vented other noises, loud and deep.
His wife joined in the chorus hot and strong;
Two furlongs off you might have heard their song.
The wench was snoring too, for company.

Alan the clerk in all this melody
Gave John a poke and said, 'Are ye awake?
Did ye ever hear sich sang for guidness sake?
There's family prayers for ye among they noddies!
Wild fire come doon and burn them up, the bodies!
Whoever heard a canny thing like that?
The devil take their souls for what they're at!
All this lang neet I shall na get nie rest.

'But never ye mind, all shall be for the best;
I tell ye, John, as sure as I'm a man,
I'm going to have that wench there, if I can!
The law grants easement when things gan amiss,
For, John, there is a law that gans like this:

"If in one point a person be aggrieved,
Then in another he shall be relieved."
    'Wor corn is stolen, nivvor doubt of that;
Ill-luck has followed us in all we're at,
And since no compensation has been offered
Against wor loss, I'll take the easement proffered.
God's soul, it shall be so indeed, none other!'
    John whispered back to him, 'Be careful, brother,
The miller is a torble man for slaughter;
If he should wake and find ye with his daughter
He might do injury to you and me.'
    'Injury? Him! I coont him nat a flea!'
    Alan rose up; towards the wench he crept.
The wench lay flat upon her back and slept,
And ere she saw him, he had drawn so nigh,
It was too late for her to give a cry,
And, in a word, they very soon got on.
Now, Alan, play! For I will speak of John.
    John lay quite still a quarter of an hour
Lamenting to himself that grapes were sour
And grumbled thus: 'Lord, what a wicked jape!
For here am I no better than an ape;
My meät has got some comfort for his harms,
He has the miller's daughter in his arms;
He took his chance, and now his needs are sped;
I'm but a sack of rubbish here in bed.
And when this jape is told in time to come
They'll say I was a softie and a bum!
I'll get up too and take what chance I may,
For God helps those that help theirsels, they say.'
    He rises, steals towards the cradle, lifts it,
And stepping softly back again, he shifts it
And lays it by his bed upon the floor.
    The miller's wife soon after ceased to snore,
Began to wake, rose up, and left the room,
And coming back she groped about in gloom,
Missing the cradle John had snatched away.
'Lord, Lord,' she said, 'I nearly went astray

And got into the students' bed.... How dreadful!
There would have been foul doings. What a bed-full!'
    At last she gropes to where the cradle stands,
And so by fumbling upwards with her hands
She found the bed, and thinking nought but good,
Since she was certain where the cradle stood,
Yet knew not where she was, for it was dark,
She well and fairly crept in with the clerk,
Then lay quite still and tried to go to sleep.
John waited for a while, then gave a leap
And thrust himself upon this worthy wife.
It was the merriest fit in all her life
For John went deep and thrust away like mad.
It was a jolly life for either lad
Till the third morning cock began to sing.
    Alan grew tired as dawn began to spring;
He had been working all the long, long night.
'Bye-bye,' he said, 'sweet Molly.... Are ye a'right?
The day has come, I cannot linger here,
But ever mair in life and death, my dear,
I am your own true clerk, or strike me deid!'
'Good-by, my sweet,' she whispered, 'take good heed ...
But first I'll tell you something, that I will!
When you are riding homewards past the mill,
By the main entrance-door, a bit behind it,
There's the half-bushel cake – you're sure to find it –
And it was made out of the very meal
You brought to grind and I helped father steal....
And, dearest heart, God have you in his keeping!'
And with that word she almost burst out weeping.
    Alan got up and thought, 'Dawn's coming on,
Better get back and creep in beside John.'
But there he found the cradle in his way.
'By God,' he thought, 'I nearly went astray!
My heed is tottering with my work to-neet,
That'll be why I cannot gan areet!
This cradle tells me I have lost my tether;
Yon must be miller and his wife together.'

And back he went, groping his weary way
And reached the bed in which the miller lay,
And thinking it was John upon the bed,
He slid in by the miller's side instead,
Grabbing his neck, and with no more ado
Said, 'Shake yourself, wake up, you pig's-head, you!
For Christ's soul, listen! O such noble games
As I have had! I tell you, by St James,
Three times the neet, from midnight into morn,
The miller's daughter helped me grind my corn
While you've been lying in your cowardly way ...'
'You scoundrel!' said the miller. 'What d'you say?
You beast! You treacherous blackguard! Filthy rat!
God's dignity! I'll murder you for that!
How dare you be so bold as to fling mud
Upon my daughter, come of noble blood?'

He grabbed at Alan by his Adam's apple,
And Alan grabbed him back in furious grapple
And clenched his fist and bashed him on the nose.
Down miller's breast a bloody river flows
Onto the floor, his nose and mouth all broke;
They wallowed like two porkers in a poke,
And up and down and up again they go
Until the miller tripped and stubbed his toe,
Spun round and fell down backwards on his wife.

She had heard nothing of this foolish strife,
For she had fallen asleep with John the clerk,
Weary from all their labors in the dark.
The miller's fall started her out of sleep.
'Help!' she screamed. 'Holy cross of Bromeholme* keep
Us! Lord! Into thy hands! To Thee I call!
Simon, wake up! The devil's among us all!
My heart is bursting, help! I'm nearly dead,
One's on my stomach, another's on my head.
Help, Simpkin, help! These nasty clerks are fighting!'

Up started John, he needed no inciting,
And groped about the chamber to and fro
To find a stick; she too was on the go,

And, knowing the corners better than them all,
Was first to find one leaning by the wall;
And by a little shaft of shimmering light
That shone in through a hole – the moon was bright –
Although the room was almost black as pitch
She saw them fight, not knowing which was which;
But there was something white that caught her eye,
On seeing which she peered and gave a cry,
Thinking it was the night-cap of the clerk.

Raising her stick, she crept up in the dark
And, hoping to hit Alan, it was her fate
To smite the miller on his shining pate,
And down he went, shouting, 'O God, I'm dying!'

The clerks then beat him well and left him lying,
And throwing on their clothes they took their horse
And their ground meal and off they went of course,
And as they passed the mill they took the cake
Made of their meal the girl was told to bake.

And thus the bumptious miller was well beaten
And done out of the supper they had eaten,
And done out of the money that was due
For grinding Alan's corn, who beat him too.
His wife was plumbed, so was his daughter. Look!
That comes of being a miller and a crook!
I heard this proverb when I was a kid,
'Do evil, and be done by as you did.'
Tricksters will get a tricking, so say I;
And God that sits in majesty on high
Bring all this company, great and small, to Glory!
Thus I've paid out the Miller with my story!

The Cook's Tale

The Cook's Prologue

ROGER the London cook while Oswald spoke
Clawed at his back rejoicing at the joke.
'Haha!' he roared. 'Haha! Christ's blessed passion!
That miller was paid out in proper fashion
For trying to argue that his house was small!
"Be careful who you bring into the hall,"
Says Solomon in Ecclesiasticus,
For guests who stay the night are dangerous.
A man can't be too careful when he brings
A stranger in among his private things.
May the Lord send me misery and care
If ever, since they called me Hodge of Ware,
I heard a miller scored off so completely!
That jest of malice in the dark came neatly.

'But God forbid that we should stop at that,
So if you'll condescend to hear my chat,
I'll tell a tale, though only a poor man;
But I will do the very best I can,
A little joke that happened in our city.'

'Well,' said our Host, 'let it be good and witty;
Now tell on, Roger, for the word's with you.
You've stolen gravy out of many a stew,
Many's the Jack of Dover you have sold*
That has been twice warmed up and twice left cold;
Many a pilgrim's cursed you, more than sparsely,
When suffering the effects of your stale parsley
Which they had eaten with your stubble-fed goose;
Your shop is one where many a fly is loose.
Tell on, my gentle Roger, and I beg
You won't be angry if I pull your leg,

Many a true word has been said in jest.'

'That's sure enough,' said Roger, 'for the rest,
"True jest, bad jest" is what the Flemings say,
And therefore, Harry Bailey, don't give way
To temper either, if I have a plan
To tell a tale about a publican
Before we part. Still, I won't tell it yet,
I'll wait until we part to pay my debt.'
And then he laughed and brightened up a bit
And he began his story. This was it.

The Cook's Tale

THERE was a prentice living in our town
Worked in the victualling trade, and he was brown,
Brown as a berry; spruce and short he stood,
As gallant as a goldfinch in the wood.
Black were his locks and combed with fetching skill;
He danced so merrily, with such a will,
That he was known as Revelling Peterkin.
He was as full of love, as full of sin
As hives are full of honey, and as sweet.
Lucky the wench that Peter chanced to meet.
At every wedding he would sing and hop
And he preferred the tavern to the shop.
   Whenever any pageant or procession
Came down Cheapside, goodbye to his profession!
He'd leap out of the shop to see the sight
And join the dance and not come back that night.
He gathered round him many of his sort
And made a gang for dancing, song and sport.
They used to make appointments where to meet
For playing dice in such and such a street,
And no apprentice had a touch so nice
As Peter when it came to casting dice.
Yet he was free with money and persisted
In being reckless rather than close-fisted.

Of this his master soon became aware;
Many a time he found the till was bare.
For when apprentices are caught in whirls
Of dancing-parties, dice, and easy girls,
They cost their master's shop a pretty penny;
Little the minstrelsy for him, if any.
Riot and theft can interchange and are
Convertible by fiddle and guitar.
Revels and honesty among the poor
Are pretty soon at strife, you may be sure.

This jolly prentice, doing little good,
Stayed with his master through his prenticehood,
Though scolded night and morning without fail,
And often led with minstrelsy to jail.*

But in the end his master, taking thought
While casting up what he had sold and bought,
Hit on a proverb as he sat and pored:
"Throw out a rotten apple from the hoard
Or it will rot the others," said the tag.
So with a squandering servant; let him brag
And he'll corrupt all servants in the place.
Far better to dismiss him in disgrace.

His master, then, gave Peterkin the sack
With curses, and forbade him to come back,
And so this jolly prentice left his shop.
Now let him revel all the night, or stop.

As there's no thief but has a pal or plucker
To help him to lay waste or milk the sucker
From whom he borrows cash or steals instead,
Peter sent round his bundle and his bed
To a young fellow of the self-same sort
Equally fond of reveling, dice and sport,
Whose wife kept shop – but that was just for giving
Her countenance; she tarted for a living....

(Of the Cook's Tale Chaucer wrote no more)

144

[GROUP B]

The Man of Law's Tale

Introduction to the Man of Law's Tale

O UR Host perceived the sun upon its arc
Of artificial day* (from dawn to dark)
Quarter way up plus half an hour or more;
And though not deeply versed in heavenly lore
He knew quite well it was the eighteenth day
Of April that is messenger to May,
And was aware the shadow of every tree
Was of the same extent and quantity
As the erected body casting it.
    So, by the shadow cast, he had the wit
To judge that Phoebus, shining clear and bright,
Had climbed some forty-five degrees in height;
So, for that day, and in these latitudes,
It must be ten o'clock, our Host concludes.
And suddenly he plucked his horse about;
'My lords,' he said, 'I would inform the rout
A quarter of the day's already gone.
Now, for the love of God and by St John,
Let us no longer waste the time, I say.
My lords, time wastes itself by night and day,
Steals from us secretly, asleep or waking,
If we are negligent. For time is making
Stealthy escape, a stream that never again
Turns to the hills, but glides on to the plain.
    'Seneca and philosophers of old
Bewail time's loss more than the loss of gold:
"Lost money is not lost beyond recall,
But loss of time brings on the loss of all."

It can return to us again, once sped,
No more than can poor Molly's maidenhead
When she has lost it in her wantonness.
Let us not molder here in idleness;
You, sir, the Man of Law, since you contracted
To tell a tale, that tale is now exacted.
You all submitted – your consent was free –
To put this case for judgment up to me.
Acquit yourself! You promised so for one,
And then at least your duty will be done.'
'Host,' he replied, 'I'm willing, make no doubt.
I never had a thought of backing out;
Promise is debt, and as I am your debtor
I'd like to keep my word, I can't say better.
Laws are for all, and he who seeks to lay them
On others should by rights himself obey them.
Our text demands it; but I make avow
I can't recall a pithy tale just now;
But Chaucer, though a little crude at times
In meter and the management of rhymes,
Has told them in such English I suppose
As he commands, for everybody knows
That if he has not told them, my dear brother,
In one book, he has told them in another.
He has told more of lovers up and down
Than even Ovid honored with renown
In his Epistles, which are very old.
Why tell them all again since they've been told?

   'In youth he wrote of Ceix and Halcyon,*
And since has celebrated every one
Of all these noble women and their lovers,
As who will seek his lengthy book discovers.
The work is called *'The Legend of Cupid's Saints,'**
And there you may perceive how Chaucer paints
Lucrece and her wide wounds, and Thisbe gored
In Babylon, and Dido's faithful sword
Because of false Aeneas, or may view
The fate of Phyllis that was hapless too,

Turned to a tree for love of Demophon.
There you may also listen to the moan
Of Deianira and Hermione,
Or Ariadne and Hypsipyle;
The barren island in the foaming sound
Is there to see, and brave Leander drowned
For Hero's love, and you may count the woes
Of Briseis or see the tear that flows,
Helen, from thee, and thee, Laodamia!
There too the cruelty of Queen Medea,
Her little children hanging by the neck,
When the false Jason turned her love to wreck!
O Hypermnestra, true Penelope,
Faithful Alcestis, how he praises thee!
But certainly he never writes a word
Of Canace – that tale should not be heard,
She loved her brother in a sinful way,
Fie on such cursed tales as that, I say! –
Nor draws on Apollonius, him of Tyre,*
How King Antiochus, in mad desire,
Bereft his daughter of her maidenhood.
The tale's too horrible, it can't be read.
He flung her on the pavement for his wooing!
But Chaucer knew quite well what he was doing
And would not soil his sermons with narration
Of such unnatural abomination.
No more will I; ignore them if we may.
What shall I do, then, for a tale to-day?
I'd rather not be likened, if you please,
To those old Muses called Pierides
– The *Metamorphoses* know what I mean* –
Nevertheless I do not care a bean
Though I plod on behind him, somewhat dim;
I speak plain prose and leave the rhymes to him.'
     And on the word, in sober-faced relation,
As you shall hear, he started this narration.

The Man of Law's Prologue

O HATEFUL grief, to suffer indigence!
By hunger, thirst and cold to be confounded,
To feel heart's shame at asking a few pence,
Or, asking none, to know yourself surrounded
By such necessity, your need is sounded
In every ear and you are left to creep
About and borrow, beg or steal your keep!

You lay the blame on Christ and bitterly
Reproach Him for misdealing wealth; the haul
Your neighbor has sets you at enmity;
You say, 'I have so little. He has all!'
'By God,' you say, 'a judgment's sure to fall
Upon him. He will feel the burning coals
Under his tail for scanting us poor souls!'

Listen to the opinions of the wise:
'Better to die than suffer indigence';
His very next-door neighbor will despise
A man for poverty. Farewell, pretense
Of reputation! Yet with better sense
The wise have said, 'Poor men are wicked men';
Beware lest wickedness should prick you, then.

If you are poor your very brother hates you,
And all your friends avoid you, sad to say.
O, you rich merchant-men, how Fortune fêtes you!
Noble and prudent folk! You've won the day;
You throw no double-aces when you play,*
But fives and sixes! Yours is the main chance
And Christmas-time for you's a time to dance!

You scour land and sea to fill your purses
And, like sagacious men, you bargain for
The fall and rise of kingdoms, you are sources

Of information, news of peace and war!
But for a merchant I should have no store
Of tales to tell you now, yet one I know,
Told to me by a merchant long ago.

The Man of Law's Tale

PART I

IN Syria once there dwelt a company
    Of wealthy merchants, serious, straight and wise,
That had a far-flung trade in spicery
And cloth-of-gold and satins of rich dyes,
All serviceable stuff that could surprise
With novelty; and business was a pleasure,
Dealing with them and bartering for their treasure.

It happened that some merchants of this sort
Made up their minds to venture out to Rome,
Whether for business dealings or for sport;
Nor were they satisfied to stay at home
And send a messenger, but crossed the foam
In person thither; and where their expectation
Of profit lay, they found accommodation.

And having made a sojourn in that town
At their good pleasure for a month or more,
It happened that the excellent renown
Of Constance, daughter of the Emperor,
Reached them with every detail answered for;
And fresh particulars from day to day
Came to these Syrians, as I shall say.

This was the common voice of every man:
'Our Emperor – God save his majesty! –
Has such a daughter, since the world began
There never was another such as she
For beauty and for goodness; she could be
The Queen of Europe, with all eyes upon her.
May God sustain her long in health and honor!

'Peerless in beauty, yet untouched by pride,
Young, but untainted by frivolity,
In all her dealings goodness is her guide,
And humbleness has vanquished tyranny.
She is the mirror of all courtesy,
Her heart the very chamber of holiness,
Her hand the minister to all distress.'

All this was true as God Himself is true;
But to our purpose: when their ships were laden
These Syrian merchants started off anew
For Syria, having seen this blissful maiden,
Happy in this as in the goods they trade in,
Pursued their business as they did before
And lived contented; I can say no more.

It happened that these merchants stood in grace
With the young Syrian Sultan. Their return
From Rome, or any other foreign place,
He met with a benevolent concern
And entertained them eagerly, to learn
The news from other kingdoms – any word
They had to tell of wonders seen and heard.

And, among other things, they made report
Of Lady Constance and with special mention
Of her nobilty, in such a sort
As to entrap the Sultan's pleased attention.
Her features filled his fancy and invention
Till all the passion of his heart was cast
On loving her as long as life should last.

In that large book that overhangs the earth
And people call the heavens, it well may be
That it was written in his stars at birth
Love was to be his death; for certainly
The death of every man is there to see
Patterned in stars, clearer than in a glass,
Could one but read how all will come to pass.

For in the stars, and many years before
His birth, the death of proud Achilles stood,
Hector's and Pompey's, Caesar's too; the War
Of Thebes, shorn Samson's death, the hardihood
Of Hercules, and Socrates the Good
And Turnus murdered, all was written plain.
Man cannot read it, he is dull of brain.

And thus it was the Sultan, to be brief,
Summoned the Privy Council of his land
And said that of his purposes the chief
Was to obtain the Lady Constance' hand,
And that at once; for they must understand
That he must perish, lacking her for wife;
Let them take thought in haste to save his life.

Various councilors said various things,
They argued and conjectured in profusion,
They brought forth many subtle reasonings
And spoke of charms and magical illusion,
But finally were drawn to the conclusion
That there was no advantage to be gained
Except by marriage; that alone remained.

They saw great difficulties in the case,
Reasoning thus (to make their feelings plain)
That there were such discrepancies to face
Between their laws and customs; it was vain
To ask a christian prince to entertain
Thoughts of alliance under the dispensation
Mahomet blessedly had given their nation.

And he replied, 'Rather than that I lose
The Lady Constance, I will be baptized;
I must be hers, in this I cannot choose.
O leave your arguments and be advised,
Can you not see my life is jeopardized?
I have a sickness she alone can cure,
It is a grief I cannot long endure.'

What need is there for further dilatation?
I say by treaties and by embassy,
And by the Holy Father's mediation,
Backed by the Church and the Nobility,
To work destruction on Mahometry
And to enlarge the blessed law of Christ,
All were agreed; the arguments sufficed.

The Sultan with his Peers in all their pride
And all his lieges were to undergo
Their christening; Constance was to be his bride,
And certain gold – how much I do not know –
Determined for the party to bestow
In surety; oaths were sworn on either side.
Fair Constance, God Almighty be your guide!

Now some of you expect, if I may guess,
That I should tell you all the preparation
Made by the Emperor in his nobleness
For Lady Constance at the celebration;
But you must know that the elaboration
Ordained for an occasion such as this
Cannot be told in a parenthesis.

For bishops were appointed to attend,
Ladies and lords and knights of high renown
And many others; let me make an end.
And all were notified throughout the town
To pray with great devotion, calling down
Christ's blessing on the match, and to implore
A prosperous journey to the Syrian shore.

At last the day of her departure came,
I say there came that day of fatal woe.
No longer might she tarry or exclaim,
For each and all were ready decked to go.
Pale Constance rose in sorrow, for the glow
Of color left her cheek as she prepared her,
Knowing too well that nothing would be spared her.

Alas, what wonder is it if she wept
At being sent into a stranger-nation
And parted from the friends that long had kept
Her tenderly, to suffer subjugation
To one she scarcely knew by reputation?
All husbands are good husbands; heretofore
Wives have established this, I say no more.

She said in tears, 'O father, your poor girl,
Your Constance, softly fostered in your love,
And O beloved mother, crown and pearl
Of all my joy, save only Christ above,
To your kind graces she that was your dove
Commends herself, and journeys to the shore
Of Syria and shall never see you more!

'Alas, alas! Forth to a barbarous nation
At once to go! But since it is your will,
May Jesus Christ that died for our salvation
Give me the strength of purpose to fulfill
His wishes! Wretched girl, to fare so ill!
And yet what matter? Woman is a thrall
Disposed and ruled over by men in all!'

No, not in Troy, when Pyrrhus broke the wall
And burnt down Ilium, nor in Thebes destroyed,
Nor yet in Rome when it was ripe to fall
To conquering Hannibal that had thrice enjoyed
The victory, was grief so unalloyed
As in her chamber when she made to go.
But go she must, whether she wept or no.

First cause of motion, cruel firmament,*
Driving the stars with thy diurnal sway
And hurling all from east to occident
That naturally would take another way,
Thy crowding force set heaven in such array
That this her first, fierce journey must miscarry
And Mars will slay this marriage, if she marry.

153

O thou unfortunate oblique degree
Of the Ecliptic, whence the cadent Mars,
Thrust from his proper angle, helplessly
Falls into *Scorpio*,* darkest house of stars!
O lord of war, whose influence debars
All hope! O feeble Luna, vainly knit
To him, thrust forth from where thou shouldest sit!

And O imprudent Emperor of Rome,
Is one time like another in such case?
Haddest thou no astrologer at home
To choose the favorable time and place
For journeying? For one of such high race,
Whose hour of birth was known to thee? But O,
We are, alas, too ignorant, or too slow.

With solemn ceremonial, as was due,
The ship for this poor maid was brought to shore;
She only said, 'Christ Jesus be with you!'
And they, 'Farewell, fair Constance!' – nothing more.
How resolute a countenance she bore!
Forth in this manner then I let her sail
And turn to other matters in my tale.

The Sultan's mother was a well of vices;
She saw the course on which her son was bent
Of giving up their ancient sacrifices,
And so for certain councilors she sent
Who came to be apprised of her intent;
And when these men of mark were gathered near
She took her seat, and said as you shall hear.

'My lords,' she said, 'you know it to a man
How that my son is purposed to abjure
The holy teaching of our *Alkoran,*
All that Mahomet had from God the Pure.
And to that God I here make promise sure
Rather to die the death than to depart
From what that Faith has written in my heart.

'What could befall us from this newer Law
But thraldom of our bodies and remorse?
For to deny Mahomet can but draw
Our souls through everlasting Hell, perforce.
But, my good lords, will you pursue a course
I shall suggest and further my endeavor,
One that will surely make us safe forever?'

They all assented, swearing to make good
Their oath to live and die with her and stand
In strength behind her; each as best he could,
Engaged to rally all his friends at hand.
This was the enterprise that she had planned
– I shall describe it to you if I may –
And thus addressing them went on to say:

'We first must make pretense to be baptized
– Cold water cannot hurt us very much –
Thereafter let a feast be organized
To pay the Sultan out, if he should touch.
Though christened white, his wife and many such
Shall find there's blood to wash away! She'll want
More water than it takes to fill a font.'

O Sultaness! Root of iniquity!
Virago, second Queen Semiramis!
O serpent masked in femininity!*
The serpent bound in Hell was like to this.
O treacherous woman to confound the bliss
Of innocence and virtue, with a spite
Bred in thy devil's nest of foul delight!

O Satan, ever envious since the day
On which they chased you out of Paradise,
Our heritage! How soon you found the way
Through Eve to woman! Our bondage is the price.
And now this christian match by your advice
Shall be undone. Of woman you have made
The instrument by which we are betrayed!

This Sultaness (on whom my imprecation!),
Having dismissed her court in secrecy
– Why spin things out into a long narration? –
Rode round to see the Sultan presently
And told him she'd renounce Mahometry
And be baptized in Christ. She had been wrong
(She said) to be a heathen for so long.

And after that she begged him for the honor
Of feasting him upon the wedding-day,
The Christians too; she'd take the work upon her
To please them all. He answered, 'As you say,'
And knelt to thank her. Having got her way
She kissed her son, and he, with gladdened heart
In speechless joy, allowed her to depart.

PART II

THE company of Christians reached the coast
Of Syria, a great and solemn rout;
Immediately the Sultan sent a post
First to his mother, then to all about,
To say his wife had come beyond a doubt
And beg her to take horse to meet his bride
And do her honor, for his kingdom's pride.

Great was the throng and splendid the array
Of Syrians and Romans in their meeting.
The mother of the Sultan, rich and gay,
Received his lady with as fond a greeting
As any mother would have shown in treating
A well-beloved daughter; so they ride
Solemnly to the city side by side.

Not Caesar threading a triumphal arch
(Whom Lucan celebrates with such a boast)
Was royaler than this exotic march

At the assembly of this blissful host.
But yet this scorpion, this malignant ghost
The Sultaness, for all her flattering,
Gathered herself most mortally to sting.

The Sultan came himself a little after,
So royal he was wonderful to see,
And welcomed her with joy and happy laughter
And in this merriment I let them be;
The fruit of it is what you'll get from me.
After a time they thought it for the best
To end their revelries and take their rest.

The day appointed came, the Sultaness,
Old harridan, fixed the feast of which I told;
Thither the host of christian people press
In general assembly, young and old.
What a display there was of kingly gold,
What danties in the dishes! As for those
They bought them all too dear before they rose.

O sudden grief that ever art near neighbor
To worldly bliss! Sprinkled with bitterness
The ends of joy in all our earthly labor!
Grief occupies the goal to which we press.
For your own safety think it is no less,
And in your day of gladness bear in mind
The unknown evil forging on behind!

Briefly to tell my story, as is fitting,
Sultan and Christians all were overthrown,
Hacked into pieces, stabbed where they were sitting,
All but the Lady Constance, spared alone.
The ancient Sultaness, accursed crone,
Helped by her friends, did all as she had planned,
Being resolved herself to rule the land.

Not one converted Syrian that under
The Sultan's leadership had shared his thought
But, ere he could start up, was hewn in sunder.
As for the Lady Constance, she was caught
And to a rudderless sailing-vessel brought
Hot-foot, and bidden learn to sail the sea,
Quit Syria and make for Italy.

She had some store of treasure, let me add
For sake of truth, and full supplies of food
Were given her, with such garments as she had,
And forth she sailed the ocean salt and rude.
O Constance, full of sweet solicitude,
O Emperor's daughter of a mighty realm,
He that is Lord of Fortune guide thy helm!

She crossed herself and with a piteous falter
Of voice, addressed the cross of Christ and said:
'Holiest cross, O rich and shining altar
Bright with the blood of pity the Lamb bled
To wash the world's iniquity, O shed
Protection from the Fiend upon me! Keep
My soul the day I drown upon the deep!

'Victorious Tree, protection of the true,
Thou that wert only worthy to up-rear
The King of Heaven in His wounds all new,
That whitest Lamb, hurt with the cruel spear,
O blessed cross, that puts the fiend in fear
Of man or woman that is signed with thee,
Help me amend my life, and succor me!'

For many a year and day this creature fled
Upon the Grecian seas, and reached the strait
Beyond Morocco, so her fortunes led.
Many a time in grief she must abate
Her sorry meals, expecting death, and wait
Till in the raging waves her vessel reach
What shore soever in the end, and beach.

It might be questioned why she was not slain,
Or who was at the banquet there to save?
To that demand I answer back again,
Who succored Daniel in the horrible cave,
Where everyone but he, master and slave,
Fell to the lions and were torn apart?
No one but God, he bore Him in his heart.

God, to proclaim the wonders of His arm
By miracle through her, would have it so,
And Christ, who is the honey to all harm,
Has chosen instruments as well we know
To work His purposes, that darkly show
To human ignorance; our feeble sense
Grasps not the prudence of His providence.

And if not murdered at the feast, what law
Kept Constance then from drowning in the sea?
And who kept Jonah in the fish's maw
Till he was spouted up at Nineveh?
It was none other, certainly, than He
Who kept the Hebrew folk from being drowned,
Crossing the sea dry-footed, safe and sound.

And who commanded the tempestuous mouth
Of the four winds that trouble land and sea
Saying, "O west and east, O north and south,
Touch with no trouble ocean, land or tree!"?
There is no such commander if not He
That walked the water; He it was who kept
This woman safe, awake or when she slept.

Where, then, for some three years upon the wave,
Got she her food and drink? And who sufficed
To Mary the Egyptian in a cave*
And fed her there? Certainly none but Christ.
Five loaves and two small fishes overpriced
The needs of the five thousand; so indeed
God's foison came to Constance in her need.

Forth over ocean then she drove and came
Safe through our stormy channel till at last,
Under a castle that I cannot name,
Far in Northumberland, the billows cast
Her vessel on the sands and held it fast
From ebb of tide to the returning crest;
There by the will of Christ she came to rest.

This castle had a Constable-in-Chief
Who came to see the wreck and, as he ought,
He searched it through and found in all her grief
This woman and the treasure she had brought.
Him, in her foreign language, she besought
For mercy, begging him to take her life
And so deliver her from earthly strife.

Latin she spoke, of a degenerate kind,
But all the same she made him understand;
And he, assured there was no more to find
Upon the vessel, brought her safe to land.
She knelt to thank him, seeing in him God's hand.
But who she was she would not utter breath,
For hope of favor or the fear of death.

She said the seas had blotted out her life
And she in truth had lost her memory.
The Constable, together with his wife,
Moved to compassion, wept in sympathy.
And Constance showed such sweet alacrity
To serve and please all people in that place
They loved her that but looked upon her face.

This Constable and Hermengild his wife
Were pagans like their neighbors everywhere;
Hermengild came to love her as her life
And Constance made so long a sojourn there,
Giving herself to weeping and to prayer,
That Jesus brought conversion of His grace,
To Hermengild, the lady of the place.

In all that land no christians dared to meet
For worship, most had fled; for long before
A pagan army and a pagan fleet
Had made their conquest of this northern shore.
To Wales had therefore fled a christian core
Of ancient Britons dwelling in our isle.
That was the refuge of the faith meanwhile.

Not wholly so, for there were some believed
And honored Christ apart in secrecy,
So that their pagan rulers were deceived.
There happened, near the castle, to be three,
One among whom was blind and could not see,
Save with that inward eyesight of the mind
That still can shed its light upon the blind.

Bright was the sun when, on a summer's day,
The Constable suggested they might go,
He, Constance and his wife, along the way
Towards the sea for half a mile or so,
Just for the pleasure of roaming to and fro.
And on their walk it chanced they met at last
This old and crooked man, with eyes shut fast.

The old, blind Briton cried, 'For Jesus' sake,
My Lady Hermengild, restore my sight!'
Now she on hearing him began to quake
For fear her husband, should it come to light
She was of Christ, would have her slain outright.
But Constance made her bold, bidding her search
And do Christ's will, as daughter of His Church.

The Constable, abashed at what he saw,
Said, 'What's all this about?' and stopped to stare.
And Constance answered, 'Sir, the power and law
Of Christ can save us from the devil's snare.'
Then she began so fully to declare
Our faith that what she said to him sufficed,
Ere evening fell, to turn his heart to Christ.

This Constable was not the over-lord
Where Constance had been found upon the strand,
But long had held the region with his sword
For Alla, king of all Northumberland.
He was a wise king with a powerful hand
Against the Scots, as everybody knows;
Let me turn back to how my story goes.

Now Satan who is ever on our track
To trick us, seeing Constance's perfection
And casting round how he might pay her back,
Filled a young knight who lived in that direction
With foul desires of such a fierce complexion
The fellow thought he'd die, so sharp the spur
Of lust, unless he had his will of her.

He wooed her fiercely; it availed him nought,
For she would yield to sin for no persuasion.
So, out of spite, he compassed in his thought
A shameful death for her by some evasion
Or stratagem, and when on some occasion
The Constable was absent, in he crept
Softly one night where Hermengilda slept.

Weary with prayer and holy meditation
She lay near Constance. Little did she note
How he, o'ermastered by the Fiend's temptation,
Had softly come upon her; then he smote
The Lady Hermengild and slit her throat,
Then laying the bloody knife beside the bed
Of Constance went his way, God strike him dead!

Next day the Constable returned again
With Alla too, king of the country round,
To find his wife was pitilessly slain.
Wringing his hands he wept and fell to ground,
And there, by Constance, in the bed he found
The bloody knife; alas, what could she say,
Out of her wits with terror and dismay?

They told the King of the unhappy deed
And also of the manner, time and place
In which they came on Constance in her need
Upon the ship, and brooding on the case
He felt a shock of pity; in her face
He saw benignity. Could such a glance
In one so lovely fall to such mischance?

And so, as when a lamb is brought to slaughter,
She stood, this innocent, before the king,
And the false knight, the villain that had sought her
Destruction, swore that she had done the thing.
The rest stood weeping by, and clamoring
That it was unimaginable she
Had done so monstrous an iniquity.

For they had ever known her virtuous
And loving to her mistress Hermengild,
And the whole household gave its witness thus,
Except the knight by whom she had been killed.
Much moved by this the gentle King was filled
With a desire for stronger proof, to hit
By deeper questioning the truth of it.

Alas, my Constance! Champion hast thou none,
Nor canst defend thyself; what wilt thou say?
But He that died for our redemption, Son
Of God who bound the fiend – and where he lay
There lies he still – shall champion thee this day!
Without an open miracle from on high
To save her, she assuredly must die.

She fell upon her knees and thus she prayed:
'Immortal God, thou who didst save Susanna
Falsely accused, and thou, merciful maid
And mother, Mary, daughter of St Anna,
Before whose child the angels sing Hosanna,
If I be innocent of this felony
Let me not die, support and succor me!'

Have you not some time seen a paler face
Among the crowd, of one who has been led
Towards his death and has obtained no grace?
Ah, what a color in his face, how dead!
Who would not know that he was sore bested
Among those other faces, singled out?
So also Constance stood, and gazed about.

O Queens abiding in prosperity,
You Duchesses and Ladies, hearts of stone
Would have compassion on her misery;
An Emperor's daughter, there she stands alone,
Without a soul to whom she can make moan!
O royal blood, standing in greatest need
And deadly fear, far are thy friends indeed!

King Alla felt compassion for her fears;
A noble heart feels pity. At her look
He was unable to restrain his tears.
At last he said, 'Let someone fetch a book,
And if this knight will swear an oath she took
The knife and killed this woman, we shall confer
And name a man for executioner.'

They brought a British book in which were written
The Gospels, and the knight stood forth alone
And swore her guilt. And, lo, the knight was smitten,
A hand appeared and struck him to the bone
Behind the neck, and down he went like stone!
His eyes burst from their sockets in his face,
In sight of all assembled in the place.

And as he fell a voice was heard to ring:
'Thou hast defamed the innocent and meek,
A daughter of the Church, before the King;
Thus hast thou done, and yet I did not speak.'
Aghast at such a marvel faces seek
Each other in amaze at the unknown,
Dreading a judgment, all but she alone.

Great was their fear and great their penitence
For having made a wrongful accusation
And felt suspicion of her innocence.
And in the end the heavenly visitation,
With all that Constance spoke in mediation,
Converted Alla; many in that place
Were also turned to Christ, O blessed grace!

The treacherous knight was slain for his untruth
By Alla's doom, there was no tarrying,
Though Constance felt deep pity for his youth.
Then Jesus in his mercy caused the king
To wed this holy maiden. Belfries ring
In solemn joy, and Constance the serene
By ordinance of Christ is made a queen.

Who grieved at this? Who was it took no part
In this rejoicing? Who but Donegild,
The mother of the King? Her tyrant heart
Felt it would burst in two, for she was filled
With raging spite at what her son had willed.
She thought it gross dishonor to his state
To take this foreign creature for his mate.

I do not choose to stuff with chaff and straw
My lengthy tale, I rather seek the corn.
Why then relate the majesty and awe
Of ceremonial marriage, or adorn
My tale with talk of trumpet and of horn?
But let me pluck the fruit out of my story;
They ate, danced, drank, they sang and were in glory.

They went to bed, as reason was and right,
For wives, albeit very holy things,
Are bound to suffer patiently at night
Such necessary pleasures as the King's,
Or others' who have wedded them with rings.
Her holiness – well, she must do without it
Just for a little, and that's all about it.

He got a boy upon her then and there,
And to the Constable and a Bishop too
Entrusted Constance, being forced to fare
Once more to Scotland; there was work to do
Against his enemies. Constance, mild and true
And humble, heavy with her child, lay still
Within her chamber, waiting on Christ's will.

Time came to fullness and she bore a boy,
Maurice they christened him. In great content
The Constable chose a man in his employ
And wrote the King a letter to be sent
By him with tidings of this glad event
And other news that brooked of no delay.
The envoy took the letter and went his way.

This man, upon a private calculation,
Rode quickly to the mother of the King
And proffered her a courteous salutation
In his own tongue: 'Madam, rejoice! I bring
You news enough to make the heavens ring
A hundred thousand times in thankful joy;
The Queen has been delivered of a boy!

'Look, here are the sealed letters with the news
Which I must bear with all the speed I can
To greet your son the King, and should you choose
To add some message, Madam, I'm your man.'
'Not at the moment,' Donegild began,
'Stay here until to-morrow, take your rest.'
And added, 'Then I'll say as I think best.'

The messenger drank deep of ale and wine,
And all the letters secretly were cheated
Out of his box; he slept there like a swine.
Another letter then was counterfeited,
But with the utmost skill, and when completed,
Directed to King Alla, to appear
As from the Constable, as you shall hear.

The letter said the Queen had been delivered,
But of some horrible fiend or creature lured
From Hell itself, and that the castle shivered
At sight of it, it could not be endured.
Its mother was an elf, they were assured,
A wandering witch of charms and sorcery.
None could abide her hateful company.

Great was King Alla's grief at what he read;
He spoke to no one of the woes he bore,
But wrote again in his own hand and said,
'Welcome the word of Christ forevermore
To me, that now am learned in His lore!
Lord, welcome be thy pleasure and thy will!
All mine I place at thy commandment still.

'Preserve this infant, be it foul or fair,
Until I come, and let my wife be nursed.
Christ, when He wills, can bless me with an heir,
One that can please me better than the first.'
He sealed the letter and his sorrow burst
In secret tears; the messenger was sent,
There was no more to do and off he went.

O messenger, sodden in drunkenness,
Strong is your breath, your limbs are all astray,
You blab the secrets that you should repress,
Your mind is gone, you chatter like a jay,
Your features are distorted, turned to clay!
Wherever there is drunkenness about
No secret can be hidden, make no doubt.

O Donegild, I have no English worthy,
Tyrant, of thy malignity and spying,
And therefore to the Devil I refer thee;
Let him make poems on your treacherous prying,
You man-shaped monster! – No, by God, I'm lying! –
You are a very fiend and I can tell,
Wherever you are, your spirit is in Hell.

The envoy left the King and once again
Reached the Queen-Mother's court to pass the night;
And Donegild was quick to entertain
The man as hospitably as she might.
He underpinned his girdle pretty tight
Boozing away, and snored with gummy eyes
All night, until the sun began to rise.

Again they stole his letters, and the pith
Of what they forged instead of them was now:
'King Alla bids the Constable forthwith,
On pain of hanging and the royal vow,
For no consideration to allow
Constance within his kingdom; let her bide
No longer than three days and half a tide.

'Into the very ship in which he found her
Let her be put and so thrust out to sea,
Her and her son, with all her gear around her,
And charge her never to return to me.'
O Constance, tremble at the harsh decree!
What dreams will haunt your troubled sleeping, filled
With dread! All this was planned by Donegild.

On the next morning when the day was full
The envoy woke and took the shortest way
Towards the castle. To the Constable
He gave the letter, who in great dismay
Cried out repeatedly, 'Alas, the day!
Lord Jesus Christ, how can the world go on
With such a mort of wickedness thereon?

'O mighty God! And can it be thy will?
Thou art a righteous Judge, how can it be
That Thou shouldest suffer innocence to spill
And leave the wicked in prosperity?
O kindest Constance! O the grief to me
To be thy executioner or pay
It with my life! There is no other way.'

They wept, both young and old, throughout the place
At this accurst command the King had sent,
And Constance with a pale and deadly face
Arose the fourth day after; down she went
Towards the ship, not seeming to resent
The will of Christ, and kneeling on the shore
She said: 'O Lord, welcome forevermore

'Thy word! He that protected me from shame
When first I came among you will allow
No shame or harm, will shield me just the same
In the salt sea, although I know not how.
As strong as ever He was, so is He now.
In Him I trust and in His mother dear,
My rudder and my sail! What need I fear?'

Her little child lay weeping in her arm,
And kneeling with him pityingly she said:
'Peace, little son, I will not do you harm!'
And then she took a kerchief from her head
And laid it on his little eyes instead;
She rocked him in her arms and lulled his cries
And up to Heaven's height she cast her eyes.

'Mary,' she said, 'O maid and mother bright,
Truth is that by a woman's egging on
Mankind was lost, condemned to death and night,
For which thy Son was rent and spit upon.
Thou sawest His torment; what comparison
Can ever be between thy sufferings there
And any other woe that man can bear?

'Thy Child thou sawest slain before thine eyes;
My little child lives still and seeks thy aid.
Thou to whom every woeful spirit cries,
Bright lady, glory of womanhood, fair maid,
Haven of refuge, star that cannot fade,
Have pity on my child! Thy gentleness
Pities all sorrowful creatures in distress.

'O little child, alas, what is thy guilt
That never sinned as yet, and couldst not do?
Why would thy hard-heart father have thee spilt?
O Constable, is there no mercy in you?
Keep my sweet child.... O, must he suffer too?
Let him but stay, or if you fear the blame,
Kiss him but once and in his father's name!'

And then she turned her gaze towards the land
And cried aloud, 'Hard husband, ah, good-by!'
And she arose and went along the strand
Towards the vessel (and the crowd drew nigh)
And still she begged her baby not to cry,
And took her leave, and with a holy heart
Crossing herself, made ready to depart.

The ship was victualed well enough, indeed
Abundantly for her in such a case,
With necessaries to supply her need
Sufficiently. Thank God for all His grace!
May He send light to shine upon her face
And waft her home! What better can I say?
Over the open sea she drove her way.

PART III

A LLA the King came home, his warfare done,
And reached the castle – that of which I told –
And asked at once to see his wife and son.
The Constable, who felt his heart turn cold,
Began to tell him plainly and unfold
What you have heard – I cannot tell it better –
Ending by shewing him his seal and letter,

Saying, 'My Lord, as you commanded me
On pain of death, I did. No less than that.'
The messenger was tortured until he

Acknowledged all, confessing full and flat
Where he had been, what places rested at
By night, and how; and so, by questioning,
They guessed the author of this dreadful thing.

The hand was recognized that wrote the letter
And mixed the venom for this cursed deed,
But how I know not, I can say no better
Than that the outcome was the King decreed
His mother should be killed, as you may read,
For false allegiance, treason and dishonor.
Thus ends old Donegild, my curse upon her!

The sorrows of King Alla night and day
Consumed him for his wife and little child;
How great his sufferings no tongue can say,
And so I turn to Constance on the wild
Paths of the sea, five years and more exiled
In grief and misery, but in the hand
Of Christ's protecting angel; she neared land.

Yes, by a heathen castle at long last
– What name it had, alas I cannot find
In my authorities – the sea upcast
Her and her child. O Saviour of mankind,
Think upon Constance, have her child in mind!
She's fallen among heathens dwelling near,
On point of perishing as you shall hear.

Down from the castle keep to see the sight
And stare at Constance many people came,
And from the castle also late that night
There came its steward, Heaven send him shame!
He was a thief that had renounced the name
Of Christ; he climbed the vessel, and made show
To lie with her, whether she would or no.

The wretched woman, overcome with grief,
Cried out for mercy, and her baby wept;
But Blessed Mary saved her from the thief,
For in the struggle, as the fellow leapt
In deadly grapple with her, he was swept
Over the side into the sea, and drowned;
And thus Christ kept her spotless, safe and sound.

Foul lust of lechery, behold thy due!
Not only dost thou darken a man's mind,
But bringst destruction on his body too.
In their beginning all thy works are blind
And in their end are grief. How many find
That not the act alone, but even the will
To set about it can deprave and kill!

How could this feeble woman have the strength
Against this scoundrel? Can you answer that?
Goliath, of immeasurable length,
How was it David came and knocked you flat,
So young and so unarmed and such a sprat?
How dared he look upon your dreadful face?
Only, one well can see, by Heaven's grace.

And who gave Judith heart and hardiness
To slay King Holofernes in his tent,
And to deliver out of their distress
The people of the Lord? My argument
Is this, that just as God Almighty sent
A spirit of vigor to them in their woe
He could send strength to Constance, even so.

Onwards her vessel through the narrow mouth
Of Ceuta and Gibraltar forged her way,
Sometimes to westward, sometimes north and south,
And sometimes east for many a weary day,
Until Christ's mother – blessed be she aye! –
Out of her endless goodness, to befriend
Poor Constance in her sorrow, made an end.

Now turn we to the Emperor of Rome
And say no more of Constance for a while;
From Syria the news had been brought home
About the Christians slaughtered, and the vile
Dishonor to his daughter by the guile
Of that foul Sultaness, accursed beast,
That had them murdered at the wedding-feast.

To take his vengeance then, the Emperor chose
A Senator and many another lord
All royally appointed, and God knows
They took revenge upon that Syrian horde;
They smote and burnt and put them to the sword
For many a day, then, to be brief, turned home
– That was the end of it – and made for Rome.

And as this Senator returned in glory
Sailing in style, the laurel on his brow,
He met a vessel, driving, says the story,
With Constance, pale and piteous, at the prow.
Nothing he knew of who she was, or how
Brought down to such condition; nor would she
Tell under threat of death her history.

He brought her back to Rome, and to his wife
He gave her with her little son, and so
Safe at the Senator's she lived her life.
Thus could Our Lady lift her out of woe
As she lifts many another here below.
There for a season Constance had her place
And lived in holy works, her gift of grace.

This Senator's wife, it happened, was her aunt;
But for all that she did not yet discern
Her niece, long-lost, in Constance. But I shan't
Delay my story longer; I return
To Alla. Long he felt his spirit yearn
And wept for Constance, who, for all his weeping,
Was safe enough in Rome, and in good keeping.

King Alla, who had doomed his mother's death,
One day was taken with a great remorse,
And, to relate the matter in a breath,
Set sail to Rome to undergo what course
Of penance that the Pope might there enforce,
Little or great, and as he sailed besought
Christ to forgive the evils he had wrought.

The news at once was bandied through the town:
'Alla the King has come on pilgrimage!'
His harbingers were going up and down
And, by a custom common in that age,
The Senator and all his lineage
Rode out, as much to show magnificence
As to receive a King with reverence.

Splendid the welcome that these noblemen
Gave to King Alla; he, no less than due,
Did equal honor in return and then,
After their meeting, in a day or two,
King Alla bade the Senator renew
Acquaintance at a feast. And, truth to tell,
The little son of Constance came as well.

Some have supposed it was at her request
The little child was taken to the feast;
– I can't know everything, I do my best –
But be that as it may, I know at least
That he was there, and by her wish released
To stand in front of Alla, after grace.
The child stood looking at the kingly face.

Seeing the child, the King began to ponder
And made remark a little later on:
'Who is that pretty infant standing yonder?'
The Senator said, 'By God and by St John,
He has a mother, but his father's gone
For all I know....' He went on to expound
The circumstance in which the child was found.

'God knows,' he then proceeded to declare,
'I never saw or heard in all my life
Of such a virtuous woman anywhere
As that boy's mother – woman, maid or wife.
And I'll be bound she'd rather have a knife
Thrust through her heart than yield herself to sin;
No one could bring her to that point, and win.'

In this child's face there was as great resemblance
To Constance as there possibly could be,
And Alla, bearing ever in remembrance
The beauty of his wife, bemusedly
Thought, 'Could the mother of the child be she
That once I had to wife?' And in his heart
He sighed, and sought occasion to depart,

Thinking, 'O Heaven! What phantoms in my head!
I should believe – unless all judgment's spent –
The seas have swallowed her and she is dead.'
And then there came the further argument,
'How do I know that Christ may not have sent
My Constance hither safe, as once before
He sent her safely to my northern shore?'

So, in the afternoon, the wondering King
Went with the Senator, upon the chance.
He took him home with honor, and made them bring
Constance in haste; he bade her to advance.
You may believe she had no thought to dance
When told the reason – whom she was to meet.
Faith, she could barely stand upon her feet.

When Alla saw his wife he greeted her
And wept. It was a moving thing to see
That first long look of recognition stir
Upon his face; he knew that it was she.
And she stood dumb in sorrow, like a tree;
Her heart was shut within its own distress
When she remembered his unnaturalness.

And twice she fell before him in a faint;
He wept and sought her pardon with the cry:
'As God above and every shining Saint
May show me mercy, dear, it was not I,
Who am as guiltless of the griefs that lie
On you as little Maurice here, whose look
Is so like yours – or blot me from God's book!'

Long was the sobbing, bitter was the pain
Before their troubled spirits came to peace,
And sad it was to hear them weep again,
As if their weeping brought them an increase
Of sorrow; and I beg you to release
Me, for the task would take me till to-morrow,
And I am weary now of so much sorrow.

But finally when all the truth was told
And when she knew him guiltless of her woes,
Their kisses fell, I think, a hundred-fold.
And such delight, such rapture then arose,
Save for the joys eternal, I suppose
Such joy as theirs has never been surpassed
Nor ever will be while the world may last.

Then, to repay her for her griefs, she pressed
Humbly upon her husband to agree
In sending a particular request
To beg her father of his majesty
To do him so much honor as to be
His guest one day at dinner, but to say
Nothing at all of her in any way.

Some men would have it that he sent his son,
Their little Maurice, to the Emperor;
But, as I think, King Alla was not one
To send a child as his ambassador
To greet the flower of christian men, who bore
So sovereign an authority; I deem
He went himself, and so it well may seem.

The Emperor vouchsafed with courtesy
To come and dine with him as he besought.
I read he gazed at Maurice eagerly,
And Constance came at once into his thought.
Alla returned once more and, as he ought,
Made ready for the feast, and all his power
Was spent in preparation for the hour.

The morning came; King Alla and his Queen
Rose early and arrayed themselves to meet
The Emperor; they were of joyful mien.
And when she saw her father in the street
She lighted down and, falling at his feet,
Said, 'Father, Constance was your child! O Sir
Have you no thought or memory of her?

'I am your daughter Constance,' then said she,
'That once you sent to Syria, as to slaughter,
And it is I that on the salty sea
Was thrust alone, to perish on the water.
Now, father dear, have mercy on your daughter
Send me no more to lands in heathen blindness,
But thank my husband here for all his kindness.'

Who could describe the joys that seemed to rend
The hearts of all those three at such a meeting?
But I must bring my story to an end
And shall delay no more, the day is fleeting.
They then sat down to dine; I leave them eating,
These happy people, with a joyfulness
Greater a thousand times than you can guess.

Maurice in time became the Emperor,
Crowned by the Pope, and proved a very limb
Of Christ and lived to strive in honor for
His holy Church. My memories are dim;
This is a tale of Constance, not of him.
In ancient Roman histories you'll find
The life of Maurice – it has left my mind.

His purpose ended, Alla chose the day
To bring his sweet and saintly wife and boy
To England, and they took the shortest way.
And there they lived in quietude and joy.
Not long it lasted; time, that can destroy
All happiness on earth, will never bide;
From day to night joy changes as the tide.

Whoever lived so happy for a day
As to have been unmoved by any sense
Of guilt or rage, unvexed by some affray,
By pride or envy, passion or offense?
And this I only say as evidence
That our felicities are of short life;
And so it was with Alla and his wife.

For death, that takes a rent from high and low,
After a year had passed, or even less,
Called for this king, and Alla had to go;
He left his Constance full of heaviness.
God send a blessing on his soul, and bless
The Lady Constance, who returning home
Set sail on her last journey back to Rome.

To Rome she came, this holy soul, at last,
And found her friends again at home and well;
All her adventures now were safely past;
She found her father in the citadel,
And weeping tears of tenderness she fell
Joyfully on her knees, pouring her praises
In thanks to God, a thousand eager phrases.

And so they lived in virtue and the giving
Of holy alms, never again to wend
Until by death divided from the living;
And so farewell! My tale is at an end.
May Jesus Christ, who in His might can send
Joy after sorrow, keep us in His grace,
Aye, every man and woman in this place!

Amen.

Epilogue to the Man of Law's Tale

OUR Host, after the Man of Law had done,
  Rose in his stirrups. 'Listen, everyone,'
He said, 'that was first-class, to say the least,
That story was. God's bones, Sir Parish Priest,
Tell us a tale! You promised it before.
You learned men are full of ancient lore,
God's dignity! You know a lot, I see.'
The Parson answered, '*Benedicite!*
What ails the man so sinfully to swear?'
Our Host retorted, 'Ho! Is Johnny there?*
I smell a Lollard in the wind!' said he.
'Good men,' our Host went on, 'attend to me;
Don't run away! By Jesu's noble passion,
We're in for something done in sermon-fashion.
This Lollard here would like to preach, that's what.'
The Skipper said, 'By thunder, he shall not!
He shan't come here to vex us with his preaching,
His commentaries and his Gospel-teaching.
We all believe in God round here,' said he,
'And he'll go starting up some heresy
And sow his tares in our clean corn, perchance;
And therefore, Host, I warn you in advance
My jolly body has a tale to tell!
And I shall ring you out so blithe a bell,
I shall be waking up the company.
It won't be much about philosophy
Or *phislyas* or curious terms in law.*
There is but little Latin in my maw!'

The Shipman's Tale

THERE was a merchant in St Denys once
  Who, being rich, was held to be no dunce.
He had a wife, unusually fair,
One of a gay, companionable air,
A thing which causes more pecunial dearth
Than all the foppish compliments are worth
That menfolk offer them at feasts and dances.
Such nods and becks and party countenances
Pass as a shadow passes on a wall.
But woe to him that has to pay for all!
The silly husband always has to pay,
He has to clothe us, he has to array*
Our bodies to enhance his reputation,
While we dance round in all this decoration.
And if he cannot pay, as it may chance,
Or won't submit to such extravagance,
Thinking his money thrown away and lost,
Then someone else will have to bear the cost
Or lend us money, and that's dangerous.

This noble merchant kept a splendid house
And all day long so many guests there were
– For he was generous and his wife was fair –
You would have been surprised; but to my tale.

His guests from up and down the social scale
Included a young monk, well-made and bold;
I judge he was some thirty winters old,
And he was always visiting the place.

Now this young monk, with his delightful face,
Was on most friendly terms with this good man
And since their first acquaintanceship began
He had been welcomed as familiarly
As it is possible for a friend to be.

And for as much as this good-natured man,
He and the monk, of whom my tale began,
Were born in the same village, the monk stated
That they were cousins, very near related;
The claim was neither questioned nor withdrawn:
Both were as glad of it as bird of dawn.
It pleased the merchant's heart, and his compliance
Had furthered this unbreakable alliance,
And each was happy to assure the other
He always would regard him as a brother.

This monk Sir John was very free in spending
Whenever he stayed there, carefully attending
To what should please; he poured out tips like wages,
Forgetting not the meanest of the pages
About the house; to each in his degree,
Master or man, he gave a gift or fee
Whenever he came – some honest kind of present –
And so, to them, his coming was as pleasant
As sunrise is to bird upon the nest.
I must have said enough, so let it rest.

The merchant, as it happened, one fine day,
Began to make arrangements for a stay
Somewhere near Bruges, to further his affairs
And buy a fresh consignment of his wares.
And so he sent a message thereupon
To Paris, and invited good Sir John
Down to St Denys so as to renew
Their pleasant company a day or two;
He and his wife would welcome it, as he
Was off to Bruges almost immediately.

This noble monk – the one I am describing –
Was glad enough, and needed little bribing;
He saw his Abbot and he got permission,
Being a man of prudence and position,
In fact a superintendent, one to ride
Inspecting abbey granges far and wide.

Off to St Denys, then, the monk has gone.
Who was so welcome as my lord Sir John,

So full of courtesy and 'cousin mine'?
He brought with him a jug of Malmsey wine
And also one of sweet Italian juice,
With these a brace of birds, as was his use.
And thus I leave them at their meat and drink,
Merchant and monk, a day or two, I think.

On the third morning up the merchant gets
In serious thought about his needs and debts
And up into his counting-house he goes
To reckon up, as you may well suppose,
All the past year and how things stood with him,
What he had spent, how the accounts would trim,
And whether his business had increased or not.

Many a ledger and money-bag he got
And laid them out upon his counting-board.
He had a deal of treasure in his hoard
And so he locked the door with an abrupt
Command that no one was to interrupt
His casting of accounts; he worked away
Sitting up there till past the prime of day.

Sir John had risen early too, to go
Into the garden. Walking to and fro
He said his office, courteous and devout.
This excellent wife then stealthily came out
Where he was walking softly in the sun
And greeted him, as she had often done.

A little girl was there for company
Beside her, under her authority,
Still subject to the rod; her mistress said:
'Ah, my dear cousin John! What, not in bed?
What's wrong with you that you are up so soon?'
'Niece,' he replied, 'a man can keep in tune
On five good hours of sleep, as I should judge,
Unless he is a poor old pallid drudge
Like all these husbands who will cower there
In bed, as in her form a weary hare
When she has had the hounds upon her tail.
But, my dear niece, why do you look so pale?

I cannot but imagine our good man
Has been at work with you since night began;
You really ought to go and take a rest.'
And he laughed merrily at his little jest,
And for his private thoughts his face turned red.

This pretty wife began to shake her head
And answered thus: 'Ah, God knows all!' said she.
'No, cousin mine, things aren't like that with me;
For by the Lord that gave me soul and life
In all the realm of France there is no wife
That has less pleasure in that sorry play.
For I may sing "Alas, and woe the day
That ever I was born!" I daren't,' said she,
'Tell anyone how matters go with me.
If only I could get away, or end
It all – Oh, I could kill myself, dear friend,
I am so terrified, so full of care....'

On hearing this the monk began to stare
And said, 'Alas, dear cousin, God forbid
That fear or grief, whatever else they did,
Should make you kill yourself! Unfold your grief;
It may be I can give you some relief,
Advice or help, perhaps; and therefore, come,
Tell me about your trouble, I'll keep mum.
Look, on this prayer-book I will take a vow
Never by chance or choice, no matter how,
To give away what you may say to me.'
'I say the same again to you,' said she,
'By God and by this prayer-book I can swear,
Though I were torn in pieces, to play fair
And never breathe a syllable or tell
A living soul, not though I went to Hell;
Not on account of cousinship, but just
Out of affection for you, love and trust.'
And having sworn, they kissed to seal the oath
And then conversed as impulse prompted both.

'Cousin,' she said, 'if I had time and space,
And I have none, especially in this place,

I could unfold a legend of my life
And what I've had to suffer as a wife.
As for my husband, though he's your relation ...'
'No!' said the monk. 'By God and my salvation!
Cousin indeed! He's no more cousin to me
Than is this leaf, here, hanging on the tree.
I call him so, but by the saints of France
I do so only for a better chance
Of seeing you – because I love you dearly
Above all other women, most sincerely.
I swear it you on my profession, love!
Tell me your troubles while he's still above,
Quick, don't hang back! And then you can be gone.'
'O my dear love,' she answered, 'sweet Sir John,
I hate to tell you.... O if I were stronger!
But it must out, I cannot bear it longer.
My husband is the very meanest man,
To me at any rate, since the world began.
It's unbecoming, since I am his wife,
To tell a soul about our private life,
Whether in bed or any other place,
And God forbid I sank to such disgrace!
I know a wife should only speak in honor
About her husband, or else fie upon her!
Only to you, the only one on earth,
This much I'll say. God help me, he's not worth
A fly upon the wall! In no respect.
But his worst fault is niggardly neglect.
For you must know that women naturally
Need to have sixty things, the same as me;
They want to have their husbands, to be candid,
Sturdy and prudent, rich and open-handed,
Obedient to their wives and fresh in bed.
But by the Lord that died for us and bled,
By Sunday next, if I am to look smart
And do my husband honor, I must part
With – well, a hundred francs; or I'm undone.
Far better not be born than to be one

184

That people slander and say cheap things about.
Yet if my husband were to find it out
I were as good as lost – ah, don't deny!
Lend me this little sum or I shall die.
Sir John, I say, lend me these hundred francs!
Trust me I will not fail you in my thanks
If only you'll oblige me as I say.
I'll pay you back, and you shall name the day,
And if there's anything else – some little task
That I can do for you – well, only ask.
And if I don't, God send as foul mischance
To me as fell to Ganelon of France!'*

    The monk gave answer in his well-bred way:
'My own dear lady, I can truly say
I weep in sympathy for what I've heard,
And here I promise you and plight my word
That when your husband has gone off to Flanders
I will deliver you from fears of slanders
For I will bring you down a hundred francs.'
And on the word he caught her by the flanks
And clasped her closely, giving her a riot
Of kisses, saying softly, 'Keep things quiet ...
And now let's have some dinner if we may,
My dial says it's past the prime of day;
You'd best be off. And be as true to me
As I to you.' 'God forbid else!' said she.

    And off she went as jolly as a lark
And told the cooks to hurry off the mark
So that they all could dine without delay.
Up to her husband then she made her way
And boldly knocked upon the counter-door.
'*Qui là?*' he said. 'It's me, dear. How much more
Have you to do up there,' she said, 'and fasting?
How long will you be reckoning up and casting
All those accounts of yours and books and things?
The devil run off with all such reckonings!
Heavens, you've had enough of it, my Own!
Come down and leave those money-bags alone.

Aren't you ashamed to leave that poor Sir John
Fasting all day while you go on and on?
What? ... Let's hear Mass, and then go in to dine.'
    'Dear wife,' he said, 'how little you divine
The complicated nature of affairs!
God save us all! Of such as deal in wares,
There's hardly two of us, as I'm alive,
Not two in twelve, I say, can hope to thrive*
Till they retire, showing a steady clearance.
All very well to make a good appearance,
To drive about the world and make a mark,
But our affairs must always be kept dark
Till we are dead, unless we are to play
At pilgrimage and keep out of the way
Of creditors. It's vital to consider
This curious world and find the highest bidder;
There's always chance to fear, and many a slip
Makes for anxiety in salesmanship.
    'I have to go to Bruges at break of day;
I shall come home as quickly as I may.
Therefore, dear wife, I beg of you to be
Courteous and meek to all in place of me.
Look after all our property with care,
See to the house; here's plenty and to spare.
Govern it well. I'll see you have enough,
But still, be thrifty over household stuff.
You've all the clothes you need, and all the stores.
I'll put some silver in that purse of yours.'
    And with that word he shut the counter-door
And came downstairs, he lingered there no more.
Quickly they all went off to Mass and prayed,
And quickly too the tables then were laid;
The merchant and his wife attacked the spread,
Sir John the monk was sumptuously fed.
    Soon after dinner, soberly, Sir John
Took him aside – this merchant – and went on
To say as follows: 'Cousin, as I see,
You're off to Bruges for some commodity.

May God and St Augustine be your guide!
Now do be careful, cousin, how you ride,
And moderate your diet; in this heat
You should be temperate in what you eat.
Well, don't let's stand on ceremony! Good-bye,
Dear cousin! God protect you from on high!
And if there's anything by night or day
That I can do to help you, only say.
Command me, and whatever be the task
It shall be done exactly as you ask.

    'Oh ... One thing. May I ask you as a friend
Before you go ... Could you contrive to lend
A hundred francs? Just for a week or two?
I have to buy some cattle to renew
A farm of ours with animals and stores.
So help me God I wish the place were yours!
You may be sure I will not fail my day,
Not if it were a thousand francs, I say.
But please tell no one of this little debt.
– You see, I haven't bought the cattle yet.
And now, good-by to you, my own dear cousin,
And for your kindness to me, thanks a dozen!'

    This noble hearted merchant thereupon
Replied, 'Good heavens, cousin! Dear Sir John,
This is indeed a very small request!
My gold is yours whenever you think best.
And not my gold alone, but all my stuff;
Take what you please, be sure you take enough.
Of course – I hardly need remind you now –
We merchants use our money like a plow.
We can get credit while our name will run,
But to be short of money is no fun;
So pay me back when you've the cash about.
Meanwhile I'm very glad to help you out.'

    He fetched a hundred francs out of his trunk
And handed them in secret to the monk,
So secretly the deal was only known
To him – this merchant – and Sir John alone.

They drank and talked and loitered for a spell;
Sir John rode back then to his abbey cell.

Day came; the merchant started on his ride
To Flanders with a prentice as his guide
And came at last to Bruges in good condition.
Once there he worked in haste without remission
And did his business, borrowed, made advances,
And never turned aside for dice or dances,
But purely as a merchant, let me say,
He spent his time, and there I let him stay.

The very Sunday after he had gone,
Back to St Denys came the good Sir John
New-tonsured and with freshly-shaven face.
There was no little boy in all the place
Nor any other person, it was plain,
But was rejoiced to see Sir John again.
And to go shortly to the point indeed
This lovely woman readily agreed
To take his hundred francs and to requite
Sir John by lying in his arms all night.
And just as was agreed, so it was done.
All night they led a life of busy fun
Till dawn came up. Then with a kindly laugh
He left, wishing good luck to all the staff,
For not a soul, there or in town about,
Had formed the least suspicion or slightest doubt
Of what had happened. Homewards, or where whim
Directed, off he rode; no more of him.

This merchant, having finished his affairs,
Turned for St Denys; thither he repairs
And cheers his wife with fun and feast and such,
But said his merchandise had cost so much
That he must needs negotiate an advance,
For he was bound by a recognizance
For twenty thousand crowns he had to pay.
He'd have to go to Paris the next day
To borrow certain sums among his friends
Which, with his ready cash, would meet his ends.

No sooner had he come into the town
Than, out of pure affection, he got down
And called upon Sir John for simple pleasure
And not at all to claim the borrowed treasure,
But just to see him, ask how he was doing
And tell him what affairs he was pursuing
As friends will do on their occasional meetings.
Sir John was most effusive in his greetings
And he as blithely chatted back and told
How prosperously he had bought and sold,
Thanks be to God, in all his merchandise,
Save that it was incumbent to devise
The raising of a loan at interest;
That done, he could afford to take a rest.

Sir John replied, 'Indeed, I am delighted
That you are safely back with matters righted;
If I were rich – we all have ups and downs –
You should not lack for twenty thousand crowns,
You were so kind to me the other day,
Lending me money; all I have to say
Is many, many thanks! God give you life!
But I returned the money to your wife
– The sum you lent – and put it in your till
At home. She'll know about it all, she will.
There was a token; she will understand.
And now you must excuse me. It's been planned
For me to join the Abbot here to-day,
He's going out of town, I cannot stay.
Best greetings to my pretty little niece
Your wife! Good-by, dear cousin, go in peace!
Let's hope it won't be long before we meet.'

This merchant, who was wary and discreet,
Soon managed to negotiate his loan;
The bond that he had signed became his own,
For he paid down the money to a franc
To certain Lombards at their Paris Bank.
He left, as merry as a popinjay,
For home, his business done in such a way

That he was bound to make to the extent
Of fully a thousand francs more than he'd spent.

   His wife was there and met him at the gate,
Just as she always did, and they sat late
That night and had a feast. He did not fret,
Knowing that he was rich and out of debt.

   At dawn this merchant started to embrace
His wife afresh, and kissed her on the face,
And up he went and made it pretty tough.
'No more!' she said. 'By God, you've had enough!'
And wantonly she gamboled for a while,
Until at last the merchant with a smile
Said, 'I'm a little cross with you, my dear,
Though I am loth to be so, never fear.
Do you know why? By God, or so I guess,
You've brought about a sort of awkwardness
Between myself, I say, and Cousin John.
You should have warned me, dear, before I'd gone,
That he had paid you back my hundred francs
By ready token. It was little thanks
He gave me when I spoke of borrowing money.
His face showed plainly that it wasn't funny.
But all the same, by God our Heavenly King,
I had no thought to ask for anything!
I beg you not to do it any more.
When off on business I must know before
If any debtor has paid you back my pence
Unknown to me, in case your negligence
Should make me ask for what's been paid already.'

   So far from being frightened or unsteady,
This wife retorted boldly thereupon:
'Then I defy that treacherous monk Sir John!
Him and his tokens! I don't care a bit!
He gave me certain moneys, I admit.
So what? A curse upon his monkish snout!
God knows I had imagined, out of doubt,
That he had given it me because of you,
To spend on my adornment, as is due

To your position, and the friendly cheer
You've always shown him as a cousin here!
But now it seems that things are out of joint.
Well then! I'll answer briefly to the point;
You've many slacker debtors than myself!
I'll pay you readily, and as for pelf,
If that should fail, from sunset to revally
I am your wife, so score it on my tally.*
I'll pay you back as promptly as I may.
I promise you I spent it in the way
Of pretty clothes; it didn't go in waste,
But, I assure you, in the best of taste,
To honor you; for goodness' sake I say
Don't be so angry, dear, let's laugh and play.
My jolly body's pledged to you instead;
By God I'll never pay except in bed!
Forgive me, dearest husband, just this while;
Turn round again and let me see you smile!'

    This merchant saw that there was no redress
And that to chide her was but foolishness,
Since nothing could be done, and was content
To say, 'Well, I forgive you what you spent,
But don't be so extravagant again;
You must economize, let that be plain.'

    And now my story's done, and may God send us
Plenty of tallying till death shall end us!
Amen.

The Prioress's Tale

Words of the Host to the Shipman and the Prioress

'WELL said, by *Corpus Dominus!*' cried our Host.*
'Long life to you! And may you sail the coast
In safety, noble skipper! Don't get sunk.
A load of lousy luck upon that monk!
Hey, fellows, watch your step for such a jape!
He took the merchant's hood and put an ape
Inside, by St Augustine, and what's more
Into his wife's hood too! Well, shut your door
Against all monks! ... What next? ... Well, let me see;
Who else shall entertain the company?'

And turning round, he checked himself, displayed
A courtesy becoming to a maid,
And said, 'My Lady Prioress, by your leave,
If I felt certain not to vex or grieve,
I'd judge it time for you to show your skill
By telling the next story, if you will.
Will you vouchsafe, dear lady, to comply?'
'Gladly,' the Prioress answered, 'I will try.'

The Prioress's Prologue

Domine, dominus noster (Psalm viii)

'O LORD, our Lord, how marvelous Thy name,
Spread through the reaches of the earth!' said she;
'Nor only are Thy precious praise and fame
Found in the mouths of men of dignity,
For in the mouths of children, such maybe
As suck the breast, the bounty of Thy ways
Can be declared in worship and in praise.

'Wherefore in honor of Thee, as best I can,
Of Thee and of that whitest lily-flower
That bare Thee, all without the touch of man,
I tell my tale and will put forth my power,
Though all unable to increase her dower
Of honor, who is honor itself, and root
Of bounty, next to Thee, her body's fruit.

'O mother-maid, maid-mother, chaste and free!
O bush unburnt, burning in Moses' sight,
Thou that didst ravish down from Deity
Upon thy humbleness the Spirit's flight
That lit upon thy heart, and in whose might
The Word took flesh, help me to tell my story
In reverence of thee and of thy glory!

'No tongue or knowledge can have confidence,
Lady, to tell thy great humility,
Thy bounty, virtue and magnificence;
For sometimes, lady, ere men pray to thee
Thou goest before in thy benignity
And through thy prayer thou gettest for each one
Light that may guide them to thy blessed Son.

'Weak is my skill in speech, O blissful Queen;
How then shall I declare thy worthiness
Or how sustain the weight of what I mean?
For as a child, a twelvemonth old or less,
That hardly has a word it can express,
Just so am I, and therefore pity me!
Guide thou the song that I shall sing for thee!'

The Prioress's Tale

IN Asia once there was a christian town
In which, long since, a Ghetto used to be
Where there were Jews, supported by the Crown

For the foul lucre of their usury,
Hateful to Christ and all his company.
And through this Ghetto one might walk or ride
For it was free and open, either side.

A little school stood for the christian flock
Down at the further end, and it was here
A heap of children, come of christian stock,
Received their early schooling year by year
And the instruction suited to their ear,
That is to say in singing and in reading
– The simple things of childhood and good breeding.

Among these children was a widow's son,
A little chorister of seven years old,
And day by day to school he used to run
And had the custom (for he had been told
To do so) should he happen to behold
An image of Christ's mother, to kneel and say
Hail Mary as he went upon his way.

Thus had this widow taught her little boy
To reverence the mother of Christ, our dear
And blissful lady, and it was his joy;
A happy child will always learn and hear.
When I remember this, the ever-near
Saint Nicholas stands in my presence, he
Who did Christ reverence in infancy.

This little child, while he was studying
His little primer, as he undertook
Sitting at school, heard other children sing
O Alma Redemptoris from their book.
Close as he dared he drew himself to look,
And listened carefully to word and part
Until he knew the opening verse by heart.

He had no notion what this Latin meant
Being so young, so tender too, so green,
But in the end, one morning there, he went
And asked a comrade what the song might mean
And why it was in use. He was so keen
To know it that he went upon his knees
Begging the boy explain it if he please.

His comrade was a boy of senior station
And answered thus: 'This song in times gone by
Was made, they say, in prayer and salutation
To greet our blessed Lady now on high,
That she may reach to help us when we die
And be our succor. That is all I know.
I can learn singing, but my grammar's slow.'

'And is this anthem made to reverence
Christ's mother?' said this innocent. 'If I may,
I certainly will show my diligence
To learn it off by heart for Christmas Day.
Though they should scold me when I cannot say
My primer, though they beat me thrice an hour,
I'll learn it in her honor, to my power.'

So every day his comrade secretly
As they went homewards taught it him by rote;
He sang it with a childlike clarity
And boldly, word by word and note by note;
And twice a day it filled his little throat,
Going to school and coming back again,
Praising Christ's mother with all his might and main.

As I have said, this child would go along
The Jewish street and, of his own accord,
Daily and merrily he sang his song
O Alma Redemptoris; as it soared,
The sweetness of the mother of our Lord
Would pierce his heart, he could not choose but pray
And sing as, to and fro, he went his way.

First of our foes, the Serpent Satan shook
Those Jewish hearts that are his waspish nest,
Swelled up and said, 'O Hebrew people, look!
Is this not something that should be redressed?
Is such a boy to roam as he thinks best,
Singing, to spite you, canticles and saws
Against the reverence of your holy laws?'

From that time forward all these Jews conspired
To chase this innocent child from the earth's face.
Down a dark alley-way they found and hired
A murderer who owned that secret place;
And as the boy passed at his happy pace
This cursed Jew grabbed him and held him, slit
His little throat and cast him in a pit.

Cast him, I say, into a privy-drain,
Where they were wont to void their excrement.
O cursed folk! O Herod come again,
What profit was there in your foul intent?
Murder will out, and nothing can prevent
God's honor spreading, even from such seed;
The blood cries out upon your cursed deed.

O martyr wedded to virginity,
Now mayest thou sing forever, being gone
To the celestial Lamb of innocency,
Of whom the great evangelist, St John,
In Patmos wrote, who says that there they don
White robes before that Lamb, and sing afresh,
That never have known woman in the flesh.

This wretched widow waited all that night,
She waited for her child, but all for nought;
And so, soon as there came the morning light
Pale on her face of dread and busy thought,
She searched his school, then up and down she sought
Elsewhere, and finally she got the news
That he was last seen in the street of Jews.

Within her breast her mother's pity closed,
She went about as one half out of mind
To every place in which, as she supposed,
There was some likelihood for her to find
Her child, and to Christ's mother, meek and kind,
She cried in heart, and in the end was brought
Among the accursed Jews, and there she sought.

She made inquiry with a piteous cry
Of every Jew inhabiting that place,
Asking if they had seen her child go by,
And they said, 'No.' But Jesus of His grace
Put in her thought, after a little space,
To come upon that alley as she cried
Where, in a pit, he had been cast aside.

Great God, that to perform Thy praise hast called
The innocent of mouth, how great Thy might!
This gem of chastity, this emerald,
This jewel of martyrdom and ruby bright,
Lying with carven throat and out of sight,
Began to sing *O Alma* from the ground
Till all the place was ringing with the sound.

The christian people going through the street
Came crowding up, astonished at the thing,
And sent to fetch the Provost to entreat
His presence, and he came and heard him sing.
The Provost, praising Christ our heavenly king
And His dear mother, honor of mankind,
Bade all the Jews be fettered and confined.

They took the child with piteous lamentation
And he was brought, still singing out his song,
In high solemnity and celebration
Towards a neighboring abbey by the throng.
His mother, swooning as they went along
Beside the bier, could not be reconciled,
A Second Rachel, weeping for her child.

The Provost then did judgment on the men
Who did the murder, and he bid them serve
A shameful death in torment there and then
On all those guilty Jews; he did not swerve.
'Evils shall meet the evils they deserve.'
And he condemned them to be drawn apart
By horses. Then he hanged them from a cart.

Still lay this innocent child upon his bier
At the high altar while a Mass was said.
The abbot and his convent then drew near
To hasten on his burial and spread
A rain of holy water on his head;
And as the drops of holy water spill
He sings *O Alma Redemptoris* still.

This abbot then, who was a holy man
As abbots are, or else they ought to be,
In invocation of the boy began
To say aloud, 'Dear child, I conjure thee
By virtue of the Holy Trinity
To say how singing is permitted thee
Although thy throat is cut, or seems to be.'

'Through to the bone my neck is cut, I know,'
Answered the child; 'and had I been confined
By natural law I should, and long ago,
Have died. But Christ, whose glory you may find
In books, wills it be also kept in mind.
So for the honor of his mother dear
I still may sing *O Alma* loud and clear.

'That well of mercy, sweetest mother of Christ,
I long have loved with all that I could bring;
This at the hour of my death sufficed
To draw her down to me. She bade me sing
This anthem till my time of burying,
As you have heard; and when my song was sung
She seemed to lay a grain upon my tongue.

And so I sing as I must sing again
For love of her, the blissful and the free,
Till from my tongue you take away the grain.
For after that, the Virgin said to me,
"My little child, behold I come for thee
When from thy tongue this grain of seed is taken.
And have no fear; thou shalt not be forsaken." '

This holy monk, this abbot, even he,
Touched the child's tongue and took away the grain;
And he gave up the ghost so peacefully,
So softly, and the marvel was so plain,
Salt fell the abbot's tears in trickling rain,
And down he fell, prostrate upon the ground,
And lay as still as one who had been bound.

And all the weeping convent also bent
To earth and praised Christ's mother with many a tear,
And after that they rose, and forth they went
Taking this little martyr from his bier,
And in a sepulcher of marble clear
Enclosed his little body, fair and sweet.
Where he now is, God grant we all may meet!

O Hugh of Lincoln, likewise murdered so
By cursed Jews, as is notorious,
(For it was but a little time ago),
Pray mercy on our faltering steps, that thus
Merciful God reach mercy down to us,
Though we be so unstable, though we vary,
In love and reverence of His mother Mary.

                                        Amen.

The Tale of Sir Topaz

Words of the Host to Chaucer

Now when they heard this miracle every man
  Was sobered; it was marvelous to see.
But in the end our Host again began
His jokes, and first he turned and looked at me;
Then he observed: 'Who might this fellow be?
What man are you, eh? Looking for a hare?
Why do you fix the ground with such a stare?

'Come nearer, man, look up, look merrily!
Make room there, gentlemen, let this man have place!
He's shaped about the waist the same as me;
He'd be a likely poppet to embrace
For any woman, small and fair of face!
There's something elvish in his countenance;
He never speaks a word in dalliance.

'Say something now, as other folk have done;
And let it be a tale of mirth; at once!'
'Host,' I replied, 'I hope you are not one
To take it in bad part if I'm a dunce;
I only know a rhyme which, for the nonce,
I learnt.' 'That's good,' he said, 'well, take your place;
It should be dainty, judging by your face.'

Chaucer's Tale of Sir Topaz

THE FIRST FIT

Listen, lords, with all your might
And I will tell you, honor bright,
 A tale of mirth and game,
About a fair and gentle knight
In battle, tournament and fight,
 Sir Topaz was his name.

And he was born in far countree
In Flanders all beyond the sea,
 At Poperinghe in that place.
His father was of high degree
And lord of all the land was he,
 As God had given him grace.

Sir Topaz grew a doughty swain,
With face like bread of whitest grain,
 His lips were red as rose,
And his complexion like a stain
Of scarlet red, and I maintain
 He had a seemly nose.

He'd saffron hair and beard as well
That down below his girdle fell,
 His shoe-leather was Spanish;
From Bruges his hose, and brown, they tell,
His costly robe was simply swell,
 It made the money vanish.

And he was great at hunting deer
And hawking down along the mere
 With goshawk on his hand;
He was an archer, never fear,
A wrestler too that had no peer,
 No peer in all the land.

201

Full many a maiden bright in bower
Lay longing for him hour by hour
  Who should have been asleep;
But he was chaste and fled the power
Of lechery, chaste as bramble-flower
  Where red the berries creep.

It so befell upon a day,
As I'll tell truly if I may,
  Sir Topaz went to ride.
He mounted on his steed of gray
And, lance in hand, he rode away,
  A long-sword by his side.

He spurred his way through forest fair
Where many a monster has its lair,
  Such as the hare and buck;
And as he went by east and north,
I tell you, and was riding forth
  He met with evil luck.

The herbs were springing in the vale;
Green ginger plants and licorice pale
  And cloves their sweetness offer,
With nutmegs too, to put in ale
No matter whether fresh or stale,
  Or else to keep in coffer.

The birds were singing, let me say,
The sparrowhawk and popinjay,
  It was a joy to hear.
The throstlecock attuned his lay,
The turtle-dove upon the spray
  Sang very loud and clear.

Sir Topaz fell in love-longing
On hearing thus the throstle sing
  And spurred away like mad.
His steed was hot with galloping
And sweated so a man could wring
  Him out, such sweat he had.

Sir Topaz, so it came to pass,
Wearied of spurring o'er the grass;
    So very fierce his courage
That down he lay as bold as brass
And eased his steed by a morass
    Where there was splendid forage.

'Saint Mary, *benedicite!*'
He said. 'What love has done to me!
    It binds my heart, no joke.
By God I dreamt all night,' said he,
'An Elf-Queen should my mistress be
    And sleep beneath my cloak.

'I'll have an Elf-Queen, I declare!
In all the world there's none so fair
    Or worthy to be mine
             In town;
All other women I resign,
An Elf shall be my Valentine
    By dell and dale and down!'

He climbed his saddle like a throne
And galloped over stile and stone
    To spy an Elfin Queen.
And soon, as fast as if he'd flown,
He found a secret place and lone,
    Sweet Fairy-land, I mean,
             So wild;
For not a soul in all that zone
There was and not a face was shown,
    No woman, not a child,

Until a mighty Giant came
On him, Sir Elephant by name,
    A perilous man indeed,
Who said, 'Sir Knight, by fire and flame
Be off! By Termagant, I'll maim
    You and your sturdy steed

                              With mace
Unless you go. The Queen of Faerie
With harp and pipe and music airy
        Has dwelling in this place.'

The Knight replied, 'By all that's blue,
To-morrow I will meet with you
        When I have got my armor;
And then I hope to make you dance
With this my slender little lance,
        And you shall be the warmer.
                              Your belly
Shall feel its prick as I advance
Ere prime of day, and it may chance
        That you'll be slain, I tell 'ee.'

Sir Topaz quickly then retired;
The Giant took a sling and fired
        Fell stones, but greatly daring
Sir Topaz swiftly left the place
And got away by God's good grace
        And by his noble bearing.

My lords, still hearken to my tale
That's merrier than the nightingale,
        And let me whisper plain
How good Sir Topaz, small and pale,
By spurring over hill and dale
        Got back to town again.

He ordered all his merry throng
To cheer him up with sport and song,
        For he would have to fight
A three-head giant, very strong,
To gain the transports that belong
        To love and lady bright.

'Come forth,' he said, 'my minstrels all,
You story-tellers in my hall,
    And tell me, while I arm,
Romances such as may befall
To Prince and Pope and Cardinal,
    And of a lover's charm.'

They fetched him first the sweetest wine,
Then mead in mazers they combine
    With lots of royal spice,
And gingerbread, exceeding fine,
And licorice and eglantyne
    And sugar, very nice.

They covered next his ivory flank
With cloth spun of the finest hank,
    With breeches and a shirt,
And over that (in case it fail)
A tunic, then a coat of mail,
    For fear he might be hurt,

And over that contrived to jerk
A hauberk (finest Jewish work
    And strong in every plate)
And over that his coat of arms,
White as a lily-flower's charms,
    In which he must debate.

His shield was of a golden red
Emblazoned with a porker's head,
    Carbuncles at the side;
And there he swore by ale and bread
That he would kill the giant dead,
    Betide what might betide!

Boiled leather on his shins had he,
His sword was sheathed in ivory,

His helm was copper bright.
His saddle was of narwhal bone,
His bridle shone like precious stone,
  Or sun, or moon at night.

Of cypress was the spear he bore,
Not made for peace, but boding war,
  The head was sharply ground.
His palfrey was of dapple-gray,
It wandered in an ambling way
  And softly trotted round
        About.
My lords, this is the opening fit!
If you want any more of it
  I'll tell you more, no doubt.

THE SECOND FIT

Now hold your tongues for charity,
My noble knights and ladies free,
  And listen to my spell,
To battle and to chivalry
And making love in wantonry
  For such is what I tell.

Men tell romances such as this
About Sir Horn, Sir Hypotis,
  Sir Bevis and Sir Guy,
Sir Libeus and Sir Pleyndamour,
But our Sir Topaz will endure
  Above these lesser fry.

His worthy steed he then bestrode
And forth upon his way he glode
  Like sparkles from a flame.
And on his crest he bore a tower
And stuck thereon a lily-flower,
  God guard him from all shame!

And as he was a valiant knight
He sought no house at evening light
    But laid him down on earth,
Wrapped in his hood, his helm a pillow,
And tied his palfrey to a willow;
    It grazed to keep its girth.

But he drank water from the well,
As did the knight Sir Percivell,
    That worthy man-at-arms,
Till on a day ...

The Host stops Chaucer's Tale of Sir Topaz

'No more of this for God's dear dignity!'
    Our Host said, suddenly interrupting me,
'I'm wearied out by your illiterate stuff.
God bless my soul! I've had about enough.
My ears are aching from your frowsty story!
The devil take such rhymes! They're purgatory!
That must be what's called doggerel-rhyme,' said he.
    'Why so?' said I, 'Why should you hinder me
In telling my tale more than another man,
Since I am giving you the best I can?'
    'By God,' he said, 'put plainly in a word,
Your dreary rhyming isn't worth a turd!
You're doing nothing else but wasting time.
Sir, in a word, you shall no longer rhyme.
Let's see if you can tell us one of those
Old tales from history; and speak in prose.
Let it be gay or have a wholesome moral.'
    'Gladly,' I said, 'Dear God, I hate a quarrel.
So let me tell a little thing in prose
That ought to give you pleasure, I suppose,
Or else it must be very hard to please you;
It has a virtuous moral to appease you;
It has been told again and yet again
By various writers; but I may explain

No one Evangelist would have sufficed
To tell us of the pains of Jesus Christ,
Nor does each tell it as the others do;
Nevertheless what each has said is true,
And all agree as to their general sense,
Though each with some degree of difference.
If some of them say more and some say less
About his piteous Passion, I should guess
– Speaking of Mark and Matthew, Luke and John –
Their meaning doubtless was agreed upon.
And therefore let me beg of you, my lords,
If you should think my story ill accords
With the original – if, for instance, more
Proverbial matter than you've heard before
Is thrust into my little treatise here
To enforce its meaning in the moral sphere,
Or if the words I use are not the same
As you have heard, I beg you not to blame
My variations; in my general sense
You won't find much by way of difference
Between the little treatise as it's known
And this, a merry story of my own.
So listen, please, to what I have to say,
And let me tell my tale as best I may.'

Chaucer's Tale of Melibee

Chaucer's prose Tale of Melibee (the tone of which is entirely serious throughout) here follows in the original. It is a dialectical homily or moral debate, exhibiting a learned store of ethical precept culled from many ancient authorities. It extends over a thousand lines or so. Among the authorities quoted are Job, Solomon, St Paul, Jesus son of Sirach, St Augustine, St Jerome, St Gregory, Pope Innocent, Ovid, Cato, Seneca, Cicero, Cassiodorus, and Petrus Alphonsus.

The principal character in the debate is Dame Prudence, the wife of Melibee, but we also hear the views of his acquaintance, Doctors, Lawyers, prudent old men and hot-headed young ones. Melibee himself offers some opinions, most of which are wisely and modestly refuted by his wife. He is, however, more talked against than talking, and is always won over, in the end, to the right view.

The principal subject of the debate is whether we should avenge a violent injury by violence, and the subject arises because, during his absence from home Melibee's daughter, Sophia, has been assaulted and wounded by three miscreants who have made a burglarious entry into his house. Should revenge be taken upon them?

In the course of the debate the following subjects arise and are dealt with learnedly and logically, for the most part by Dame Prudence:

how to purify one's heart of anger, covetousness and impetuosity, how to keep one's opinions to oneself and distinguish true friends from false ones, fools and flatterers; how to examine any advice proffered and when to change one's advisers;

whether women are to be trusted, and whether their advice can ever be good, and if so, whether husbands ought to submit themselves to their direction (Dame Prudence wins heavily on this);

whether to take a private revenge is (a) dangerous, (b) justifiable morally, (c) in this case expedient (in parenthesis, why does God permit evil? No one knows): the outcome of violence is uncertain, one cannot be sure of success in vengeance. It is better to agree or compound with one's enemies. But would not this involve a loss of prestige? Prestige considered;

the importance of not making God your enemy, to whom vengeance belongs. If you reconcile yourself with Him, He will reconcile your enemies with you.

The enemies of Melibee are then sent for; Dame Prudence sees them privately and points out the superiority of a peaceful settlement. They are astonished and delighted.

Melibee decides to let them off with a fine. Dame Prudence persuades him to forgive them altogether.

His enemies then return before Melibee, who forgives them utterly, but not before he has rebuked them severely and pointed out his own magnanimity. This is perhaps the only point he scores.

Nothing is said of what happened to Sophia or whether she recovered from her injuries. The homily is immediately followed by

The Monk's Tale

Words of the Host to the Monk

WHEN I had done my tale of Melibee
And of Dame Prudence's benignity,
Our Host exclaimed, 'As I'm an honest man,
And by the precious bones of Madrian,
I'd rather have had my wife to hear this tale,
Good soul, than have a barrelful of ale!
She never shows such patience when with me
As Prudence showed in handling Melibee.
God's bones! Whenever I go to beat those knaves
My tapsters, out she comes with clubs and staves,
"Go on!" she screams – and it's a caterwaul –
"You kill those dogs! Break back and bones and all!"
'If any of my neighbors when in church
Fails to acknowledge her, or gives a lurch
And bumps against her, as may be the case,
No sooner home, she's ramping in my face,
"You wretched coward," she cries, "avenge your wife!
By *corpus* bones," she says, "give me your knife

And you shall have my distaff and go spin!"
   'That's how the evenings end and days begin.
"My word!" she says. "Things are in pretty shape;
I've married a milksop or a cowardly ape
Who lets himself be downed by every sot
And daren't stand up to back his wife, that's what!"
   'Such is my daily life; unless I fight,
By God, she turns me out of doors at night
Lost, if I show the slightest sign of tardiness
Or seem less than a lion in fool-hardiness!
Sooner or later, thanks to all her labors,
I shall be driven to murdering the neighbors;
For, knives out, I'm an ugly customer,
Though I confess I can't stand up to her.
Her arm is pretty tough as, by St Victor,
You'd find were you to wound or contradict her!
But now let's drop the subject and pass on.
   'My lord the Monk, don't look so woe-begone,
For it's your turn to tell a story, sir.
Why, look! We've almost got to Rochester!
Forward, my lord, and don't hold up our game.
But, on my honor, I don't know your name;
Sir John, perhaps? Why have you kept it from us?
Or should I say Sir Alban, or Sir Thomas?
What monastery have they shut you in?
I vow to God you have a pretty skin!
There was fine pasturage where you were sent,
You're nothing like a ghost or penitent!
By God, I bet you are some officer-feller,
Some worthy sexton – keeper of the cellar!
For by my father's soul, in my opinion,
When you're at home, you're in your own dominion.
You are no novice, cloistered in retreat,
A boss, more likely, wily and discreet.
And, more than that, you've brawn and bones as well,
Do yourself properly, too, as I can tell.
God send confusion on the foolish skunk
That first persuaded you to be a monk!

You would have put a hen to pretty use,
Had you permission as you have the juice
To exercise your pleasure in procreation!
You could have done your part to build the nation.
Alas, who put you in so wide a cope?
Damnation take me, but if I were Pope,
Not only you but many a mighty man
Going about the world with tonsured pan
Should have a wife; for look, the world's forlorn!
Religion has got hold of all the corn
Of procreation, laymen are but shrimps.
Weak trees make sorry seedlings! That's what skimps
Our heirs and children, makes them all so slender
And feeble that they hardly can engender.
And that's what makes our wives so apt to cope
Religious people; there they have some hope
Of honest coin to pay the debts of Venus;
We laymen hardly have a groat between us!

'But don't be angry, sir, at what I say;
Many a true word has been said in play!'

This worthy Monk took all without offense
And said, 'Sir, I will do my diligence
To tell you all a tale or two, or three,
As far as may conform with decency.
And if you care to hear, as our assessor,
I'll tell the *Life of Edward the Confessor;*
Or else I have some tragedies to tell;
I have at least a hundred in my cell.

'*Tragedy* means a certain kind of story,
As old books tell, of those who fell from glory,
People that stood in great prosperity
And were cast down out of their high degree
Into calamity, and so they died.
Such tales are usually versified
In six-foot lines they call *Hexameter*.
Many are told in prose if you prefer,
And other meters suited to the stuff;
This explanation ought to be enough.

'Now listen, therefore, if you care to hear.
But first I beg you not to be severe
If my chronology in all these things,
Be they of popes, of emperors or kings,
Forsake the order in which they fell of yore
And I put some behind and some before;
They come to my remembrance but by chance;
Accept excuses for my ignorance.'

The Monk's Tale

IN Tragic Manner I will now lament
The griefs of those who stood in high degree
And fell at last with no expedient
To bring them out of their adversity.
For sure it is, if Fortune wills to flee,
No man may stay her course or keep his hold;
Let no one trust a blind prosperity.
Be warned by these examples, true and old.

LUCIFER

With Lucifer, although an angel he
And not a man, I purpose to begin.
For notwithstanding angels cannot be
The sport of Fortune, yet he fell through sin
Down into Hell, and he is yet therein.
O Lucifer, brightest of angels all,
Now thou art Satan, and canst never win
Out of thy miseries; how great thy fall!

ADAM

Consider Adam, made by God's own finger,
And not begotten of man's unclean seed,
He that in Eden was allowed to linger
– Now called Damascus – and had power at need

213

Over all Paradise, save that decreed
And single tree prohibited. Than he
None ever on earth stood higher, till his deed
Drove him to labor, Hell and misery.

SAMSON

Long ere his birth, by an annunciation,
Samson was heralded by an angel bright,
Who marked him out for God in consecration.
He stood forth nobly while he had his sight;
There never was another of such might,
Or hardihood of mind for might to borrow;
And yet he let his secret come to light,
He told his wife, and killed himself for sorrow.

Samson, this noble warrior of Zion,
Having no weapon by him for the fray
But his bare hands, yet slew and tore a lion
While walking to his wedding, on the way.
His treacherous wife so pleased him with her play
She coaxed his secrets forth; with double face
She then betrayed them to his foes that lay
In wait, and took another in his place.

And Samson took, in his avenging ire,
And lashed three hundred foxes in a band
Tying their tails, then set the tails on fire
(To every tail he bound a fiery brand)
And burnt up every cornfield in the land
And every vine and olive in a mass
Of flame, and slew a thousand with his hand,
No weapon but the jaw-bone of an ass;

But having slain them, was so parched with thirst
He was near lost, yet prayed the Lord on high
To show that favor He had showed at first
And send His servant water lest he die;

Then from that very jaw-bone, which was dry,
Out of a molar tooth, there sprang a well,
And there he drank enough to satisfy
His thirst; God sent His help, as *Judges* tell.

And then at Gaza on a certain night
By force he rent apart the city gate,
Bore off the pieces on his back, in spite
Of what the Philistines in fierce debate
Could do, and then he set them up in state
High on a hill. O Samson, dear thy worth!
Hadst thou not blabbed thy secrets to thy mate,
None ever could have matched thee upon earth!

This Samson never drank of mead or wine,
His head no razor ever touched, or shear;
This precept was enjoined by the divine
Messenger-angel – all his strength lay here,
Lodged in his locks. And fully twenty year
He was a Judge and ruler of Israel;
Yet the day came to him for many a tear
And it was by a woman that he fell.

It was his love, Delilah, even she;
To her he owned that all his power lay
Within his hair, and to the enemy
She sold her lover sleeping, as he lay
Upon her breast; she bade them cut away
His locks, revealed his secret to those spies,
And so they found him there, an easy prey.
They bound him fast and put out both his eyes.

But yet before his hair was clipped and shaved
There was no thong or lashing that could bind
His arm; and now they took him and encaved
Him in a prison, set him there to grind

A quern! O Samson, strongest of mankind,
O sometime Judge in glory and in power,
Now mayst thou weep although thine eyes are blind!
Fled is thy joy, and come thy bitter hour.

Perished this captive wretch as I shall say;
His foes prepared a feast, and for their jeers
Made him their fool and bade him to display
Amidst a temple, thronged in crowded tiers,
His strength; and yet he set them by the ears.
He grasped two pillars, shook and made them fall,
And the whole temple, shaken from its piers,
Crashed down and slew him, and his foemen all.

That is to say, not Magistrates alone
But some three thousand others also slain
In the huge ruin of their temple of stone.
Of Samson I will say no more; but gain
A warning from his story, old and plain:
Men should keep counsel, and not tell their wives
Secrets that it concerns them to retain,
Touching the safety of their limbs and lives.

HERCULES

For Hercules, victor of sovereign power,
His labors sing his praise and lasting fame,
Who in his time was human strength in flower.
He slew a lion and he skinned the same;
He robbed the Centaurs of their boasted name;
He slew the Harpies, cruel birds and fell;
He robbed the golden apples, overcame
Their dragon-guard, drove Cerberus from Hell,

And slew Busiris the tyrannical,
And made his horses eat him, flesh and bone;
He brought about the fiery serpent's fall,
Made one of Acheloüs' horns his own,

Killed the fierce Cacus in his cave of stone
And left Antaeus the Gigantic dead;
He met the grisly boar and laid it prone,
And last he shouldered heaven overhead.

Was never hero since the world began
That slew so many monsters as did he.
Throughout the world his reputation ran,
What with his strength and magnanimity.
All kingdoms of the earth he went to see,
None said him nay, none equaled him in worth,
And the Chaldean prophet named Trophee
Says he set pillars up to bound the earth.

He had a lover, this redoubted man,
Her name was Deianira, fresh as May;
And as the learned tell us, she began
To fashion him a shirt, to make him gay.
O fatal shirt! Alas, alas, I say!
Poison was subtly woven in its mesh;
Ere he had worn it scarcely half a day,
From every bone there fell away his flesh.

But some authorities would thus excuse her,
Saying that Nessus made the shirt, not she;
Let that be as it may, I won't accuse her;
He wore it anyhow, and certainly
Blackness began to rot his flesh, and he
Raked burning coals upon himself and died,
Having perceived there was no remedy
And scorning death by poison, out of pride.

Thus fell the famous, mighty Hercules.
Who then may trust the dice at Fortune's throw,
Who in this thronging world delights to seize
On the unwary and to lay him low?

Wise is the man that well has learnt to know
Himself; beware! When Fortune would elect
To trick a man, she plots his overthrow
By such a means as he would least expect.

NEBUCHADNEZZAR

The mighty throne, the precious stores of treasure,
The glorious scepter and the diadem
That once belonged to King Nebuchadnezzar
Tongue cannot tell, hard to describe one gem
Among them! Twice he took Jerusalem
And, from the Temple, bore the vessels plighted
To God, and to his realm he carried them
In Babylon, where he gloried and delighted.

The fairest children of the royal line
Of Israel he gelded, and this done,
Made each of them a thrall and let them pine
In servitude. Daniel of these was one,
Wisest among them all, or under sun.
He could expound the dreams whose visitation
Troubled the King; Chaldean there was none
That could interpret their signification.

This proud king made an image out of gold;
Its height was sixty cubits and its frame
Seven in breadth. He ordered young and old
To bow before this idol and acclaim
Its glory; in a furnace of red flame
Any that disobeyed him should be flung.
But Daniel would not stoop to such a shame
Nor would his two companions. They were young.

This king of kings, so mighty and elate,
Supposed that God who sits in majesty
Could never rob him of his kingly state,
Yet he was cast from it, and suddenly.

Forth in the rain, thinking himself to be
An animal, he went and fed without,
On hay, as oxen do; and there dwelt he
Among the beasts, till time had come about.

And like an eagle's feathers grew his hair,
His nails were like the talons of a bird,
Till God released him of his madness there
For certain years; and the king's heart was stirred
In thanks to God. With many a tearful word
He swore to sin no more, and till the hour
Of death, when at the last he was interred,
He recognized God's mercy and His power.

BELSHAZZAR

He had a son, Belshazzar was his name,
Who held the throne after his father's day,
But took no warning from him all the same,
Proud in his heart and proud in his display,
And an idolater as well, I say.
His high estate on which he so had prided
Himself, by Fortune soon was snatched away,
His kingdom taken from him and divided.

He made a feast and summoned all his lords,
A certain day, in mirth and minstrelsy,
And called a servant, as the Book records,
'Go and fetch forth the vessels, those,' said he,
'My father took in his prosperity
Out of the Temple of Jerusalem,
That we may thank our gods for the degree
Of honor he and I have had of them.'

His wife, his lords and all his concubines
Drank on as long as appetite would last
Out of these vessels, filled with sundry wines.
The king glanced at the wall; a shadow passed

As of an armless hand, and writing fast.
He quaked for terror, gazing at the wall;
The hand that made Belshazzar so aghast
Wrote *Mene, Tekel, Peres,* that was all.

In all the land not one magician there
Who could interpret what the writing meant;
But Daniel soon expounded it, 'Beware,'
He said, 'O king! God to your father lent
Glory and honor, kingdom, treasure, rent;
But he was proud and did not fear the Lord.
God therefore punished that impenitent
And took away his kingdom, crown and sword.

'He cast him from the company of men
To make his habitation in the dew
Among the beasts, eat grass and tread the fen
In rain and drought, until at last he knew
By grace and reason God alone is true
And has dominion over crowns and creatures.
Then God at last was minded to renew
His mercy and restored his realm and features.

'But you, his son, are proud, though well you know
The truth of all these things that I have told;
You are a rebel before God, his foe,
Having defiled his vessels of pure gold;
Your wife and all your wenches have made bold
To do the like and drink of many a wine
In honor of false gods, accurst of old.
But God will punish you, and this his sign!

'That hand was sent of God, that on the wall
Wrote *Mene, Tekel, Peres,* as you see;
Your reign is done, you have been weighed, and fall;
Your kingdom is divided and shall be
Given to Persians and to Medes,' said he.
They slew the King Belshazzar the same night,
Darius took his throne and majesty,
Though taking them neither by law nor right.

My lords, from this the moral may be taken
That there's no lordship but is insecure.
When Fortune flees a man is left forsaken
Of glory, wealth and kingdom; all's past cure.
Even the friends he has will not endure,
For if good fortune makes your friends for you
Ill fortune makes them enemies for sure,
A proverb very trite and very true.

ZENOBIA*

Palmyra (say the Persians) had a queen,
Zenobia; one accounted to possess
A noble nature, and in arms so keen
And hardy none could match her, they profess.
Her lineage and her breeding were no less
Than of a Persian royally descended;
I will not call her first in loveliness
But say her beauty could not be amended.

I find that from her childhood she had fled
The offices of women, for she went
Off to the wildness of the woods to shed
The blood of forest deer, her bow she bent
On them, still swift of foot when they were spent;
And as she grew to woman she would kill
Leopard and lion too, and once she rent
A bear apart; she ruled the beasts at will.

She dared them all, would thrust into a den,
Or course upon the mountains through the night,
Taking her sleep in bushes; as for men
She was a wrestler and could win a fight
Against a stripling of whatever might;
None could resist her arm and none elude.
And she had kept her maiden honor bright,
Not deigning to be vanquished or subdued.

At last her friends prevailed and she was married
To one Prince Odenathus of that land,
Albeit that she long refused and tarried;
And yet it is as well to understand
He was reluctant too to give his hand,
Having like fantasies. When knit together
Nevertheless their union proved a bland
And happy one, they came to love each other,

Save for one thing; she never would consent
To let him lie with her, except it be
Once only, for it was her clear intent
To have a child, to leave posterity;
And therefore when she knew that certainly
She had conceived no child from such an act,
She then permitted him his fantasy
Again, but only once; and that is fact.

And when she was with child by him at last
She suffered no more toying at that game
Until the fortieth day was fully past,
Then she permitted him to do the same;
And Odenathus, whether wild or tame,
Could get no more of her. She would aver
It was no more than lechery and shame
To woman, for a man to play with her.

Two sons she had by Odenathus then,
Whom she brought up in virtue and in learning.
Now let us turn back to our tale again;
I say once more a creature so discerning,
So much esteemed, so lavish and so burning
In warlike zeal, so courteous by her birth,
You never could have found although returning
From search in all the corners of the earth.

Her splendor of array may not be told,
Whether in clothing or in store of treasure,
For she was clad in jewelry and gold.
In spite of all her hunting she found leisure

For languages, and learnt them in full measure;
And she applied herself to many, feeling
The study of a book to be a pleasure
That taught the way to power and high dealing.

And briefly to continue with my story,
Her husband was as powerful as she;
They conquered many kingdoms of great glory
Far in the Orient, they held in fee
Cities belonging to the majesty
Of Rome itself, and made their conquests thrive.
They never fled before an enemy
So long as Odenathus was alive.

As for her battles (should you wish for reading)
Against Shapur the King, and more as well,
With all the details of the whole proceeding,
What title won, what captured citadel,
And how at length she came to grief and fell
Besieged, made captive – all that she endured –
Study my master Petrarch, he can tell;
He wrote enough about her, be assured.

When Odenathus died, she mightily
Held all those kingdoms in her sovereign hand
And was so cruel to her enemy
There was no king or prince in all the land
But felt that it was grace enough to stand
In safety and secured from war and riot,
And treated with her, that they might disband;
Let her make wars so long as they had quiet.

And neither Claudius the Emperor
Nor his successor Gallienus ran
The danger of provoking her to war;
No, nor Armenian or Egyptian,
No Syrian either or Arabian
Dared take the field against her in a fight,
Lest she should slay them, or her conquering van
Put them in all its multitude to flight.

In royal robe her sons were wont to go,
Heirs of their father's kingdoms, one and all;
Their names Hermanno and Thymalaö,
Or such at least are what the Persians call
The pair. But Fortune's honey turns to gall;
Fortune withdrew her shining countenance
From this great queen and brought about her fall.
And she was plunged in sorrow and mischance.

For when Aurelian came upon the scene
With Rome beneath his government and sway,
He planned a mighty vengeance on the queen,
And, gathering his legions, took his way
Against Zenobia; to be brief, I say,
He routed her, enslaved and brought her home
In fetters with her children, there they lay!
And having conquered, he returned to Rome.

Amongst the other trophies of the war
There was her golden chariot, richly gemmed;
And great Aurelian, Roman emperor,
Returned with it in glory and condemned
The queen to walk before his Triumph, hemmed
By shouting crowds, gold chains about her throat,
And still, as rank allowed her, diademed,
And there were jewels crusted on her coat.

O alas, Fortune! She that once had been
Terror of kings and of imperial powers,
Jeered at and gaped upon! A noble queen
That oft had worn the helmet through long hours
Of battle, and had taken towns and towers,
Now wears a mob-cap on her royal head,
She that had held a scepter wreathed with flowers
Carries a distaff in her hand instead!

KING PETER OF SPAIN*

O noble, worthy Peter, glory of Spain,
Whom Fortune held so high in majesty,
How bitterly should we lament thy pain,
Who, by thy brother driven forth to flee,
After a siege wert caught by treachery,
And thus betrayed wert taken to his tent,
Where, with his own bare hands, he murdered thee
And gained succession to thy throne and rent!

Upon an argent field an eagle sable*
Caught on a lime-rod gules (if you can read
This riddle) brewed the treason and was able
– O 'wicked nest'! – to do a wicked deed!
No Oliver of Charlemagne he, to heed
Honor and truth, but Brittany's mishap,
A Ganelon-Oliver corrupt in greed
It was that brought this King to such a trap!

KING PETER OF CYPRUS*

O Peter King of Cyprus, fine and true,
That conqueredst Alexandria by the right
Of arms, and didest woe on heathens too,
Thy very liegemen envied thee, and spite
(No other cause) against thy chivalrous might
Moved them to murder thee upon the morrow
There, on thy bed! Thus Fortune with a light
Turn of her wheel brings men from joy to sorrow.

BERNABO VISCONTI OF LOMBARDY*

Great Bernabo Visconti of Milan,
God of indulgence, scourge of Lombardy,
Should I not tell of thee, unhappy man,
That scaled the summit of felicity?
Thy brother's son, so doubly bound to thee.
Being thy nephew and thy son-in-law,
Yet in his prison wrought thy misery
And death, but how or why I never saw.

COUNT UGOLINO OF PISA

There is no tongue of pity that has power
To tell Count Ugolino's tragedy.
A little out of Pisa stands a tower;
There in that tower he was imprisoned, he
And all his little children. There were three,
Of whom the eldest-born was barely five.
O Fortune! It was grievous cruelty
To put such birds in such a cave, alive!

He was condemned to perish in that prison,
For Bishop Ruggieri had framed lies
Against him, and the city folk had risen,
Believing all the Bishop could devise,
And jailed him as I said without supplies,
Save for some water and a little meat,
But these so scant and poor, you may surmise
That there was scarce enough for them to eat.

And on a certain day when came the hour
At which their food was usually brought,
The jailer shut the portals of the tower.
He heard it well enough, but he said nought;
There came upon his heart at once the thought
That they were minded he should starve to death.
'Alas that I was born!' he said, and sought
In vain to check his tears and calm his breath.

His younger son – just three – ah, it is cruel
To think of him! – said, 'Father dear, why weep?
When will the prison-jailer bring our gruel?
Is there no bread, a morsel, in the keep?
I am so hungry that I cannot sleep.
If only I could sleep till I were dead!
Hunger no more would then have power to creep.
There's nothing I should like so much as bread.'

Thus day by day the little child would cry
Till on his father's bosom down he lay,
And said, 'Farewell, dear father, I must die!'
And kissed him; and he died that very day.
Seeing him dead his father, ashen-gray,
Bit on his arm and cried, 'Ah, wretched me!
Bitterest Fortune, thou hast had thy way,
Thy false wheel turns against me, as I see!'

The other children thought it must be hunger
That made him bite upon his arm, not pain.
'Ah father, don't, don't do it!' cried the younger,
'But rather eat the flesh upon us twain;
Our flesh you gave us, take it back again
And eat enough!' Thus both the children cried,
But in a day or two, their grief in vain,
They crept into his lap and there they died.

He in despair sat on, and slowly starved.
Thus, mighty once, he met his end in jail;
Fortune foreclosed on his estate and carved
His greatness from him. Of this tragic tale,
Those who wish more, and on a nobler scale,
Should turn to read the great Italian poet
Dante* by name; they will not find him fail
In any point or syllable, I know it.

NERO

Though Nero was a vicious man who lusted
As fiercely as a fiend who treads the deep
(Says Suetonius, and he may be trusted),
He ruled the whole wide world; 'twas his to keep.
East, west, north, south, he scoured it o'er to reap
Its rubies, sapphires, pearls of orient white ...
And his embroidered garments, heap on heap,
Blazed with them richly; gems were his delight.

A prouder, more fastidious ostentation
Of pomp no emperor has ever shown;
A dress once worn he had no inclination
To see again, would scarcely seem to own.
His many nets of golden mesh were thrown
To fish the Tiber with, just to amuse him.
His pleasures were his laws, he made it known
That there was nothing Fortune could refuse him.

And Rome, to please his palate for sensations,
He burnt; he killed his senators in play,
Just for the fun of hearing lamentations
And shrieks of pain; with his own sister lay;
Murdered his brother; carved his dreadful way
Into his mother's womb, only to know
Where he had been conceived. Alas the day
That ever man should treat his mother so!

Yet at the sight of it he shed no tear
But 'A fine woman once, she was,' he said.
Wonder it is that he could so appear
To sit in judgment on her beauty dead!
And then he bade a table to be spread
And drank some wine but showed no other grief.
Where power and a cruel heart are wed
How deep the poison, challenging belief!

In youth they gave him an instructor; he
Taught him to read and taught him gentle breeding.
He was the flower of morality
At that far time, according to my reading.
And for a while he mastered him, succeeding
In putting his intelligence to use
With suppleness and wisdom. Tyranny
And vice in him were not as yet let loose.

This Seneca – the man of whom I speak –
Made Nero fear him, but he went in dread
Of Seneca because he chose to speak
In the rebuke of wickedness instead

Of punishing him. 'An emperor,' he said,
'Shuns tyranny and follows virtue's path.'
So Nero cut his veins for him and bled
The man to death, he killed him in a bath.

It had been Nero's practice, I should judge,
When he was young, to mutiny and rise
Against his master; he could bear a grudge
And killed him for it, so we may surmise.
Nevertheless this Seneca the wise
Preferred to perish thus lest worse disaster
Should overtake him in another guise.
Thus Nero murdered his beloved master.

But as it happened Fortune cared no longer
To cherish Nero in his soaring pride.
Though he was strong enough yet she was stronger
And thus she thought: 'By God, I let him ride
Far too indulgently upon the tide
Of vice, and lend the title that protects
An emperor. By Heaven, he shall slide
Out of his seat, and when he least expects.'

One night the citizens of Rome revolted
Against his tyrannies and mad ambition,
And when he heard them mutiny he bolted
Alone and sought his friends for coalition.
The more he knocked and begged them for admission
The more they shut their doors and said him nay.
And then he saw that of his own perdition
He was sole author and he fled away.

The people yelled for him and rumbled round
So that their shouts were dinning in his ear:
'Where's Nero? Where's the tyrant? Treacherous hound!'
He almost went out of his mind for fear.
Pitifully he prayed the gods to hear
And succor him; in vain, they would not shield him.
Distraught, and knowing that his end was near,
He ran into a garden that concealed him.

He found two peasants in the garden there
Seated beside a bonfire glowing red,
And he approached these peasants with a prayer
To kill him and by smiting off his head
To shield his body after, he was dead,
From mutilation or an act of shame.
And then he slew himself, for all was said.
And Fortune laughed at having made her game.

HOLOFERNES*

There never was a captain served a king
Who brought so many countries in subjection
Or one more famous then for everything
Touching the fields of war and insurrection,
Or more presumptuous by predilection
Than Holofernes. Fortune ever fair
Kissed him with such a lecherous affection
He lost his head before he was aware.

It was not only that he made a wraith
Of the world's wealth and plundered liberty,
He made his enemies renounce their faith:
'Nebuchadnezzar is your God,' said he,
'You shall adore none other that may be!'
There was no city dared stand up to him
Save one that proved a rebel to decree,
Bethulia, and her priest Eliachim.

But watch how Holofernes met his fate;
Drunken amid his host he lay one night
In his enormous, barn-like tent of state.
For all his pomp, his majesty and might,
Judith, a woman, had the strength to smite.
Off went his sleepy head, and from the tent
She crept away before the morning light,
Bearing his head with her, and home she went.

KING ANTIOCHUS THE ILLUSTRIOUS*

What need to tell of King Antiochus
Or to describe his royal panoply,
His overweening pride, his venomous
Ill-doing? There was never such as he.
Read what is said of him in *Maccabee,*
Read those proud words so arrogantly spoken,
And why he fell from his felicity
Upon a hill-side, festering and broken.

Fortune indeed had so enhanced his pride
That verily he thought to take his stand
Among the stars themselves or turn aside
To lift and weigh a mountain in his hand,
Or warn the flood of ocean from the land.
But it was God's own people he most hated
And slew by torture, steel and firebrand.
He thought his pride could never be abated.

Because Nicanor once and Timothy
Had by the Jews been mightily defeated,
His hatred swelled for Israel. Hastily
He made his chariot ready and when seated
He vowed and swore that they should all be treated
To something of his spite, that they should rue it;
Jerusalem he said should be deleted.
He was prevented ere he came to do it.

God smote him for these menacing recitals
With an invisible and cureless blain
That carved his guts and bit into his vitals.
Afflicted with intolerable pain,
He yet had little reason to complain;
It was a just revenge, for he had often
Carved out the guts of other men to gain
His ends; their tortures did not make him soften.

He gave the word to summon all his hosts
When suddenly, before he was aware,
God daunted his presumption and his boasts,
For down he fell out of his chariot there.
It tore his limbs and flesh, the bone lay bare;
No longer could he either walk or ride,
But only could be carried in a chair
All bruised and lacerated, back and side.

The vengeance of the Lord smote cruelly;
Pestilent worms within his body crept
So that he stank with such obscenity
Not one of all the servants, that he kept
To guard him when awake or when he slept,
Could bear the stench or look upon his features.
And in this agony he wailed and wept
And knew that God was lord of all his creatures.

To all his host and to himself no less
The carrion stench that rose from every vent
Was unendurable in loathsomeness;
They could not carry him. In redolent
And agonizing pain, within his tent
Upon a hill, this thief and homicide,
Who made so many suffer and lament
Wretchedly perished, the reward of pride.

ALEXANDER*

The story of Alexander is so famous
That it is known to everyone at least
In part, unless he be an ignoramus.
He conquered the wide world from west to east
By force of arms, and as his fame increased
Men gladly sued to have him for their friend.
He brought to naught the pride of man and beast
Wherever he came, as far as the world's end.

And never can comparison be made
Of him with any other; at his face
Kingdoms would quake, the whole world was afraid.
He was the flower of knighthood and of grace,
The heir of Fortune and in nothing base;
Save wine and women there was naught could part
Him from his high designs or take their place,
He was a man so leonine of heart.

What praise were it to him though I should tell
Of great Darius and a thousand more,
Kings, princes, generals, dukes and earls as well,
Conquered by him and brought to grief in war?
As far as men may ride from shore to shore
Of the wide world, the world was his to hold.
Though I should speak forever on the score
Of knightly honor, his could not be told.

Twelve years he reigned, so say the *Maccabees,*
And was King Philip's son, of Macedon,
First to be king over the land of Greece.
Alas that Alexander, such a son,
So gentle, so magnanimous, were one
To die by poison from the men he kept!
But Fortune threw him aces for the run*
Of sixes thrown before. She little wept.

Who then will give me tears that I may plain
The death of greatness that was never rough,
Of generous feeling that had held domain
Over the world and thought it not enough?
His was a spirit brimming with the stuff
Of high design. Ah, help me to speak shame
Of poisoners and of the foul rebuff
Of fickle Fortune, whom alone I blame.

JULIUS CAESAR

By wisdom, manhood and the works of war,
From humble bed to royal majesty,
Arose great Julius Caesar, conqueror,
Who won the occident by land and sea
By strength of arms or by diplomacy
And made of each a Roman tributary
And last was emperor himself, till he
Was picked by Fortune for her adversary.

O Caesar that in Thessaly excelled
Against your father-in-law great Pompey's sway,
The whole of orient chivalry was held
In whose command, far as the dawn of day!
Your valor was enough to take and slay
All but a few that fled with him, your spell
Held the whole east in terror and dismay.
Give thanks to Fortune for she served you well!

Yet for a little while I will bewail
This Pompey's fate, the noble governor
Of Rome who fled the battle, for the tale
Tells of a man of his, a perjurer
Who smote his head off, for he hoped to stir
Some gratitude in Caesar, so he brought
The head to him. O Pompey, Justicer
Of all the east, alas that thou wert caught!

To Rome once more this Julius turned, to don
The laurel-wreath, triumphant and elate.
But Brutus Cassius* as time went on,
One that had ever envied his estate,
Made a conspiracy in subtle hate
Against this Julius, gave the treacherous vow,
And chose the place where he should meet his fate
By dagger-thrust, and I shall tell you how.

Up to the Capitol this Julius went
A certain day, as he was wont to do.
There he was taken by the malcontent,
False-hearted Brutus and his scheming crew,
They stabbed him there with daggers through and
    through,
Many the wounds, and there they let him die.
After one dagger-stroke, or maybe two,
He never groaned, unless the stories lie.

He was a soldier with a manly heart;
So dear to him was honest decency
That deeply as he felt his gashes smart
He sought to shroud his person, casting free
His cloak about his hips and privity,
And in the trance of dying, though he knew
It was his death, he held in memory
The things of seemliness and order due.

I recommend you Lucan for this story,
And Suetonius and Valerius too.
They write of these two conquerors in their glory
And in their end, how both of them once knew
Fortune to be their friend, and how she grew
To be their foe. No man may trust her long,
Beware of her in everything you do
And think of these great leaders, once so strong.

CROESUS

Rich Croesus, King of Lydia long ago,
Whom even Persian Cyrus held in dread,
Was yet cut short in all his pride and show
And led out to be burnt; but as they led
Him to the stake, such rain from overhead
Came down, it quenched the fire and he escaped.
He failed to take the warning, be it said;
Fate kept him for the gallows, where he gaped.

For having thus evaded death by fire,
Nothing would stop him making war again.
He thought that Fortune meant to raise him higher,
After his luck in being saved by rain,
And he presumed he never could be slain.
Moreover being favored by a vision
That cockered up his heart, he felt so vain
He set himself to vengeance and derision.

He dreamt that he was perching in a tree
With Jupiter to wash him, back and side,
While Phoebus with a towel fair to see
Was drying him. This was what swelled his pride.
He told his daughter who was at his side,
Knowing her versed in mysteries, it would seem,
And asked her what the vision signified.
And thus she started to expound his dream:

'This tree,' she told him, 'signifies a gibbet
And Jupiter betokens snow and rain,
While Phoebus with his towel must exhibit
The streaming sun, to dry you off again.
You will be hanged, my father, that is plain;
The rain shall wash you and the sun shall bake.'
And thus his daughter warned him, but in vain;
Her name Phanýa, if I not mistake.

Hanged, then, was Croesus, this tremendous king;
His royal scepter was of no avail.
Tragedy is no other kind of thing,
Nor tunes her song save only to bewail
How Fortune, ever fickle, will assail
With sudden stroke the kingdoms of the proud
And, when men trust in her, she then will fail
And cover her bright face as with a cloud....

Words of the Knight and the Host

'Ho, my good sir, no more!' exclaimed the Knight.
What you have said so far no doubt is right,
And more than right, but still a little grief
Will do for most of us in my belief.
As for myself, I take a great displeasure
In tales of those who once knew wealth and leisure
And then are felled by some unlucky hit.
But it's a joy to hear the opposite,
For instance, tales of men of low estate
Who climb aloft and growing fortunate
Remain secure in their prosperity;
That is delightful as it seems to me
And is a proper sort of tale to tell.'
    'That's certain, by St Paul's and by its bell!'
Our Host joined in. 'This Monk, he talks too loud;
All about "Fortune covered with a cloud"
– I don't know what – and as for "Tragedy,"
You heard just now, what has to be must be.
It does no good to grumble and complain,
What's done is done. Moreover, it's a pain,
As you have said, to hear about disaster;
Let's have no more of it. God bless you, master,
It's an offense, you're boring us, that's why!
Such talk as that's not worth a butterfly,
Gives no enjoyment, doesn't help the game.
In short Sir Monk – Sir Peter – what's-your-name –
I heartily beg you'll talk of something else.
But for the clink and tinkle of those bells
That hang your bridle round on every side,
By my salvation, by the Lord that died,
I simply should have fallen down asleep
Into the mud below, however deep.
Your story then would have been told in vain,
For, quoting the authorities again,

"When lecturers find their audiences decrease
It does them little good to say their piece."
Give us a word or two on hunting, say.'
'No,' said the Monk, 'I'm in no mood to-day
For fun. Ask someone else, I've said enough.'
    Our Host, whose language was a little rough,
Seeing a Priest beside the Nun, went on:
'Come here, you priest, step forward, you, Sir John,
And tell a tale to make our troubles pack.
Cheer yourself up although you ride a hack.
What if your ugly horse is poor and thin?
If it will serve you, never care a pin!
And always keep your heart up – that's the test!'
'Yes,' he replied, 'yes, Host, I'll do my best,
Not to be merry would deserve reproach.'
And he immediately began to broach
His story to us, as we all rode on,
This charming priest and kindly man, Sir John.

The Nun's Priest's Tale

ONCE, long ago, there dwelt a poor old widow
    In a small cottage by a little meadow
Beside a grove and standing in a dale.
This widow-woman of whom I tell my tale
Since the sad day when last she was a wife
Had led a very patient, simple life.
Little she had in capital or rent,
But still by making do with what God sent
She kept herself and her two daughters going.
Three hefty sows – no more – were all her showing,
Three cows as well; there was a sheep called Molly.
    Sooty her hall, her kitchen melancholy,

And there she ate full many a slender meal;
There was no *sauce piquante* to spice her veal,
No dainty morsel ever passed her throat,
According to her cloth she cut her coat.
Repletion never left her in disquiet
And all her physic was a temperate diet,
Hard work for exercise and heart's content.
And rich man's gout did nothing to prevent
Her dancing, apoplexy struck her not;
She drank no wine, nor white nor red had got.
Her board was mostly served with white and black,
Milk and brown bread, in which she found no lack;
Broiled bacon or an egg or two were common,
She was in fact a sort of dairy-woman.

She had a yard that was enclosed about
By a stockade and a dry ditch without,
In which she kept a cock called Chanticleer.
In all the land for crowing he'd no peer;
His voice was jollier than the organ blowing
In church on Sundays, he was great at crowing.
Far, far more regular than any clock
Or abbey bell the crowing of this cock.
The equinoctial wheel and its position*
At each ascent he knew by intuition;
At every hour – fifteen degrees of movement –
He crowed so well there could be no improvement.
His comb was redder than fine coral, tall
And battlemented like a castle wall,
His bill was black and shone as bright as jet,
Like azure were his legs and they were set
On azure toes with nails of lily white,
Like burnished gold his feathers, flaming bright.

This gentlecock was master in some measure
Of seven hens, all there to do his pleasure.
They were his sisters and his paramours,
Colored like him in all particulars;
She with the loveliest dyes upon her throat
Was known as gracious Lady Pertelote.

Courteous she was, discreet and debonair,
Companionable too, and took such care
In her deportment, since she was seven days old
She held the heart of Chanticleer controlled,
Locked up securely in her every limb;
O such a happiness his love to him!
And such a joy it was to hear them sing,
As when the glorious sun began to spring,
In sweet accord *My Love is far from land**
– For in those far off days I understand
All birds and animals could speak and sing.

    Now it befell, as dawn began to spring,
When Chanticleer and Pertelote and all
His wives were perched in this poor widow's hall
(Fair Pertelote was next him on the perch),
This Chanticleer began to groan and lurch
Like someone sorely troubled by a dream,
And Pertelote who heard him roar and scream
Was quite aghast and said, 'O dearest heart,
What's ailing you? Why do you groan and start?
Fie, what a sleeper! What a noise to make!'
'Madam,' he said, 'I beg you not to take
Offense, but by the Lord I had a dream
So terrible just now I had to scream;
I still can feel my heart racing from fear.
God turn my dream to good and guard all here,
And keep my body out of durance vile!
I dreamt that roaming up and down a while
Within our yard I saw a kind of beast,
A sort of hound that tried or seemed at least
To try and seize me ... would have killed me dead!
His color was a blend of yellow and red,
His ears and tail were tipped with sable fur
Unlike the rest; he was a russet cur.
Small was his snout, his eyes were glowing bright.
It was enough to make one die of fright.
That was no doubt what made me groan and swoon.'
    'For shame,' she said, 'you timorous poltroon!

Alas, what cowardice! By God above,
You've forfeited my heart and lost my love.
I cannot love a coward, come what may.
For certainly, whatever we may say,
All women long – and O that it might be! –
For husbands tough, dependable and free,
Secret, discreet, no niggard, not a fool
That boasts and then will find his courage cool
At every trifling thing! By God above,
How dare you say for shame, and to your love,
That anything at all was to be feared?
Have you no manly heart to match your beard?
And can a dream reduce you to such terror?
Dreams are a vanity, God knows, pure error.
Dreams are engendered in the too-replete
From vapors in the belly, which compete
With others, too abundant, swollen tight.

   'No doubt the redness in your dream to-night
Comes from the superfluity and force
Of the red choler in your blood. Of course;
That is what puts a dreamer in the dread
Of crimsoned arrows, fires flaming red,
Of great red monsters making as to fight him,
And big red whelps and little ones to bite him;
Just so the black and melancholy vapors
Will set a sleeper shrieking, cutting capers
And swearing that black bears, black bulls as well,
Or blackest fiends are haling him to Hell.
And there are other vapors that I know
That on a sleeping man will work their woe,
But I'll pass on as lightly as I can.

   'Take Cato now, that was so wise a man,
Did he not say, "Take no account of dreams"?
Now, sir,' she said, 'on flying from these beams,
For love of God do take some laxative;
Upon my soul that's the advice to give
For melancholy choler; let me urge
You free yourself from vapors with a purge.

And that you may have no excuse to tarry
By saying this town has no apothecary,
I shall myself instruct you and prescribe
Herbs that will cure all vapors of that tribe,
Herbs from our very farmyard! You will find
Their natural property is to unbind
And purge you well beneath and well above.
Now don't forget it, dear, for God's own love!
Your face is choleric and shows distension;
Be careful lest the sun in his ascension
Should catch you full of humors, hot and many.
And if he does, my dear, I'll lay a penny
It means a bout of fever or a breath
Of tertian ague. You may catch your death.

   'Worms for a day or two I'll have to give
As a digestive, then your laxative.
Centaury, fumitory, caper-spurge
And hellebore will make a splendid purge;
And then there's laurel or the blackthorn berry,
Ground-ivy too that makes our yard so merry;
Peck them right up, my dear, and swallow whole.
Be happy, husband, by your father's soul!
Don't be afraid of dreams. I'll say no more.'

   'Madam,' he said, 'I thank you for your lore,
But with regard to Cato all the same,
His wisdom has, no doubt, a certain fame,
But though he said that we should take no heed
Of dreams, by God in ancient books I read
Of many a man of more authority
Than ever Cato was, believe you me,
Who say the very opposite is true
And prove their theories by experience too.
Dreams have quite often been significations
As well of triumphs as of tribulations
That people undergo in this our life.
This needs no argument at all, dear wife,
The proof is all too manifest indeed.

   'One of the greatest authors one can read

Says thus: there were two comrades once who went
On pilgrimage, sincere in their intent.
And as it happened they had reached a town
Where such a throng was milling up and down,
And yet so scanty the accommodation,
They could not find themselves a habitation,
No, not a cottage that could lodge them both;
And so they separated, very loath,
Under constraint of this necessity
And each went off to find some hostelry,
And lodge whatever way his luck might fall.

'The first of them found refuge in a stall
Down in a yard, with oxen and a plow.
His friend found lodging for himself somehow
Elsewhere, by accident or destiny
Which governs all of us and equally.

'Now it so happened, long ere it was day,
This fellow had a dream, and as he lay
In bed it seemed he heard his comrade call,
"Help! I am lying in an ox's stall
And shall to-night be murdered as I lie.
Help me, dear brother, help or I shall die!
Come in all haste!" Such were the words he spoke;
The dreamer, lost in terror, then awoke.
But once awake he paid it no attention,
Turned over and dismissed it as invention,
It was a dream, he thought, a fantasy.
And twice he dreamt this dream successively.

'Yet a third time his comrade came again,
Or seemed to come, and said, "I have been slain.
Look, look! my wounds are bleeding wide and deep.
Rise early in the morning, break your sleep
And go to the west gate. You there shall see
A cart all loaded up with dung," said he,
"And in that dung my body has been hidden.
Boldly arrest that cart as you are bidden.
It was my money that they killed me for."

'He told him every detail, sighing sore,

And pitiful in feature, pale of hue.
This dream, believe me, Madam, turned out true;
For in the dawn as soon as it was light,
He went to where his friend had spent the night;
And when he came upon the cattle-stall
He looked about him and began to call.

'The innkeeper, appearing thereupon,
Quickly gave answer, "Sir, your friend has gone.
He left the town a little after dawn."
The man began to feel suspicious, drawn
By memories of his dream – the western gate,
The dung-cart – off he went, he would not wait,
Towards the western entry. There he found,
Seemingly on its way to dung some ground,
A dung-cart loaded on the very plan
Described so closely by the murdered man.
So he began to shout courageously
For right and vengeance on the felony,
"My friend's been killed! There's been a foul attack,
He's in that cart and gaping on his back!
Fetch the authorities, get the sheriff down
– Whosever job it is to run the town –
Help! My companion's murdered, sent to glory!"

'What need I add to finish off the story?
People ran out and cast the cart to ground,
And in the middle of the dung they found
The murdered man. The corpse was fresh and new.

'O blessed God, that art so just and true,
Thus thou revealest murder! As we say,
"Murder will out." We see it day by day.
Murder's a foul, abominable treason,
So loathsome to God's justice, to God's reason,
He will not suffer its concealment. True,
Things may lie hidden for a year or two,
But still "Murder will out," that's my conclusion.

'All the town officers in great confusion
Seized on the carter and they gave him hell,
And then they racked the innkeeper as well,

And both confessed. And then they took the wrecks
And there and then they hanged them by their necks.
  'By this we see that dreams are to be dreaded.
And in the self-same book I find embedded,
Right in the very chapter after this
(I'm not inventing, as I hope for bliss)
The story of two men who started out
To cross the sea — for merchandise no doubt —
But as the winds were contrary they waited.
It was a pleasant town, I should have stated,
Merrily grouped about the haven-side.
A few days later with the evening tide
The wind veered round so as to suit them best;
They were delighted and they went to rest
Meaning to sail next morning early. Well,
To one of them a miracle befell.
  'This man as he lay sleeping, it would seem,
Just before dawn, had an astounding dream.
He thought a man was standing by his bed
Commanding him to wait, and thus he said:
"If you set sail to-morrow as you intend,
You will be drowned. My tale is at an end."
  'He woke and told his friend what had occurred
And begged him that the journey be deferred
At least a day, implored him not to start.
But his companion, lying there apart,
Began to laugh and treat him to derision.
"I'm not afraid," he said, "of any vision,
To let it interfere with my affairs;
A straw for all your dreamings and your scares.
Dreams are just empty nonsense, merest japes;
Why, people dream all day of owls and apes,
All sorts of trash that can't be understood,
Things that have never happened and never could.
But as I see you mean to stay behind
And miss the tide for willful sloth of mind
God knows I'm sorry for it, but good day!"
And so he took his leave and went his way.

'And yet, before they'd covered half the trip
– I don't know what went wrong – there was a rip
And by some accident the ship went down,
Her bottom rent, all hands aboard to drown
In sight of all the vessels at her side
That had put out upon the self-same tide.

'So, my dear Pertelote, if you discern
The force of these examples you may learn
One never should be careless about dreams,
For undeniably I say it seems
That many are a sign of trouble breeding.

'Now, take St Kenelm's life which I've been reading;
He was Kenulphus' son, the noble King
Of Mercia. Now, St Kenelm dreamt a thing
Shortly before they murdered him one day.
He saw his murder in a dream, I say.
His nurse expounded it and gave her reason
On every point and warned him against treason.
But as the saint was only seven years old
All that she said about it left him cold.
He was so holy, how could visions hurt?

'By God, I willingly would give my shirt
To have you read his legend as I've read it;
And, Madam Pertelote, upon my credit,
Macrobius wrote of dreams and can explain us
The vision of young Scipio Africanus,
And he affirms that dreams can give a due
Warning of things that later on come true.

'And then there's the Old Testament – a manual
Well worth your study; see the *Book of Daniel*.
Did Daniel think a dream was vanity?
Read about Joseph too and you will see
That many dreams – I do not say that all –
Give cognizance of what is to befall.

'Look at Lord Pharaoh, king of Egypt! Look
At what befell his butler and his cook.
Did not their visions have a certain force?
But those who study history of course

Meet many dreams that set them wondering.
  'What about Croesus too, the Lydian king,
Who dreamt that he was sitting in a tree,
Meaning he would be hanged? It had to be.
  'Or take Andromache, great Hector's wife;
The day on which he was to lose his life
She dreamt about, the very night before,
And realized that if Hector went to war
He would be lost that very day in battle.
She warned him; he dismissed it all as prattle
And sallied forth to fight, being self-willed,
And there he met Achilles and was killed.
The tale is long and somewhat overdrawn,
And anyhow it's very nearly dawn,
So let me say in very brief conclusion
My dream undoubtedly fortells confusion,
It bodes me ill, I say. And, furthermore,
Upon your laxatives I set no store,
For they are venomous. I've suffered by them
Often enough before and I defy them.

  'And now, let's talk of fun and stop all this.
Dear Madam, as I hope for Heaven's bliss,
Of one thing God has sent me plenteous grace,
For when I see the beauty of your face,
That scarlet loveliness about your eyes,
All thought of terror and confusion dies.
For it's as certain as the Creed, I know,
Mulier est hominis confusio
(A Latin tag, dear Madam, meaning this:
"Woman is man's delight and all his bliss"),
For when at night I feel your feathery side,
Although perforce I cannot take a ride,
Because, alas, our perch was made too narrow,
Delight and solace fill me to the marrow
And I defy all visions and all dreams!'
  And with that word he flew down from the beams,
For it was day, and down his hens flew all,
And with a chuck he gave the troupe a call

For he had found a seed upon the floor.
Royal he was, he was afraid no more.
He feathered Pertelote in wanton play
And trod her twenty times ere prime of day.
Grim as a lion's was his manly frown
As on his toes he sauntered up and down;
He scarcely deigned to set his foot to ground
And every time a seed of corn was found
He gave a chuck, and up his wives ran all.
Thus royal as a prince who strides his hall
Leave we this Chanticleer engaged on feeding
And pass to the adventure that was breeding.

Now when the month in which the world began,
March, the first month, when God created man,
Was over, and the thirty-second day
Thereafter ended, on the third of May,
It happened that Chanticleer in all his pride,
His seven wives attendant at his side,
Cast his eyes upward to the blazing sun,
Which in the sign of *Taurus* then had run
His twenty-one degrees and somewhat more,
And knew by nature and no other lore
That it was nine o'clock. With blissful voice
He crew triumphantly and said, 'Rejoice,
Behold the sun! The sun is up, my seven.
Look, it has climbed forty degrees in heaven,
Forty degrees and one in fact, by this.
Dear Madam Pertelote, my earthly bliss,
Hark to those blissful birds and how they sing!
Look at those pretty flowers, how they spring!
Solace and revel fill my heart!' He laughed.

But in that moment Fate let fly her shaft;
Ever the latter end of joy is woe,
God knows that worldly joy is swift to go.
A rhetorician with a flair for style
Could chronicle this maxim in his file
Of Notable Remarks with safe conviction.
Then let the wise give ear; this is no fiction.

My story is as true, I undertake,
As that of good Sir Lancelot du Lake
Who held all women in such high esteem.
Let me return full circle to my theme.

A coal-tipped fox of sly iniquity
That had been lurking round the grove for three
Long years, that very night burst through and passed
Stockade and hedge, as Providence forecast,
Into the yard where Chanticleer the Fair
Was wont, with all his ladies, to repair.
Still in a bed of cabbages he lay
Until about the middle of the day
Watching the cock and waiting for his cue,
As all these homicides so gladly do
That lie about in wait to murder men.
O false assassin, lurking in thy den!
O new Iscariot, new Ganelon!
And O Greek Sinon,* thou whose treachery won
Troy town and brought it utterly to sorrow!
O Chanticleer, accursed be that morrow
That brought thee to the yard from thy high beams!
Thou hadst been warned, and truly, by thy dreams
That this would be a perilous day for thee.

But that which God's foreknowledge can foresee
Must needs occur, as certain men of learning
Have said. Ask any scholar of discerning;
He'll say the Schools are filled with altercation
On this vexed matter of predestination,
Long bandied by a hundred thousand men.
How can I sift it to the bottom then?
The Holy Doctor St Augustine shines
In this, and there is Bishop Bradwardine's*
Authority, Boethius'* too, decreeing
Whether the fact of God's divine foreseeing
Constrains me to perform a certain act
– And by 'constraint' I mean the simple fact
Of mere compulsion by necessity –
Or whether a free choice is granted me

To do a given act or not to do it,
Though, ere it was accomplished, God foreknew it,
Or whether Providence is not so stringent
And merely makes necessity contingent.
    But I decline discussion of the matter;
My tale is of a cock and of the clatter
That came of following his wife's advice
To walk about his yard on the precise
Morning after the dream of which I told.
    O women's counsel is so often cold!
A woman's counsel brought us first to woe,
Made Adam out of Paradise to go,
Where he had been so merry, so well at ease.
But, for I know not whom it may displease
If I suggest that women are to blame,
Pass over that; I only speak in game.
Read the authorities to know about
What has been said of women; you'll find out.
These are the cock's words, and not mine, I'm giving;
I think no harm of any woman living.
    Merrily in her dust-bath in the sand
Lay Pertelote. Her sisters were at hand
Basking in sunlight. Chanticleer sang free,
More merrily than a mermaid in the sea
(For *Physiologus* reports the thing*
And says how well and merrily they sing).
And so it happened as he cast his eye
Towards the cabbage at a butterfly
It fell upon the fox there, lying low.
Gone was all inclination then to crow.
'Cok cok,' he cried, giving a sudden start,
As one who feels a terror at his heart,
For natural instinct teaches beasts to flee
The moment they perceive an enemy,
Though they had never met with it before.
    This Chanticleer was shaken to the core
And would have fled. The fox was quick to say
However, 'Sir! Whither so fast away?

Are you afraid of me that am your friend?
It would be worse than fiendish to intend
Some violence or villainy upon you;
Dear sir, I was not even spying on you!
Truly I came to do no other thing
Than just to lie and listen to you sing.
You have as merry a voice as God has given
To any angel in the courts of Heaven;
To that you add a musical sense as strong
As had Boethius who was skilled in song.
My Lord your Father (God receive his soul!),
Your mother too – how courtly, what control! –
Have honored my poor house, to my great ease;
And you, sir, too, I should be glad to please.
For, when it comes to singing, I'll say this
(Else may these eyes of mine be barred from bliss),
There never was a singer I would rather
Have heard at dawn than your respected father.
All that he sang came welling from his soul
And how he put his voice under control!
The pains he took to keep his eyes tight shut
In concentration – then the tip-toe strut,
The slender neck stretched out, the delicate beak!
No singer could approach him in technique
Or rival him in song, still less surpass.
I've read the story in *Burnel the Ass*,*
Among some other verses, of a cock
Whose leg in youth was broken by a knock
A clergyman's son had given him, and for this
He made the father lose his benefice.
But certainly there's no comparison
Between the subtlety of such an one
And the discretion of your father's art
And wisdom. Oh, for charity of heart,
Can you not emulate your sire and sing?'
    This Chanticleer began to beat a wing
As one incapable of smelling treason,
So wholly had this flattery ravished reason.

Alas, my lords! there's many a sycophant
And flatterer that fill your courts with cant
And give more pleasure with their zeal forsooth
Than he who speaks in soberness and truth.
Read what *Ecclesiasticus* records
Of flatterers. 'Ware treachery, my lords!

This Chanticleer stood high upon his toes,
He stretched his neck, his eyes began to close,
His beak to open; with his eyes shut tight
He then began to sing with all his might.

Sir Russel Fox then leapt to the attack,
Grabbing his gorge he flung him o'er his back
And off he bore him to the woods, the brute,
And for the moment there was no pursuit.

O Destiny that may not be evaded!
Alas that Chanticleer had so paraded!
Alas that he had flown down from the beams!
O that his wife took no account of dreams!
And on a Friday, too, to risk their necks!
O Venus, goddess of the joys of sex,
Since Chanticleer thy mysteries professed
And in thy service always did his best,
And more for pleasure than to multiply
His kind, on thine own day is he to die?

O Geoffrey, thou my dear and sovereign master*
Who, when they brought King Richard to disaster
And shot him dead, lamented so his death,
Would that I had thy skill, thy gracious breath,
To chide a Friday half so well as you!
(For he was killed upon a Friday too.)
Then I could fashion you a rhapsody
For Chanticleer in dread and agony.

Sure never such a cry or lamentation
Was made by ladies of high Trojan station,
When Ilium fell and Pyrrhus with his sword
Grabbed Priam by the beard, their king and lord,
And slew him there as the *Aeneid* tells,
As what was uttered by those hens. Their yells

Surpassed them all in palpitating fear
When they beheld the rape of Chanticleer.
Dame Pertelote emitted sovereign shrieks
That echoed up in anguish to the peaks
Louder than those extorted from the wife
Of Hasdrubal when he had lost his life
And Carthage all in flame and ashes lay.
She was so full of torment and dismay
That in the very flames she chose her part
And burnt to ashes with a steadfast heart.
O woeful hens, louder your shrieks and higher
Than those of Roman matrons when the fire
Consumed their husbands, senators of Rome,
When Nero burnt their city and their home,
Beyond a doubt that Nero was their bale!

Now let me turn again to tell my tale;
This blessed widow and her daughters two
Heard all these hens in clamor and halloo
And, rushing to the door at all this shrieking,
They saw the fox towards the covert streaking
And, on his shoulder, Chanticleer stretched flat.
'Look, look!' they cried. 'O mercy, look at that!
Ha! Ha! the fox!' and after him they ran,
And stick in hand ran many a serving man,
Ran Coll our dog, ran Talbot, Bran and Shaggy,
And with a distaff in her hand ran Maggie,
Ran cow and calf and ran the very hogs
In terror at the barking of the dogs;
The men and women shouted, ran and cursed,
They ran so hard they thought their hearts would burst,
They yelled like fiends in Hell, ducks left the water
Quacking and flapping as on point of slaughter,
Up flew the geese in terror over the trees,
Out of the hive came forth the swarm of bees;
So hideous was the noise – God bless us all,
Jack Straw and all his followers in their brawl*
Were never half so shrill, for all their noise,
When they were murdering those Flemish boys,

As that day's hue and cry upon the fox.
They grabbed up trumpets made of brass and box,
Of horn and bone, on which they blew and pooped,
And therewithal they shouted and they whooped
So that it seemed the very heavens would fall.

   And now, good people, pay attention all.
See how Dame Fortune quickly changes side
And robs her enemy of hope and pride!
This cock that lay upon the fox's back
In all his dread contrived to give a quack
And said, 'Sir Fox, if I were you, as God's
My witness, I would round upon these clods
And shout, "Turn back, you saucy bumpkins all!
A very pestilence upon you fall!
Now that I have in safety reached the wood
Do what you like, the cock is mine for good;
I'll eat him there in spite of every one."

   The fox replying, 'Faith, it shall be done!'
Opened his mouth and spoke. The nimble bird,
Breaking away upon the uttered word,
Flew high into the tree-tops on the spot.
And when the fox perceived where he had got,
'Alas,' he cried, 'alas, my Chanticleer,
I've done you grievous wrong, indeed I fear
I must have frightened you; I grabbed too hard
When I caught hold and took you from the yard.
But, sir, I meant no harm, don't be offended,
Come down and I'll explain what I intended;
So help me God I'll tell the truth – on oath!'
'No,' said the cock, 'and curses on us both,
And first on me if I were such a dunce
As let you fool me oftener than once.
Never again, for all your flattering lies,
You'll coax a song to make me blink my eyes;
And as for those who blink when they should look,
God blot them from his Everlasting Book!'
'Nay, rather,' said the fox, 'his plagues be flung
On all who chatter that should hold their tongue.'

Lo, such it is not to be on your guard
Against the flatterers of the world, or yard,
And if you think my story is absurd,
A foolish trifle of a beast and bird,
A fable of a fox, a cock, a hen,
Take hold upon the moral, gentlemen.
    St Paul himself, a saint of great discerning,
Says that all things are written for our learning;
So take the grain and let the chaff be still.
And, gracious Father, if it be thy will
As saith my Saviour, make us all good men,
And bring us to his heavenly bliss.
                    Amen.

Words of the Host to the Nun's Priest

'Sir Priest,' our Host remarked in merry tones,
   'Blest be your breeches and your precious stones,
That was a merry tale of Chanticleer!
If you had only been a secular
You would have trodden a pretty fowl, no doubt,
Had you the heart, your muscles would hold out;
You look as if you needed hens, I mean,
Yes, more than seven. Seven times seventeen!
Just look what brawn he has, this gentle priest,
And what a neck! His chest's not of the least.
As for his eyes, they're like a sparrow-hawk's,
And his complexion like a box of chalks;
He needs no dyes imported from the East
Or Portugal. Good luck to you, Sir Priest,
For telling a fine tale!' And saying thus
He turned, as you shall hear, to one of us.

Here follows the Physician's Tale.

[GROUP C]

The Physician's Tale

L IVY has handed down a tale to us
     About a knight surnamed Virginius.
He was a man of honorable birth,
Rich, well-befriended and of sterling worth.
   This knight had had a daughter by his wife;
There were no other children in his life.
Of an excelling loveliness was she,
Above all others that a man might see.
Nature had shown a sovereign diligence
In forming her to such an excellence,
As if she wished to say, 'Look! I am Nature,
And this is how I form and paint a creature
When so I choose. Who dares a counterfeit?
No, not Pygmalion, though he forge and beat,
Color and carve forever; I maintain
That Zeuxis or Apelles would work in vain
To color or to carve, to forge or beat,
Should they presume to try a counterfeit.
For He that is the Maker-Principal
Appointed me his vicar-general
To fashion creatures, all that ever were,
And paint them as I please; for in my care
Lies all that's under moon and, wax or wane,
I form them all. I do not work for gain;
My Lord and I are leagued in close accord.
I made her for the worship of my Lord,
And so I do with all my other creatures
Whatever be their color or their features.'
This was, I think, what Nature meant to say.
   The maiden was fourteen on whose array

Nature had spent her care with such delight.
For just as she can paint a lily white,
Redden a rose and teach it to unfurl
Her petals, so she touched this noble girl
Ere she was born; her limbs so lissom she
Had touched with color where they ought to be.
Phoebus her mass of tresses with a gleam
Had dyed in burnish from his golden stream,
And if her beauty was beyond compare,
Her virtue was a thousand times more rare.
There lacked no quality in her to move
The praises sober wisdom would approve.
Chaste of her body and her soul was she,
And so she flowered in her virginity
With all humility and abstinence
In temperate and patient innocence,
With modesty of bearing and of dress
And showed in speech a modesty no less.
Though I dare say as wise as Pallas, she
Was simple in her words and womanly;
She used no fancy terms in affectation
Of learning, but according to her station
She spoke; in all and everything she said
She showed that she was good and gently bred.
Shamefast she was, in maiden shamefastness,
And constant in her heart. She was express
In conquering sloth to fill the busy hour;
Over her mouth had never Bacchus power,
For wine and youth swell Venus and desire,
Much as when oil is cast upon the fire.
Indeed her native goodness unconstrained
So prompted her that she had often feigned
Some sickness to escape from company
Where there was likelihood of ribaldry,
As well there may be; junketings and dances
Are good occasion for lascivious glances.
Such things as these may soon too easily
Make a child bold and ripe, as one can see;

That's very dangerous and long has been,
For all too soon she learns to play the queen
And show how bold she is, when she's a wife.

And all you ladies that in middle life
Are put in charge of younger gentlefolk,
Pray do not think I speak as to provoke
Your anger; think that your appointment springs
From either one or other of two things,
Either that you were chaste and did not fail
To guard your honor, or that you were frail,
And therefore, knowing well the ancient dance,
You have forsaken your intemperance
Forever. Teach them then for Jesu's sake
And never slacken; virtue is at stake.
Just as a poacher who forsakes his crimes
And leaves his trade in villainy betimes
Makes the best gamekeeper – he's just the man –
Keep you your charges; if you will you can.
Never belittle or connive at vice
Lest you should pay damnation as the price;
For those who do are traitors, never doubt it,
And so give heed to what I say about it.
Top of all treason, sovereign pestilence,
Is the betrayal done on innocence.

You Fathers and you Mothers, let me add,
However many children you have had,
Yours is the duty of their supervision
As long as they are bound by your decision.
Beware lest the example you present,
Or your neglect in giving chastisement
Cause them to perish; otherwise I fear
If they should do so, you will pay it dear.
Shepherds too soft who let their duty sleep
Encourage wolves to tear the lambs and sheep.
One parable's enough, you understand;
Let me return to what I had in hand.

This girl who is the theme of my address
Was such as not to need a governess.

The way she lived, if other girls would look,
Could teach them more of goodness than a book
In all that should concern a virtuous maid,
She was so prudent, bountiful and staid;
And common fame was eager to confess
Her matchless beauty and her kindliness.
Lovers of virtue praised her and gave proof
Of her deserts, though envy stood aloof,
Envy that glowers at favor like a thief
And gloats to see another come to grief
(A phrase that St Augustine noted down).

   This girl one morning went into the town
Towards the temple, with her mother too,
As one may see a girl will often do.
Now at that time there was a judge in charge
Over the city and the land at large,
And so it happened that he cast his eye
Upon this girl as she was passing by
And narrowly appraised her. As he viewed
Her loveliness, a sudden change of mood
Entered his heart and, feeling himself caught
By her attraction, secretly he thought,
'I'll have that girl whether I sink or swim!'
At once the devil entered into him,
Whose machinations then began to stir
And teach him how to have his will of her.
He knew quite well that neither force nor fee
Could suit his purpose in the least degree,
For she had powerful friends and what was more
Her sovereignty of goodness closed the door
On his desires, he could not hope to win
Her soul or body to an act of sin.
So, after much reflection, he sent down
For a known blackguard living in the town,
As low in cunning tricks as he was bold.
He came; in secret then the tale was told
And having heard it he was made to swear
Never to tell a soul, and should he dare

So much as whisper, he should lose his head.
When he agreed to all that had been said
Of his accursed plan, the judge was glad
And gave him precious gifts, the best he had.

When they had framed their whole conspiracy
From point to point to suit the lechery
That was to be enacted on the sly
(Though you shall hear about it by and by)
Home went the fellow. Claudius was his name.
This treacherous judge that was so lost to shame
Was surnamed Appius – for the thing's no fable
But quite historical, and many able
Historians will vouch the gist of it –
This treacherous judge, I tell you, set his wit
To work and went about without delay
To gratify his lust. There came a day
When the false judge (authorities report)
As was his custom took his seat in court
And gave his judgment upon various cases.
All of a sudden in this fellow races
Crying, 'My Lord, I beg with your permission
For justice in my pitiful petition
Touching my suit against Virginius.
If he denies it, says it was not thus,
Then I shall prove it and produce good witness
To testify the truth of it, and fitness.'

'In absence,' said the judge, 'of the accused
Definitive award must be refused.
Summon him, state your case, and I will hear it
Gladly; you shall have justice, never fear it.'

Virginius came to learn the judge's will,
And instantly they read the cursed bill;
These were the terms of it, as you shall hear:

'To you, Lord Appius, it shall appear
On showing of your poor servant Claudius
How that a certain knight, Virginius,
Against the law, against all equity,
And an express injunction lodged by me,

Retains a servant that is mine by right,
One that was stolen from my house by night
When she was very young. I can support
The charge on witness, may it please the court.
My lord the judge, whatever he may say
The girl is not his daughter and I pray
My slave may be restored, by your good will.'
This was the tenor of his cursed bill.

Virginius stared in horror at the churl,
But quickly, ere he could defend his girl
And prove it on his honor as a knight,
Or bring a host of witness, as he might,
That all was false his enemy had stated,
This cursed judge, who never so much as waited
To hear the answer of Virginius,
Spoke out at once and gave his judgment thus:
'I rule this fellow is to have his slave
Immediately. The case is very grave.
Your house shall not protect her. Fetch the girl.
I say the court awards her to the churl.'

And when Virginius, this excellent knight,
Had understood the judge's doom aright,
And knew his daughter on compulsion must
Be handed over to the judge's lust,
Home he returned and seated in his hall
He sent a servant, bidding him to call
His daughter to him, and with ashen face
Deathly and cold, gazed on her lowly grace.
Fatherly pity pierced him to the heart
And yet he did not falter in his part.

'Daughter,' he said, 'Virginia, I must name
The ways that lie before you, death or shame.
One you must take. Alas that I was born!
O judgment undeserved! O my forlorn
And innocent girl, to die upon the knife!
O my dear daughter, ender of my life,
You that I fostered up with such delight,
Whose thought has never left me day or night,

O daughter, you that are my last of woe
And last of any joy that I shall know,
Be patient, O my gem of chastity,
And take your death, for that is my decree.
And it is love, not hate, would have you dead;
My pitying hand must strike, and take your head.
Alas that ever Appius saw your face
To give false judgment in a treacherous case!'
He told her then all you have heard before
Of what had happened; I need say no more.

   'O mercy, dearest father!' said the maid,
And as she spoke she came to him and laid
Her arms about his neck, as oft she did,
And the tears flooded under either lid.
Thus as she wept, 'O father dear,' said she,
'Am I to die? Is there no remedy?'
'None, none, my dearest daughter. Hope is dead.'
'O give me time, dear father,' then she said,
'Let me lament my death a little space,
For Jephtha gave his daughter so much grace
As to allow her time to sorrow in
Before he slew her. She had done no sin,
God knows, but ran, the first among them all,
To welcome him in solemn festival.'
And on the word she fell into a swoon;
But when her faintness passed she rose as soon
And thus addressed her father, unafraid,
'Blessed be God that I shall die a maid!
I take my death rather than take my shame,
So do your will upon me in God's name!'

   And having spoken thus the child implored
That he would smite her softly with his sword
And then once more she fainted and lay still.
Her father sorrowful in heart and will
Smote off her head and took it by the hair,
Sought out the judge and gave it to him there
Sitting in judgment, in the open court.
When he beheld it, Livy makes report,

He rose and gave the order to his men
To take the knight and hang him. There and **then**
A thousand men came surging from the city
Thrusting their way into the court, in pity
And hope to save the knight; the news had **flown,**
The treacherous iniquity was known;
For there had been suspicion of the thing
Bred from the way the churl had sought to **bring**
His charge against the knight with the consent
Of Appius. They knew his lecherous bent,
And so it was the people had arisen.
They took that judge and cast him into prison
And there he slew himself; and Claudius,
Him that was instrument to Appius,
They took and would have hanged upon a **tree,**
But that Virginius in clemency
Begged for his exile. They could scarce **refuse,**
Else he would certainly have got his dues.
The rest were hanged, the greater and the **less,**
That had been party to this cursedness.

Here one can see how sin is paid its wages;
Beware, for no one knows how God engages,
Or when He smites the sinner, or how the **worm**
Of conscience will bring terror to the firm
In wickedness, however secretly,
Though none should know of it but God and he.
Be he illiterate or a man of learning,
How soon the blow will fall there's no discerning.
I offer you this counsel; let it make you
Forsake your sins before your sins forsake you.

Words of the Host to the Physician and to the Pardoner

OUR Host began a violent tirade.
  'God's nails and blood,' he said, 'alas, **poor maid!**
What a low blackguard! What a treacherous **judge!**
Death to all lawyers that will bribe and fudge

To trap you, be they judge or advocate!
Well, the poor girl was killed at any rate.
Alas, her beauty cost her all too dear!
Just as I always say, it's pretty clear
The handsome gifts that fate and nature lend us
Most often are the very ones that end us.
Her beauty was her death as one might say;
How pitifully she was made away!
Those gifts that I was mentioning just now
Do us more harm than good, one must allow.
Well, my dear sir, if I may speak sincere,
Your tale was truly pitiful to hear.
Nevertheless, pass on. No sense in fretting.
God's blessing on you, Doctor, not forgetting
Your various urinals and chamber-pots,
Bottles, medicaments and cordial tots
And boxes brimming all with panaceas,
God's blessing on them all and St Maria's!
You look a proper fellow! Pills and pellets!
St Ronyan, you've a figure like a prelate's!
Don't I say well? – although I lack the art
To talk like you; your story touched my heart,
It gave me heart-disease, or very near.
By corpus bones! I'll need a dose, I fear,
Or else a good wet draught of malted ale
If someone doesn't tell a cheerful tale.
I'm lost in pity for that poor girl dead.
Come on, old chum and Pardoner,' he said,
'Tell us a funny story, break a joke!'
'Right, by St Ronyan! but I'll have a soak
First at this pub. I've got a thirst to slake,'
Said he, 'I'll drink and eat a bit of cake.'

    Outcry arose among the gentlefolk.
'No, no, don't let him tell a dirty joke!
Tell something with a moral, something clear
And profitable, and we'll gladly hear.'
'Granted,' he said, 'but first I'll have to think;
I'll ponder something decent while I drink.'

The Pardoner's Tale

The Pardoner's Prologue

'M Y lords,' he said, 'in churches where I preach
I cultivate a haughty kind of speech
And ring it out as roundly as a bell;
I've got it all by heart, the tale I tell.
I have a text, it always is the same
And always has been, since I learnt the game,
Old as the hills and fresher than the grass,
Radix malorum est cupiditas.

'But first I make pronouncement whence I come,
Show them my bulls in detail and in sum,
And flaunt the papal seal for their inspection
As warrant for my bodily protection,
That none may have the impudence to irk
Or hinder me in Christ's most holy work.
And then I tell them, as occasion calls,
Some anecdotes of popes and cardinals,
Of patriarchs and even bishops too,
And speak some words in Latin – just a few –
To put a saffron tinge upon my preaching
And stir devotion with a spice of teaching.
Then I bring all my long glass bottles out
Cram-full of bones and ragged bits of clout,
Relics they are, at least for such are known.
Then, cased in metal, I've a shoulder-bone,
Belonging to a sheep, a holy Jew's.
"Good men," I say, "take heed, for here is news.
Take but this bone and dip it in a well;
If cow or calf, if sheep or ox should swell
From eating adders or from being stung,
Take water from that well and wash its tongue,

And it will then recover. Furthermore,
Where there is pox or scab or other sore,
All animals that water at that well
Are cured at once. Take note of what I tell.
If the good man – the owner of the stock –
Goes once a week, before the crow of cock,
Fasting, and takes a draught of water too,
Why then, according to that holy Jew,
He'll find his cattle multiply and sell.

   ' "And it's a cure for jealousy as well;
For if your husband's prone to jealous wrath,
Use the same water when you make his broth
And he will always trust you. It's a curtain
On your behavior, though he knew for certain
That several clergy had enjoyed your love.

   ' "Now look; I have a mitten here, a glove.
Whoever wears this mitten on his hand
Will multiply his grain. He sows his land
And up will come abundant wheat or oats,
Providing that he gives me a few groats.

   ' "Good men and women, here's a word of warning;
If there is anyone in church this morning
Guilty of sin so far beyond expression
Revolting he's ashamed to make confession,
Or if some woman young or old's in touch
With man, and cuckolding her husband, such
Shall neither have the power nor the grace
To offer to my relics in this place.
But those who can acquit themselves of blame
Can all come up and offer in God's name,
And I will shrive them by the authority
Committed in this papal bull to me."

   'That trick's been worth a hundred marks a year
Since I became a Pardoner, never fear.
I stand up in my pulpit with a frown
Like any priest, and when they've all sat down
I preach upon the text you heard before
And tell a hundred lying mockeries more.

I take great pains, and stretching out my neck
To east and west I crane about and peck,
Just like a pigeon sitting on a barn.
My hands and tongue together spin the yarn
And all my antics are a joy to see.
The curse of avarice and cupidity
Is all my sermon, for it frees the pelf.
Out come the pence, and specially for myself,
For my exclusive purpose is to win
And not at all to castigate their sin.
Once dead what matter how their souls may fare?
They can go blackberrying, for all I care!

    Believe me, many a sermon or devotive
Exordium issues from an evil motive.
Some titillate their folk by flattery
Gaining promotion by hypocrisy;
Some preach from vanity and some from hate.
For want of other methods of debate
I sometimes choose a victim for my tongue
And as he can't escape he sits there stung
By slanderous defamation. Thus he's paid
For injuring me, or others of my trade.
For though I never mention him by name
The congregation guesses all the same
From certain hints that everybody knows,
And so I take revenge upon our foes
And spit my venom forth, while I profess
Holy and true – or seeming holiness.

    'But let me briefly make my purpose plain;
I preach for nothing but for greed of gain
And use the same old text, as bold as brass,
Radix malorum est cupiditas.
The vice on which I pour my emphasis
Is what I live by, namely avarice.
And yet however guilty of that sin
Myself, with others I have power to win
Them from it, I can bring them to repent;
But that is not my principal intent.

Covetousness is both the root and stuff
Of all I preach. That ought to be enough.

'Well, then I give examples thick and fast
From bygone times, old stories from the past;
A yokel mind loves stories from of old,
Being the kind it can repeat and hold.
What! Do you think, as long as I can preach
And get their silver for the things I teach,
That I will live in poverty, from choice?
That's not the counsel of my inner voice!
No, I will preach and beg from kirk to kirk;
For I'll not do an honest job of work,
No, nor make baskets like St. Paul to gain
My livelihood, for I won't beg in vain.
I'll copy no apostle ever born!
I will have money, wool and cheese and corn,
Though it were given me by the poorest lad
Or poorest village widow, though she had
A string of starving children, all agape.
No, let me drink the liquor of the grape
And keep a jolly wench in every town!

'But listen, gentlemen; to bring things down
To a conclusion, would you like a tale?
Now, as I've drunk a draught of corn-ripe ale,
By God it stands to reason I can strike
On some good story that you all will like.
For, though I am a wholly vicious man,
Don't think I can't tell moral tales. I can!
Here's one I often preach when out for winning;
Now please be quiet. Here is the beginning.'

The Pardoner's Tale

Iɴ Flanders once there was a company
Of youngsters haunting vice and ribaldry,
Riot and gambling, stews and public-houses
Where each with harp, guitar or lute carouses,

Dancing and dicing day and night, and bold
To eat and drink far more than they can hold,
Doing thereby the devil sacrifice
Within that devil's temple of cursed vice,
Abominable in superfluity,
With oaths so damnable in blasphemy
That it's a grisly thing to hear them swear.
Our dear Lord's body they will rend and tear
As if the Jews had rent Him not enough;
And at the sin of others every tough
Will laugh, and presently the dancing-girls,
Small pretty ones, come in and shake their curls,
With youngsters selling fruit, and ancient bawds,
And girls with cakes and music, devil's gauds
To kindle and blow the fires of lechery
That are so close annexed to gluttony.
Witness the Bible, which is most express
That lust is bred of wine and drunkenness.

Look how the drunken and unnatural Lot
Lay with his daughters, though he knew it not;
He was too drunk to know what he was doing.

Take Herod too, his tale is worth pursuing.
Replete with wine and feasting, he was able
To give the order at his very table
To kill the innocent Baptist, good St John.

Seneca has a thought worth pondering on;
No difference, he says, that he can find
Between a madman who has lost his mind
And one who is habitually mellow
Except that madness, when it takes a fellow,
Lasts longer, on the whole, than drunkenness.
O cursed gluttony, our first distress!
Cause of our first confusion, first temptation,
The very origin of our damnation,
Till Christ redeemed us with his blood again!
O infamous indulgence! Cursed stain
So dearly bought! And what has it been worth?
Gluttony has corrupted all the earth.

Adam, our father, and his wife no less,
From Paradise to labor and distress
Were driven for that vice, they were indeed.
While she and Adam fasted, so I read,
They were in Paradise; when he and she
Ate of the fruit of that forbidden tree
They were at once cast forth in pain and woe.
O gluttony, it is to thee we owe
Our griefs! O if we knew the maladies
That follow on excess and gluttonies,
Sure we would diet, we would temper pleasure
In sitting down at table, show some measure!
Alas the narrow throat, the tender mouth!
Men labor east and west and north and south
In earth, in air, in water – Why, d'you think?
To get a glutton dainty meat and drink!
How well of this St Paul's Epistle treats!
'Meats for the belly, belly for the meats,
But God shall yet destroy both it and them.'
Alas, the filth of it! If we contemn
The name, how far more filthy is the act!
A man who swills down vintages in fact
Makes a mere privy of his throat, a sink
For cursed superfluities of drink!
    So the Apostle said, whom tears could soften:
'Many there are, as I have told you often,
And weep to tell, whose gluttony sufficed
To make them enemies of the cross of Christ,
Whose ending is destruction and whose God
Their belly!' O thou belly! stinking pod
Of dung and foul corruption, that canst send
Thy filthy music forth at either end,
What labor and expense it is to find
Thy sustenance! These cooks that strain and grind
And bray in mortars, transubstantiate
God's gifts into a flavor on a plate
To please a lecherous palate. How they batter
Hard bones to put some marrow on your platter,

Spicery, root, bark, leaf – they search and cull it
In the sweet hope of flattering a gullet!
Nothing is thrown away that could delight
Or whet anew lascivious appetite.
Be sure a man whom such a fare entices
Is dead indeed, though living in his vices.

    Wine is a lecherous thing and drunkenness
A squalor of contention and distress.
O drunkard, how disfigured is thy face,
How foul thy breath, how filthy thy embrace!
And through thy drunken nose a stertorous snort
Like 'samson-samson' – something of the sort.
Yet Samson never was a man to swig.
You totter, lurch and fall like a stuck pig,
Your manhood's lost, your tongue is in a burr.
Drunkenness is the very sepulcher
Of human judgment and articulation.
He that is subject to the domination
Of drink can keep no secrets, be it said.
Keep clear of wine, I tell you, white or red,
Especially Spanish wines which they provide
And have on sale in Fish Street and Cheapside.
That wine mysteriously finds its way
To mix itself with others – shall we say
Spontaneously? – that grow in neighboring regions.*
Out of the mixture fumes arise in legions,
So when a man has had a drink or two,
Though he may think he is at home with you
In Cheapside, I assure you he's in Spain
Where it was made, at Lepé I maintain,
Not even at Bordeaux. He's soon elate
And very near the 'samson-samson' state.

    But seriously, my lords, attention, pray!
All the most notable acts, I dare to say,
And victories in the Old Testament,
Won under God who is omnipotent,
Were won in abstinence, were won in prayer.
Look in the Bible, you will find it there.

Or else take Atilla the Conqueror;
Died in his sleep, a manner to abhor,
In drunken shame and bleeding at the nose.
A general should live sober, I suppose.
Moreover call to mind and ponder well
What was commanded unto Lemuel
– Not Samuel but Lemuel I said –
Read in the Bible, that's the fountain-head,
And see what comes of giving judges drink.
No more of that. I've said enough, I think.

Having put gluttony in its proper setting
I wish to warn you against dice and betting.
Gambling's the very mother of robbed purses
Lies, double-dealing, perjury, and curses,
Manslaughter, blasphemy of Christ, and waste
Of time and money. Worse, you are debased
In public reputation, put to shame.
'A common gambler' is a nasty name.

The more exalted such a man may be
So much the more contemptible is he.
A gambling prince would be incompetent
To frame a policy of government,
And he will sink in general opinion
As one unfit to exercise dominion.

Stilbon, that wise ambassador whose mission
Took him to Corinth, was of high position;
Sparta had sent him with intent to frame
A treaty of alliance. When he came,
Hoping for reinforcement and advice,
It happened that he found them all at dice,
Their very nobles; so he quickly planned
To steal away, home to his native land.
He said, 'I will not lose my reputation
Or compromise the honor of my nation
By asking dicers to negotiate.
Send other wise ambassadors of state,
For on my honor I would rather die
Than be a means for Sparta to ally

With gamblers; Corinth, glorious in honor,
Shall take no such alliances upon her
As dicers make, by any act of mine!'
He showed his sense in taking such a line.

Again, consider King Demetrius;
The King of Parthia – history has it thus –
Sent him a pair of golden dice in scorn,
To show he reckoned him a gambler born
Whose honor, if unable to surmount
The vice of gambling, was of no account.
Lords can amuse themselves in other ways
Honest enough, to occupy their days.

Now let me speak a word or two of swearing
And perjury; the Bible is unsparing.
It's an abominable thing to curse
And swear, it says; but perjury is worse.
Almighty God has said, 'Swear not at all,'
Witness St Matthew, and you may recall
The words of Jeremiah, having care
To what he says of lying: 'Thou shalt swear
In truth, in judgment and in righteousness.'
But idle swearing is a sin, no less.
Behold and see the tables of the Law
Of God's Commandments, to be held in awe;
Look at the third where it is written plain,
'Thou shalt not take the name of God in vain.'
You see He has forbidden swearing first;
Not murder, no, nor other thing accurst
Comes before that, I say, in God's commands.
That is the order; he who understands
Knows that the third commandment is just that.
And in addition, let me tell you flat,
Vengeance on him and all his house shall fall
That swears outrageously, or swears at all.
'God's precious heart and passion, by God's nails
And by the blood of Christ that is at Hailes,*
Seven's my luck, and yours is five and three;
God's blessed arms! If you play false with me

I'll stab you with my dagger!' Overthrown
By two small dice, two bitching bits of bone,
They reach rage, perjury, cheating, homicide.
O for the love of Jesu Christ who died
For us, abandon curses, small or great!
But, sirs, I have a story to relate.

It's of three rioters I have to tell
Who, long before the morning service bell,
Were sitting in a tavern for a drink.
And as they sat, they heard the hand-bell clink
Before a coffin being borne to church.
One called the tavern-lad and with a lurch
Said to him, 'Run along and ask – look spry –
Whose corpse is in that coffin passing by;
And see you get the name correctly too.'
'Sir,' said the boy, 'no need, I promise you;
Two hours before you came here I was told.
He was a friend of yours in days of old,
But suddenly killed last night in an attack,
There on the bench, dead drunk and on his back.
There came a privy thief, they call him Death,
Who kills us all round here, and in a breath
He speared him through the heart; he never stirred.
And then Death went his way without a word.
He's killed a thousand in the present plague,
And, sir, it doesn't do to be too vague
If you should meet him; you had best be wary.
Be on your guard with such an adversary,
Be primed to meet him everywhere you go,
That's what my mother said. It's all I know.'
The publican joined in with, 'By St Mary.
What the child says is right; you'd best be wary,
This very year he killed, in a large village
A mile away, man, woman, serf at tillage,
Page in the household, children – all there were.
Yes, I imagine that he lives round there.
It's well to be prepared in these alarms,
He might do dirt on you.' 'What's that? God's arms!'

The rioter said, 'Is he so fierce to meet?
I'll search for him, by Jesus, street by street.
God's blessed bones! I'll register a vow!
Here, chaps! The three of us together now,
Hold up your hands, like me, and we'll be brothers
In this affair, and each defend the others.
We'll kill this double-crosser Death, I say;
Away with him as he has made away
With all our friends. God's dignity! To-night!'

They made their bargain, swore with appetite,
These three, to live and die for one another
As brother-born might swear to his born brother.
And up they started in their drunken rage
And made towards this village which the page
And publican had spoken of before.
Many and grisly were the oaths they swore,
Tearing Christ's blessed body to a shred;
'If we can only catch him, Death is dead!'

When they had gone not fully half a mile,
Just as they were about to cross a stile,
They came upon a very poor old man
Who humbly greeted them and thus began,
'God look to you, my lords, and give you quiet!'
To which the proudest of these men of riot
Gave back the answer, 'What, old fool? Give place!
Why are you all wrapped up except your face?
Why live so long? Isn't it time to die?'

The old, old fellow looked him in the eye
And said, 'Because I never yet have found,
Though I have walked to India, searching round
Village and city on my pilgrimage,
One who would change his youth to have my age.
And so my age is mine and must be still
Upon me, for such time as God may will.

'Not even Death, alas, will take my life;
So, like a wretched prisoner at strife
Within himself, I walk alone and wait
About the earth, which is my mother's gate,

Knock-knocking with my staff from night to noon
And crying, "Mother, open to me soon!
Look at me, mother, won't you let me in?
See how I wither, flesh and blood and skin!
Alas! When will these bones be laid to rest?
Mother, I would exchange – for that were best –
The wardrobe in my chamber, standing there
So long, for yours! Aye, for a shirt of hair
To wrap me in!" She has refused her grace,
Whence comes the pallor of my withered face.

'But it dishonored you when you began
To speak so roughly, sir, to an old man,
Unless he had injured you in word or deed.
It says in holy writ, as you may read,
"Thou shalt rise up before the hoary head
And honor it." And therefore be it said
"Do no more harm to an old man than you,
Being now young, would have another do
When you are old" – if you should live till then.
And so may God be with you, gentlemen,
For I must go whither I have to go.'

'By God,' the gambler said, 'you shan't do so,
You don't get off so easy, by St John!
I heard you mention, just a moment gone,
A certain traitor Death who singles out
And kills the fine young fellows hereabout.
And you're his spy, by God! You wait a bit.
Say where he is or you shall pay for it,
By God and by the Holy Sacrament!
I say you've joined together by consent
To kill us younger folk, you thieving swine!'
'Well, sir,' he said, 'if it be your design
To find out Death, turn up this crooked way
Towards that grove. I left him there to-day
Under a tree, and there you'll find him waiting.
He isn't one to hide for all your prating.
You see that oak? He won't be far to find.
And God protect you that redeemed mankind,

Aye, and amend you!' Thus that ancient man.
    At once the three young rioters began
To run, and reached the tree, and there they found
A pile of golden florins on the ground,
New-coined, eight bushels of them as they thought.
No longer was it Death those fellows sought,
For they were all so thrilled to see the sight,
The florins were so beautiful and bright,
That down they sat beside the precious pile.
The wickedest spoke first after a while.
'Brothers,' he said, 'you listen to what I say.
I'm pretty sharp, although I joke away.
It's clear that Fortune has bestowed this treasure
So as to let us live our lives in pleasure.
Light come, light go! We'll spend it as we ought.
God's precious dignity! Who would have thought
This morning was to be our lucky day?

    'If one could only get the gold away,
Back to my house, or else to yours, perhaps –
For as you know, the gold is ours, chaps –
We'd all be at the top of fortune, hey?
But certainly it can't be done by day.
People would call us robbers – a strong gang,
So our own property would make us hang.
No; we must bring this treasure back by night
Some prudent way, and keep it out of sight.
And so as a solution I propose
We draw for lots and see the way it goes.
The one who draws the longest, lucky man,
Shall run to town as quickly as he can
To fetch us bread and wine – but keep things dark –
While two remain in hiding here to mark
Our heap of treasure. If there's no delay,
When night comes down we'll carry it away,
All three of us, wherever we have planned.'

    He gathered lots and hid them in his hand
Bidding them draw for where the luck should fall.
It fell upon the youngest of them all,

And off he ran at once towards the town.

    As soon as he had gone the first sat down
And thus began a parley with the other:
'You know that you can trust me as a brother;
Let me point out the advantage to you there.
Our friend has gone, as you are well aware,
And here's a lot of gold that is to be
Divided equally amongst us three.
Nevertheless, if I could shape things thus
So that we shared it out — the two of us —
Wouldn't you take it as a friendly turn?'

    'How?' said the other. 'Maybe I can learn,
But still he knows the gold's with me and you;
What can we tell him? What are we to do?'

    'Is it a bargain,' said the first, 'or no?
For I can tell you in a word or so
What's to be done to bring the thing about.'
'Trust me,' the other said, 'you needn't doubt
My word. I won't betray you, I'll be true.'

    'Well,' said his friend, 'you see that we are two,
And two are twice as powerful as one.
Now look; when he comes back, get up in fun
And have a wrestle with him, just a rag;
Then I'll jump up and slice him through the bag
While he is struggling, thinking it a game;
You draw your dagger too and do the same.
Then all this money will be ours to spend,
Divided equally of course, dear friend.
Then we can gratify our lusts and fill
The day with dicing at our own sweet will.'
Thus these two miscreants agreed to slay
The third and youngest, as you heard me say.

    The youngest, as he ran towards the town,
Kept turning over, rolling up and down
Within his heart the beauty of those bright
New florins, saying, 'Lord, to think I might
Have all that treasure to myself alone!
Could there be anyone beneath the throne

Of God so happy as I then should be?'
　　And so the Fiend, our common enemy,
Was given power to put it in his thought
That there was always poison to be bought,
And that with poison he could kill his friends.
To men in such a state the Devil sends
Thoughts of this kind, and has a full permission
To lure them on to sorrow and perdition;
For this young man was utterly content
To kill them both and never to repent.
　　And on he ran, he had no thought to tarry,
Came to the town, found an apothecary
And said, 'Sell me some poison if you will,
I have a lot of rats I want to kill
And there's a polecat too about my yard
That takes my chickens and it hits me hard;
But I'll get even, as is only right,
With vermin that destroy a man by night.'
　　The chemist answered, 'I've a preparation
Which you shall have, and by my soul's salvation
If any living creature eat or drink
A mouthful, ere he has the time to think,
Though he took less than makes a grain of wheat,
You'll see him fall down dying at your feet;
Yes, die he must, and in so short a while
You'd hardly have the time to walk a mile,
The poison is so strong, you understand.'
　　This cursed fellow grabbed into his hand
The box of poison and away he ran
Into a neighboring street, and found a man
Who lent him three large bottles. He withdrew
And deftly poured the poison into two.
He kept the third one clean, as well he might,
For his own drink, meaning to work all night
Stacking the gold and carrying it away.
And when this rioter, this devil's clay,
Had filled his bottles up with wine, all three,
Then back to join his comrades sauntered he.

Why make a sermon of it? Why waste breath?
Exactly in the way they'd planned his death
They fell on him and slew him, two to one.
Then said the first of them when this was done,
'Now for a drink. Sit down and let's be merry,
For later on there'll be the corpse to bury.'
And, as it happened, reaching for a sup,
He took a bottle full of poison up
And drank; and his companion, nothing loth,
Drank from it also, and they perished both.

There is, in Avicenna's long relation*
Concerning poison and its operation,
Trust me, no ghastlier section to transcend
What these two wretches suffered at their end.
Thus these two murderers received their due,
So did the treacherous young poisoner too.

O cursed sin! O blackguardly excess!
O treacherous homicide! O wickedness!
O gluttony that lusted on and diced!
O blasphemy that took the name of Christ
With habit-hardened oaths that pride began!
Alas, how comes it that a mortal man,
That thou, to thy Creator, Him that wrought thee,
That paid His precious blood for thee and bought thee,
Art so unnatural and false within?
    Dearly beloved, God forgive your sin
And keep you from the vice of avarice!
My holy pardon frees you all of this,
Provided that you make the right approaches,
That is with sterling, rings, or silver brooches.
Bow down your heads under this holy bull!
Come on, you women, offer up your wool!
I'll write your name into my ledger; so!
Into the bliss of Heaven you shall go.
For I'll absolve you by my holy power,
You that make offering, clean as at the hour

When you were born.... That, sirs, is how I preach.
And Jesu Christ, soul's healer, aye, the leech
Of every soul, grant pardon and relieve you
Of sin, for that is best, I won't deceive you.

    One thing I should have mentioned in my tale,
Dear people. I've some relics in my bale
And pardons to, as full and fine I hope
As any in England, given me by the Pope.
If there be one among you that is willing
To have my absolution, for a shilling
Devoutly given, come! and do not harden
Your hearts, but kneel in humbleness for pardon;
Or else, receive my pardon as we go.
You can renew it every town or so,
Always provided that you still renew
Each time, and in good money, what is due.
It is an honor for you to have found
A pardoner with his credentials sound,
Who can absolve you, as you ply the spur,
In any accident that may occur.
For instance – we are all at Fortune's beck –
Your horse may throw you down and break your neck.
What a security it is to all
To have me here among you and at call
With pardon for the lowly and the great,
When soul leaves body for the future state!
And I advise our Host here to begin,
The most enveloped of you all in sin.
Come forward, Host, you shall be first to pay,
And kiss my holy relics right away.
Only a groat. Come on, unbuckle your purse!'

    'No, no,' said he, 'not I, and may the curse
Of Christ descend upon me if I do!
You'll have me kissing your old breeches too
And swear they were the relic of a saint
Although your fundament supplied the paint!
Now by St Helen and the Holy Land
I wish I had your cullions in my hand

Instead of relics in a reliquarium;
Have them cut off and I will help to carry 'em.
We'll have them shrined for you in a hog's turd.'

The Pardoner said nothing, not a word;
He was so angry that he couldn't speak.
'Well,' said our Host, 'if you're for showing pique,
I'll joke no more, not with an angry man.'

The worthy Knight immediately began,
Seeing the fun was getting rather rough,
And said, 'No more, we've all had quite enough.
Now, Master Pardoner, perk up, look cheerly!
And you, Sir Host, whom I esteem so dearly,
I beg of you to kiss the Pardoner.

'Come, Pardoner, draw nearer, my dear sir.
Let's laugh again and keep the ball in play.'
They kissed, and we continued on our way.

[GROUP D]

The Wife of Bath's Tale

The Wife of Bath's Prologue

'I F there were no authority on earth
Except experience, mine, for what it's worth,
(And that's enough for me) all goes to show
That marriage is a misery and a woe;
For let me say, if I may make so bold,
My lords, since when I was but twelve years old,
Thanks be to God Eternal evermore,
Five husbands have I had at the church door;
Yes, it's a fact that I have had so many,
All worthy in their way, as good as any.

'Someone said recently for my persuasion
That as Christ only went on one occasion

To grace a wedding – in Cana of Galilee –
He taught me by example there to see
That it is wrong to marry more than once.
Consider, too, how sharply, for the nonce,
He spoke, rebuking the Samaritan
Beside the well, Christ Jesus, God and man.
"Thou hast had five men husband unto thee
And he that even now thou hast," said He,
"Is not thy husband." Such the words that fell;
But what He meant thereby I cannot tell.
Why was her fifth – explain it if you can –
No lawful spouse to the Samaritan?
How many might have had her, then, to wife?
I've never heard an answer all my life
To give the number final definition.
People may guess or frame a supposition,
But I can say for certain, it's no lie,
God bade us all to wax and multiply.
That kindly text I well can understand.
Is not my husband under God's command
To leave his father and mother and take me?
No word of what the number was to be,
Then why not marry two or even eight?
And why speak evil of the married state?

'Take wise King Solomon of long ago;
We hear he had a thousand wives or so.
And would to God it were allowed to me
To be refreshed, aye, half so much as he!
He must have had a gift of God for wives,
No one to match him in a world of lives!
This noble king, one may as well admit,
On the first night threw many a merry fit
With each of them, he was so much alive.
Blessed be God that I have wedded five!
Welcome the sixth, whenever he appears.
I can't keep continent for years and years.
No sooner than one husband's dead and gone
Some other christian man shall take me on,

For then, so says the Apostle, I am free
To wed, o' God's name, where it pleases me.
Wedding's no sin, so far as I can learn.
Better it is to marry than to burn.

'What do I care if people choose to see
Scandal in Lamech for his bigamy?
I know that Abraham was a holy man,
And Jacob too, for all that I can scan,
Yet each of them, we know, had several brides,
Like many another holy man besides.
Show me a time or text where God disparages
Or sets a prohibition upon marriages
Expressly, let me have it! Show it me!
And where did He command virginity?
I know as well as you do, never doubt it,
All the Apostle Paul has said about it;
He said that as for precepts he had none.
One may advise a woman to be one;
Advice is no commandment in my view.
He left it in our judgment what to do.

'Had God commanded maidenhood to all
Marriage would be condemned beyond recall,
For clearly, if the seed were never sown,
How ever could virginity be grown?
Paul did not dare command, let matters rest,
His Master having given him no behest.
There's a prize offered for virginity;
Catch as catch can! Who's in for it? Let's see!

'It is not everyone who hears the call;
On whom God wills He lets His power fall.
The Apostle was a virgin, well I know;
Nevertheless, though all his writings show
He wished that everyone were such as he,
It's all mere counsel to virginity.
And as for being married, he lets me do it
Out of indulgence, so there's nothing to it
In marrying me, suppose my husband dead;
There's nothing bigamous in such a bed.

Though it were good a man should never touch
A woman (meaning here in bed and such)
And dangerous to assemble fire and tow
– What this allusion means you all must know –
He only says virginity is fresh,
More perfect than the frailty of the flesh
In married life – except when he and she
Prefer to live in married chastity.

   'I grant it you. I'll never say a word
Decrying maidenhood although preferred
To frequent marriage; there are those who mean
To live in their virginity, as clean
In body as in soul, and never mate.
I'll make no boast about my own estate.
As in a noble household, we are told,
Not every dish and vessel's made of gold,
Some are of wood, yet earn their master's praise,
God calls His folk to Him in many ways.
To each of them God gave His proper gift,
Some this, some that, and left them to make shift.

   'Virginity is perfect, unforsaken,
Continence too, devoutly undertaken.
But Christ, who of perfection is the Well,
Bade not that everyone should go and sell
All that he had and give it to the poor
To follow in His footsteps, that is sure.
He spoke to those that would live perfectly,
And by your leave, my lords, that's not for me.
I will bestow the flower of life, the honey,
Upon the acts and fruit of matrimony.

   'Tell me to what conclusion, or in aid
Of what, were generative organs made?
And for what profit were those creatures wrought?
You take my word they were not made for naught.
Gloze as you will and plead the explanation
That they were only made for the purgation
Of urine, little things of no avail
Except to know a female from a male,

And nothing else. Did somebody say no?
Experience knows well it isn't so.
The learned may rebuke me, or be loath
To think it so, but they were made for both,
That is to say both use and pleasure in
Engendering, except in case of sin.
Why else the proverb written down and set
In books: "A man must yield his wife her debt"?
What means of paying her can he invent
Unless he use his silly instrument?
It follows they were fashioned at creation
Both to purge urine and for propagation.

'But I'm not saying everyone is bound
Who has such harness as you heard me expound
To go and use it breeding; that would be
To show too little care for chastity.
Christ was a virgin, fashioned as a man,
And many of his saints since time began
Were ever perfect in celibacy.
I'll speak no evil of virginity.
Let them be pure wheat loaves of maidenhead
And let us wives be known for barley-bread;
Yet Mark can tell that barley-bread sufficed
To freshen many at the hand of Christ.
In that estate to which God summoned me
I'll persevere; I'm not pernickety.
In wifehood I will use my instrument
As freely as my Maker me it sent.
If I turn difficult, God give me sorrow!
My husband, he shall have it eve and morrow
Whenever he likes to come and pay his debt,
I won't prevent him! I'll have a husband yet
Who shall be both my debtor and my slave
And bear his tribulation to the grave
Upon his flesh, as long as I'm his wife.
For mine shall be the power all his life
Over his proper body, and not he,
Just as St Paul has given it out to me

In bidding husbands love their wives, I say.
That's an opinion suits me every way.'
　　The Pardoner, as she was going on,
Started and said, 'By God and by St John,
Madam, that's preaching no one could surpass!
I was about to marry, but alas
If I shall have to pay for it so dear
There'll be no marrying for me this year!'
　　'You wait,' she said, 'my story's not begun.
You'll taste another brew before I've done;
You'll find it isn't quite so nice as beer.
For while the tale is telling you shall hear
Of all the tribulations man and wife
Can have; I've been an expert all my life,
That is to say myself have been the whip.
So please yourself whether you want to sip
At that same cask of marriage I shall broach;
Be cautious before making the approach,
For I'll give instances, and more than ten.
And those who won't be warned by other men
By other men shall suffer their correction.
So Ptolemy has said in this connection.*
You read his *Almagest*; you'll find it there.'
　　'Madam, I put it to you as a prayer,'
The Pardoner said, 'go on as you began!
Tell us your tale, spare not for any man.
Instruct us younger men in your technique.'
'Gladly,' she answered, 'if I am to speak.
But still I hope the company won't reprove me
Though I should speak as fantasy may move me,
And please don't be offended at my views;
They're really only offered to amuse.
　　'Now, gentlemen, I'll on and tell my tale
And as I hope to drink good wine and ale
I'll tell the truth. Those husbands that I had,
Three of them were good and two were bad.
The three that I call 'good' were rich and old.
They could indeed with difficulty hold

The articles that bound them all to me;
(No doubt you understand my simile).
So help me God, I have to laugh outright
Remembering how I made them work at night!
And, faith, I set no store by it; no pleasure
It was to me. They'd given me their treasure,
I had no need to do my diligence
To win their love or show them reverence.
They loved me well enough, so, heavens above,
Why should I make a dainty of their love?

   'A knowing woman's work is never done
To get a lover if she hasn't one,
But as I had them eating from my hand
And as they'd yielded me their gold and land,
Why then take trouble to provide them pleasure
Unless to profit and amuse my leisure?
I set them so to work, I'm bound to say;
Many a night they sang, "Alack the day!"
Never for them the flitch of bacon, though,
That some have won in Essex at Dunmow!*
I governed them so well and held the rein
So firmly they were rapturously fain
To go and buy me pretty things to wear;
They were delighted if I spoke them fair.
God knows how spitefully I used to scold them.

   'Listen, I'll tell you how I used to hold them,
You knowing women, who can understand.
First put them in the wrong, and out of hand.
No one can be so bold – I mean no man –
At lies and swearing as a woman can.
This is no news, as you'll have realized,
To knowing ones, but to the misadvised.
A knowing wife if she is worth her salt
Can always prove her husband is at fault,
And even though the fellow may have heard
Some story told him by a little bird
She knows enough to prove the bird is crazy
And get her maid to witness she's a daisy,

With full agreement, scarce solicited.
But listen. Here's the sort of thing I said:
   ' "Now, sir old dotard, what is that you say?
Why is my neighbor's wife so smart and gay?
She is respected everywhere she goes.
I sit at home and have no decent clothes.
Why haunt her house? What are you doing there?
Are you so amorous? Is she so fair?
What, whispering secrets to our maid? For shame,
Sir ancient lecher! Time you dropped that game.
And if I see my gossip or a friend
You scold me like a devil! There's no end
If I as much as stroll towards his house.
Then you come home as drunken as a mouse,
You mount your throne and preach, chapter and verse
– All nonsense – and you tell me it's a curse
To marry a poor woman – she's expensive;
Or if her family's wealthy and extensive
You say it's torture to endure her pride
And melancholy airs, and more beside.
And if she has a pretty face, old traitor,
You say she's game for any fornicator
And ask what likelihood will keep her straight
With all those men who lie about in wait.

   ' "You say that some desire us for our wealth,
Some for our shapeliness, our looks, our health,
Some for our singing, others for our dancing,
Some for our courtesy and dalliant glancing,
And some because our hands are soft and small;
By your account the devil gets us all.

   ' "You say what castle wall can be so strong
As to hold out against a siege for long?
And if her looks are foul you say that she
Is hot for every man that she can see,
Leaping upon them with a spaniel's airs
Until she finds a man to buy her wares.
Never was goose upon the lake so gray
But that she found a gander, so you say.

You say it's hard to keep a girl controlled
If she's the kind that no one wants to hold.
That's what you say as you stump off to bed,
You brute! You say no man of sense would wed,
That is, not if he wants to go to Heaven.
Wild thunderbolts and fire from the seven
Planets descend and break your withered neck!

   ' "You say that buildings falling into wreck,
And smoke, and scolding women, are the three
Things that will drive a man from home. Dear me!
What ails the poor old man to grumble so?

   ' "You say we hide our faults to let them show
Once we are safely married, so you say.
There's a fine proverb for a popinjay!

   ' "You say that oxen, asses, hounds and horses
Can be tried out on various ploys and courses;
And basins too, and dishes when you buy them,
Spoons, chairs and furnishings, a man can try them
As he can try a suit of clothes, no doubt,
But no one ever tries a woman out
Until he's married her; old dotard crow!
And then you say she lets her vices show.

   ' "You also say we count it for a crime
Unless you praise our beauty all the time,
Unless you're always poring on our faces
And call us pretty names in public places;
Or if you fail to treat me to a feast
Upon my birthday – presents at the least –
Or to respect my nurse and her gray hairs,
Or be polite to all my maids upstairs
And to my father's cronies and his spies.
That's what you say, old barrelful of lies!

   ' "Then there's our young apprentice, handsome Johnny;
Because he has crisp hair that shines as bonny
As finest gold, and squires me up and down
You show your low suspicions in a frown.
I wouldn't have him, not if you died to-morrow!

   ' "And tell me this, God punish you with sorrow,

Why do you hide the keys of coffer doors?
It's just as much my property as yours.
Do you want to make an idiot of your wife?
Now, by the Lord that gave me soul and life,
You shan't have both, you can't be such a noddy
As think to keep my goods and have my body!
One you must do without, whatever you say.
And do you need to spy on me all day?
I think you'd like to lock me in your coffer!
'Go where you please, dear wife,' you ought to offer,
'Amuse yourself! I shan't give ear to malice,
I know you for a virtuous wife, Dame Alice.'
We cannot love a husband who takes charge
Of where we go. We like to be at large.

  ' "Above all other men may God confer
His blessing on that wise astrologer
Sir Ptolemy who, in his *Almagest,*
Has set this proverb down: 'Of men the best
And wisest care not who may have in hand
The conduct of the world.' I understand
That means, 'If you've enough, you shouldn't care
How prosperously other people fare.'
Be sure, old dotard, if you call the bluff,
You'll get your evening rations right enough.
He's a mean fellow that let's no man handle
His lantern when it's just to light a candle;
He has lost no light, he hasn't felt a strain;
And you have light enough, so why complain?
  ' "And when a woman tries a mild display
In dress or costly ornament, you say
It is a danger to her chastity,
And then, bad luck to you, start making free
With Bible tags in the Apostle's name;
'And in like manner, chastely and with shame,
You women should adorn yourselves,' said he,
'And not with braided hair or jewelry
With pearl or golden ornament.' What next!
I'll pay as much attention to your text

And rubric in such things as would a gnat.
    ' "And once you said that I was like a cat,
For if you singe a cat it will not roam
And that's the way to keep a cat at home.
But when she feels her fur is sleek and gay
She can't be kept indoors for half a day
But off she takes herself as dusk is falling
To show her fur and go a-caterwauling.
Which means if I feel gay, as you suppose,
I shall run out to show my poor old clothes.
    ' "Silly old fool! You and your private spies!
Go on, beg Argus with his hundred eyes
To be my bodyguard, and try his skill!
But yet he shan't, I say, against my will.
I'll pull him by the beard, believe you me!
    ' "And once you said that principally three
Misfortunes* trouble earth, east, west and north,
And no man living could endure a fourth.
My dear sir shrew, Jesu cut short your life!
You preach away and say a hateful wife
Is reckoned to be one of these misfortunes.
Is there no other trouble that importunes
The world and that your parables could condemn?
Must an unhappy wife be one of them?
    ' "Then you compared a woman's love to Hell,
To barren land where water will not dwell,
And you compared it to a quenchless fire,
The more it burns the more is its desire
To burn up everything that burnt can be.
You say that just as worms destroy a tree
A wife destroys her husband and contrives,
As husbands know, the ruin of their lives."
    'Such was the way, my lords, you understand
I kept my older husbands well in hand.
I told them they were drunk and their unfitness
To judge my conduct forced me to take witness
That they were lying. Johnny and my niece
Would back me up. Lord, how they longed for peace,

292

Poor dears! I tortured them without remorse,
For I could bite and whinney like a horse
And launch complaints when things were all my fault;
I'd have been lost if I had called a halt.
First to the mill is first to grind your corn;
I attacked first and they were overborne,
Glad to apologize and even suing
Pardon for what they'd never thought of doing.

'I'd tackle one for wenching, out of hand,
Although so ill the man could hardly stand,
Yet he felt flattered in his heart because
He thought it showed how fond of him I was.
I swore that all my walking out at night
Was just to keep his wenching well in sight.
That was a dodge that made me shake with mirth;
But all such wit is given us at birth.
Lies, tears and spinning are the things God gives
By nature to a woman, while she lives.
So there's one thing at least that I can boast,
That in the end I always ruled the roast;
Cunning or force was sure to make them stumble,
And always keeping up a steady grumble.

'But bed-time above all was their misfortune;
That was the place to scold them and importune
And balk their fun. I never would abide
In bed with them if hands began to slide
Till they had promised ransom, paid a fee;
And then I let them do their nicety.
And so I tell this tale to every man,
"It's all for sale and let him win who can."
No empty-handed man can lure a bird.
His pleasures were my profit; I concurred,
Even assumed fictitious appetite
Though bacon never gave me much delight.
And that's the very fact that made me chide them.
And had the Pope been sitting there beside them
I wouldn't have spared them at their very table,
But paid them out as far as I was able.

I say, so help me God Omnipotent,
Were I to make my will and testament
I owe them nothing, paid them word for word
Putting my wits to use, and they preferred
To give it up and take it for the best
For otherwise they would have got no rest.
Though they might glower like a maddened beast
They got no satisfaction, not the least.

 'I then would say, "My dear, just take a peep!
What a meek look on Willikin our sheep!
Come nearer, husband, let me kiss your cheek;
You should be just as patient, just as meek;
Sweeten your heart. Your conscience needs a probe.
You're fond of preaching patience out of Job,
And so be patient; practice what you preach,
And if you don't, my dear, we'll have to teach
You that it's nice to have a quiet life.
One of us must be master, man or wife,
And since a man's more reasonable, he
Should be the patient one, you must agree.

 ' "What ails you, man, to grumble so and groan?
Just that you want my what-not all your own?
Why, take it, man! It's yours all said and done.
St Peter! How you like your bit of fun!
Well, if I were to sell my *belle chose,*
I could go walking fresher than a rose;
But I will keep it for your private tooth.
By God, you are to blame, and that's the truth."

 'That's how my first three husbands were undone.
Now let me tell you of my last but one.

 'He was a reveler, was number four;
That is to say he kept a paramour.
And I was young, ah, ragery's the word,
Stubborn and strong and jolly as a bird.
Play me the harp and I would dance and sing,
Believe me, like a nightingale in spring,
If I had had a draught of sweetened wine.

 'Metellius, that filthy lout – the swine

294

Who snatched a staff and took his woman's life
For drinking wine – if I had been his wife
He never would have daunted me from drink.
Whenever I take wine I have to think
Of Venus, for as cold engenders hail
A lecherous mouth begets a lecherous tail.
A woman in her cups has no defense,
As lechers know from long experience.

   'But Christ! Whenever it comes back to me,
When I recall my youth and jollity,
It fairly warms the cockles of my heart!
This very day I feel a pleasure start,
Yes, I can feel it tickling at the root.
Lord, how it does me good! I've had my fruit,
I've had my world and time, I've had my fling!
But age that comes to poison everything
Has taken all my beauty and my pith.
Well, let it go, the devil go therewith!
The flour is gone, there is no more to say,
And I must sell the bran as best I may;
But still I mean to find my way to fun....
Now let me tell you of my last but one.

   'I told you how it filled my heart with spite
To see another woman his delight,
By God and all His saints I made it good!
I carved him out a cross of the same wood,
Not with my body – just by breaking jokes
And flirting, making up to other folks.
I fried him properly in his own grease
Of jealousy and rage; he got no peace.
By God on earth I was his purgatory,
For which I hope his soul may be in glory.
God knows he sang a sorry tune, he flinched,
And bitterly enough, when the shoe pinched.
And God and he alone can say how grim,
How many were the ways I tortured him.

   'He died when I came back from Jordan Stream
And he lies buried under the rood-beam,

Albeit that his tomb can scarce supply us
With such a show as that of King Darius
– Apelles sculped it in a sumptuous taste –
But costly burial would have been a waste.
Farewell to him, God give his spirit rest!
He's in his grave, he's nailed up in his chest.

'Now of my fifth, last husband let me tell.
God never let his soul be sent to Hell!
And yet he was my worst, and many a blow
He struck me still can ache along my row
Of ribs, and will until my dying day.

'But in our bed he was so fresh and gay,
So coaxing, so persuasive.... Heaven knows
Whenever he wanted it – my *belle chose* –
Though he had beaten me in every bone
He still could wheedle me to love, I own.
I think I loved him best, I'll tell no lie.
He was disdainful in his love, that's why.
We women have a curious fantasy
In such affairs, or so it seems to me.
When something's difficult, or can't be had,
We crave and cry for it all day like mad.
Forbid a thing, we pine for it all night,
Press fast upon us and we take to flight;
We use disdain in offering our wares.
A throng of buyers sends prices up at fairs,
Cheap goods have little value, they suppose;
And that's a thing that every woman knows.

'My fifth and last – God keep his soul in health! –
The one I took for love and not for wealth,
Had been at Oxford not so long before
But had left school and gone to lodge next door,
Yes, it was to my godmother's he'd gone.
God bless her soul! *Her* name was Alison.
She knew my heart and more of what I thought
Than did the parish priest, and so she ought!
She was my confidante, I told her all.
For had my husband pissed against a wall

Or done some crime that would have cost his life,
To her and to another worthy wife
And to my niece, because I loved her well,
I'd have told everything there was to tell.
And so I often did, and Heaven knows
It used to set him blushing like a rose
In very shame, and he would blame his folly
In letting out his secrets to poor Polly.

'And so one time it happened that in Lent,
As I so often did, I rose and went
To see her, ever wanting to be gay
And go a-strolling, March, April and May,
From house to house for chat and village malice.

'Johnny (the boy from Oxford) and Dame Alice
And I myself, into the fields we went.
My husband was in London all that Lent;
All the more fun for me – I only mean
The fun of seeing people and being seen
By cocky lads; for how was I to know
Where or what graces Fortune might bestow?
And so I made a round of visitations,
Went to processions, festivals, orations,
Preachments and pilgrimages, watched the carriages
They use for plays and pageants, went to marriages,
And always wore my gayest scarlet dress.

'These worms, these moths, these mites, I must confess
Got little chance to eat it, by the way.
Why not? Because I wore it every day.

'Now let me tell you all that came to pass.
We sauntered in the meadows through the grass
Toying and dallying to such extent,
Johnny and I, that I grew provident
And I suggested, were I ever free
And made a widow, he should marry me.
And certainly – I do not mean to boast –
I ever was more provident than most
In marriage matters and in other such.
I never think a mouse is up to much

That only has one hole in all the house;
If that should fail, well, it's good-by the mouse.

'I let him think I was as one enchanted
(That was a trick my godmother implanted)
And told him I had dreamt the night away
Thinking of him, and dreamt that as I lay
He tried to kill me. Blood had drenched the bed.
"But still it was a lucky dream," I said,
"For blood betokens money, I recall."
It was a lie. I hadn't dreamt at all.
'Twas from my godmother I learnt my lore
In matters such as that, and many more.

'Well, let me see ... what had I to explain?
Aha! By God, I've got the thread again.

'When my fourth husband lay upon his bier
I wept all day and looked as drear as drear,
As widows must, for it is quite in place,
And with a handkerchief I hid my face.
Now that I felt provided with a mate
I wept but little, I need hardly state.

'To church they bore my husband on the morrow
With all the neighbors round him venting sorrow,
And one of them of course was handsome Johnny.
So help me God I thought he looked so bonny
Behind the coffin! Heavens, what a pair
Of legs he had! Such feet, so clean and fair!
I gave my heart, I put it in his cage.

'He was, I think, some twenty years of age
And I was forty then, to tell the truth.
But still I always had a coltish tooth.
Yes, I'm gap-toothed; it suits me well I feel,
It is the print of Venus and her seal.
So help me God I was a lusty one,
Fair, young and well-to-do, and full of fun!
And truly, as my husbands said to me,
I had the finest *quoniam* that might be.
Venus had sent me feeling from the stars
And my heart's boldness came to me from Mars.

Venus gave me desire and lecherousness
And Mars my hardihood, or so I guess,
Born under Taurus and with Mars therein.
Alas, alas, that ever love was sin!
And so I followed natural inclination
In virtue of my natal constellation;
I couldn't refuse, seeing what stars I had,
My chamber of Venus to a likely lad.
The mark of Mars is still upon my face
And also in another privy place.
For as I may be saved by God above,
I never used discretion when in love
But ever followed on my appetite
Whether the lad was short, long, black or white.
Little I cared, if he was fond of me,
How poor he was, or what his rank might be.

'What shall I say? Before the month was gone
This gay young student, my delightful John,
Had married me in solemn festival.
I handed him the money, lands and all
That ever had been given me before;
This I repented later, more and more.
He stopped my gadding round, my hide-and-seek,
By God, he smote me once upon the cheek
Because I tore a page out of his book,
And that's the reason why I'm deaf. But look,
Stubborn I was, just like a lioness;
In argument and wrangling, pitiless.
I went off gadding as I had before
From house to house, however much he swore.
Because of that he used to preach and scold,
Drag Roman history up from days of old,
How one Simplicius Gallus left his wife
Deserting her completely all his life,
Only for poking out her head one day
Without a hat upon the public way.

'Some other Roman – I forget his name –
Because his wife went to a summer's game

Without his knowledge, left her in the lurch.
 'And he would take the Bible up and search
For proverbs in Ecclesiasticus,
Particularly one that has it thus:
"Suffer no wicked woman to gad about."
And then would come the saying (need you doubt?)
  A man who seeks to build his house of sallows,
  A man who spurs a blind horse over fallows,
  Or lets his wife make pilgrimage to Hallows,
  Is worthy to be hanged upon the gallows.
But all for naught. I didn't give a hen
For all his proverbs and his wise old men.
I wouldn't be rebuked at any price;
I hate a man who points me out my vice,
And so, God knows, do many more than I.
That drove him raging mad, you may rely.
No more would I forbear with him, I promise.

 'Now let me tell you truly by St Thomas
About that book and why I tore the page
And how he smote me deaf in very rage.

 'He had a book, he kept it on his shelf,
And night and day he read it to himself
And laughed aloud, although it was quite serious.
He called it *Theophrastus and Valerius.**
There was another Roman, much the same,
A cardinal; St Jerome was his name.
He wrote a book against Jovinian,
Bound up together with Tertullian,
Chrysippus, Trotula and Heloise,
(An abbess, lived near Paris). And with these
Were bound the parables of Solomon,
With Ovid's *Art of Love* another one.
All these were bound together in one book
And day and night he used to take a look
At what it said, when he had time and leisure
Or had no occupation but his pleasure.

 'It was a book that dealt with wicked wives;
He knew more legends of them and their lives

Than there are good ones mentioned in the Bible.
For take my word for it, there is no libel
On women that the clergy will not paint,
Except when writing of a woman-saint,
But never good of other women, though.
Who called the lion savage? Do you know?
By God, if women had but written stories
Like those the clergy keep in oratories,
More had been written of man's wickedness
Than all the sons of Adam could redress.
Children of Mercury* and we of Venus
Keep up the contrariety between us;
Mercury stands for wisdom, thrift and science,
Venus for revel, squandering and defiance.
Their several natures govern their direction;
One rises when the other's in dejection.
And thus the works of Mercury are halted
In *Pisces,* just where Venus is exalted,
And Venus falls where Mercury is raised,
And women therefore never can be praised
By learned men, old scribes who cannot do
The works of Venus more than my old shoe.
These in their dotage sit them down to frowse
And say that women break their marriage-vows!

'Now to my purpose as I told you; look,
Here's how I got a beating for a book.
One evening Johnny, glowering with ire,
Sat with his book and read it by the fire.
And first he read of Eve whose wickedness
Brought all mankind to sorrow and distress,
Root-cause why Jesus Christ Himself was slain
And gave His blood to buy us back again.
Aye, there's the text where you expressly find
That woman brought the loss of all mankind.

'He read me then how Samson as he slept
Was shorn of all his hair by her he kept,
And by that treachery Samson lost his eyes.
And then he read me, if I tell no lies,

All about Hercules and Deianire;
She tricked him into setting himself on fire.

'He left out nothing of the miseries
Occasioned by his wives to Socrates.
Xantippe poured a piss-pot on his head.
The silly man sat still, as he were dead,
Wiping his head, but dared no more complain
Than say, "Ere thunder stops, down comes the rain."

'Next of Pasiphaë the Queen of Crete;*
For wickedness he thought that story sweet;
Fie, say no more! It has a grisly sting,
Her horrible lust. How could she do the thing!

'And then he told of Clytemnestra's lechery
And how she made her husband die by treachery.
He read that story with a great devotion.

'He read me what occasioned the commotion
By which Amphiaraüs lost his life;
My husband had the legend of his wife
Eriphyle, who for a gaud in gold
Went to the Greeks in secret, and she told
Them where to find him, in what hiding-place.
At Thebes it was; he met with sorry grace.

'Of Livia and Lucilia then he read,
And both of course had killed their husbands dead,
The one for love, the other out of hate.
Livia prepared some poison for him late
One evening and she killed him out of spite,
Lucilia out of lecherous delight.
For she, in order he might only think
Of her, prepared an aphrodisiac drink;
He drank it and was dead before the morning.
Such is the fate of husbands; it's a warning.

'And then he told how one Latumius
Lamented to his comrade Arrius
That in his orchard-plot there grew a tree
On which his wives had hanged themselves, all three,
Or so he said, out of some spite or other;
To which this Arrius replied, "Dear brother,

Give me a cutting from that blessed tree
And planted in my garden it shall be!"
'Of wives of later date he also read,
How some had killed their husbands when in bed,
Then night-long with their lechers played the whore
While the poor corpse lay fresh upon the floor.

'One drove a nail into her husband's brain
While he was sleeping and the man was slain,
Others put poison in their husbands' drink.
He spoke more harm of us than heart can think
And knew more proverbs too, for what they're worth,
Than there are blades of grass upon the earth.

' "Better," says he, "to share your habitation
With lion, dragon, or abomination
Than with a woman given to reproof.
Better," says he, "take refuge on the roof
Than with an angry wife, down in the house;
They are so wicked and cantankerous
They hate the things their husbands like," he'd say.

"A woman always casts her shame away
When she casts off her smock, and that's in haste.
A pretty woman, if she isn't chaste,
Is like a golden ring in a sow's snout."

'Who could imagine, who could figure out
The torture in my heart? It reached the top.
And when I saw that he would never stop
Reading this cursed book, all night no doubt,
I suddenly grabbed and tore three pages out
Where he was reading, at the very place,
And fisted such a buffet in his face
That backwards down into the fire he fell.

'Then like a maddened lion, with a yell
He started up and smote me on the head,
And down I fell upon the floor for dead.

'And when he saw how motionless I lay
He was aghast and would have fled away,
But in the end I started to come to.
"O have you murdered me, you robber, you,

To get my land?" I said. "Was that the game?
Before I'm dead I'll kiss you all the same."

'He came up close and kneeling gently down
He said, 'My love, my dearest Alison,
So help me God, I never again will hit
You, love; and if I did, you asked for it.
Forgive me!" But for all he was so meek
I up at once and smote him on the cheek
And said, "Take that to level up the score!
Now let me die. I can't speak any more."

'We had a mort of trouble and heavy weather
But in the end we made it up together.
He gave the bridle over to my hand,
Gave me the government of house and land,
Of tongue and fist, indeed of all he'd got.
I made him burn that book upon the spot.
And when I'd mastered him, and out of deadlock
Secured myself the sovereignty in wedlock,
And when he said, "My own and truest wife,
Do as you please for all the rest of life,
But guard your honor and my good estate,"
From that day forward there was no debate.
So help me God I was as kind to him
As any wife from Denmark to the rim
Of India, and as true. And he to me.
And I pray God that sits in majesty
To bless his soul and fill it with his glory.
Now, if you'll listen, I will tell my story.'

Words between the Summoner and the Friar

THE Friar laughed when he had heard all this.
'Well, Ma'am,' he said, 'as God may send me bliss,
This is a long preamble to a tale!'
But when the Summoner heard the Friar rail,
'Just look at that!' he cried. 'God's arms and skin!
These meddling friars are always butting in!

Don't we all know a friar and a fly
Go buzzing into every dish and pie!
What do you mean with your "preambulation"?
Amble yourself, trot, do a meditation!
You're spoiling all our fun with your commotion.'
The Friar smiled and said, 'Is that your notion?
I promise on my word before I go
To find occasion for a tale or so
About a summoner that will make us laugh.'
'Well, damn your eyes, and on my own behalf,'
The Summoner answered, 'mine be damned as well
If I can't think of several tales to tell
About the friars that will make you mourn
Before we get as far as Sittingbourne.
Have you no patience? Look, he's in a huff!'

  Our Host called out, 'Be quiet, that's enough!
Shut up, and let the woman tell her tale.
You must be drunk, you've taken too much ale.
Now, Ma'am, you go ahead and no demur.'
'All right,' she said, 'it's just as you prefer,
If I have license from this worthy friar.'
'Nothing,' said he, 'that I should more desire.'

The Wife of Bath's Tale

WHEN good King Arthur ruled in ancient days,
  A king that every Briton loves to praise,
This was a land brim-full of fairy folk.
The Elf-Queen and her courtiers joined and broke
Their elfin dance on many a green mead,
Or so was the opinion once, I read,
Hundreds of years ago, in days of yore.
But no one now sees fairies any more,
For now the saintly charity and prayer
Of holy friars seem to have purged the air;
They search the countryside through field and stream
As thick as motes that speckle a sun-beam,

Blessing the halls, the chambers, kitchens, bowers,
Cities and boroughs, castles, courts and towers,
Thorpes, barns and stables, outhouses and dairies,
And that's the reason why there are no fairies.
Wherever there was wont to walk an elf
To-day there walks the holy friar himself
As evening falls or when the daylight springs,
Saying his mattins and his holy things,
Walking his limit round from town to town.
Women can now go safely up and down,
By every bush or under every tree;
There is no other incubus but he,
So there is really no one else to hurt you
And he will do no more than take your virtue.

Now it so happened, I began to say,
Long, long ago in good King Arthur's day,
There was a knight who was a lusty liver.
One day as he came riding from the river
He saw a maiden walking all forlorn
Ahead of him, alone as she was born.
And of that maiden, spite of all she said,
By very force he took her maidenhead.

This act of violence made such a stir,
So much petitioning of the king for her,
That he condemned the knight to lose his head
By course of law. He was as good as dead
(It seems that then the statutes took that view)
But that the queen and other ladies too
Implored the king to exercise his grace
So ceaselessly, he gave the queen the case
And granted her his life, and she could choose
Whether to show him mercy or refuse.

The queen returned him thanks with all her might,
And then she sent a summons to the knight
At her convenience, and expressed her will:
'Sir, your position is precarious still,'
She said, 'you're on the edge of an abyss.
Yet you shall live if you can tell me this.

306

What is the thing that women most desire?
Beware the ax and say as I require.
  'If you can't answer on the moment, though,
I will concede you this: you are to go
A twelvemonth and a day to seek and learn
Sufficient answer, then you shall return.
I shall take gages from you to extort
Surrender of your body to the court.'
  Sad was the knight and sorrowfully sighed,
But there! What option had he? He'd been tried.
And in the end he chose to go away
And to return after a year and day
Armed with such answer as there might be sent
To him by God. He took his leave and went.
  He knocked at every house, searched every place,
Yes, anywhere that offered hope of grace.
What could it be that women wanted most?
But all the same he never touched a coast,
Country or town in which there seemed to be
Any two people willing to agree.
  Some said that women wanted wealth and treasure,
Honor said some, some jollity and pleasure;
Some gorgeous clothes and others fun in bed
And 'to be widowed and remarried,' said
Yet others. Some the thing that really mattered
Was that we should be gratified and flattered.
That's very near the truth, it seems to me;
A man can win us best with flattery.
Attentiveness and making a great fuss
About a woman, that's what fetches us.
  But others said a woman's real passion
Was liberty, behaving in what fashion
Might please her best, and not to be corrected
But told she's wise, encouraged and respected.
Truly there's not a woman in ten score
Who has a fault and someone rubs the sore
But she will kick if what he says is true;
You try it out and you will find so too.

However vicious we may be within
We like to be thought wise and void of sin.

Some people said that what we women treasure
Is to be thought dependable in pleasure,
Steadfast in keeping secrets from the jealous,
Not prone to blab the things a man may tell us.
But that opinion isn't worth a rush!
Good Lord, a woman keep a secret? Tush!
Remember Midas? Will you hear the tale?

Among some other little things now stale,
Ovid relates that Midas, it appears,
Had grown a great big pair of ass's ears
Under his flowing locks. As best he might
He kept this foul deformity from sight.
His wife – she was the only one that knew –
Was trusted by him, and he loved her too.
He begged her not to tell a living creature
That he possessed so horrible a feature.

She wouldn't tell for all the world, she swore,
It would be villainy, a sin what's more,
To earn her husband such a filthy name,
Besides it would redound to her own shame.
Nevertheless she thought she would have died
Keeping this secret bottled up inside;
It seemed to swell her heart and she, no doubt,
Thought it was on the point of bursting out.

Fearing to speak of it to woman or man,
Down to a reedy marsh she quickly ran
And reached the sedge. Her heart was all on fire
And, as a bittern bumbles in the mire,
She whispered to the water, near the ground,
'Betray me not, O water, with thy sound!
I have told no one yet, but it appears
My husband has a pair of ass's ears!
Ah! My heart's well again, the secret's out!
I couldn't have kept it longer, I don't doubt.'
So, as you see, we women can't keep mum
For very long, but out the secrets come.

For what became of Midas, if you care
To turn up Ovid you will find it there.

    This knight that I am telling you about
Perceived at last he never would find out
What it could be that women loved the best.
Faint was the soul within his sorrowful breast
As home he went, he dared no longer stay;
His year was up and now it was the day.

    As he rode home in a dejected mood,
Suddenly, at the margin of a wood,
He saw a dance upon the leafy floor
Of four and twenty ladies, nay, and more.
Eagerly he approached, in hope to learn
Some words of wisdom ere he should return;
But lo! Before he came to where they were,
Dancers and dance all vanished into air!
There wasn't a living creature to be seen
Save one old woman crouched upon the green.
A fouler-looking creature I suppose
Could scarcely be imagined. She arose
And said, 'Sir knight, there's no way on from here.
Tell me what you are looking for, my dear,
For peradventure that were best for you;
We old, old women know a thing or two.'

    'Dear Mother,' said the knight, 'alack the day!
I am as good as dead if I can't say
What thing it is that women most desire;
If you could tell me I would pay your hire.'

    'Give me your hand,' she said, 'and swear to do
Whatever I shall next require of you
– If so to do should lie within your might –
And you shall know the answer before night.'

    'Upon my honor,' he answered, 'I agree.'

    'Then,' said the crone, 'I dare to guarantee
Your life is safe, I shall make good my claim.
Upon my life the queen will say the same.
Show me the very proudest of them all
In costly coverchief or jeweled caul

That dare say no to what I have to teach.
Let us go forward without further speech.'
And then she crooned her gospel in his ear
And told him to be glad and not to fear.

They came to court. This knight, in full array,
Stood forth and said, 'O Queen, I've kept my day
And kept my word and have my answer ready.'

There sat the noble matrons and the heady
Young girls, and widows too, that have the grace
Of wisdom, all assembled in that place,
And there the queen herself was throned to hear
And judge his answer. Then the knight drew near
And silence was commanded through the hall.

The queen then bade the knight to tell them all
What thing it was that women wanted most.
He stood not silent like a beast or post,
But gave his answer with the ringing word
Of a man's voice and the assembly heard:

'My liege and lady, in general,' said he,
'Women desire the self-same sovereignty*
On husbands as they have on those that love them,
And would be set in mastery above them;
That is your greatest wish. Now spare or kill
Me as you please, I stand here at your will.'

In all the court not one that shook her head
Or contradicted what the knight had said;
Maid, wife and widow cried, 'He's saved his life!'

And on the word up started the old wife,
The one the knight saw sitting on the green,
And cried, 'Your mercy, sovereign lady queen!
Before the court disperses, do me right!
'Twas I who taught this answer to the knight,
For which he swore, and pledged his honor to it,
That the first thing I asked of him he'd do it,
So far as it should lie within his might.
Before this court I ask you then, sir knight,
To keep your word and take me for your wife;
For well you know that I have saved your life.

If this be false, deny it on your sword!'
   Alas!' he said, 'Old lady, by the Lord
I know indeed that such was my behest,
But for God's love think of a new request,
Take all my goods, but leave my body free.'
'A curse on us,' she said, 'if I agree!
I may be foul, I may be poor and old,
Yet will not choose to be, for all the gold
That's bedded in the earth or lies above,
Less than your wife, nay, then your very love!'
'My love?' said he. 'By Heaven, my damnation!
Alas that any of my race and station
Should ever make so foul a misalliance!'
Yet in the end his pleading and defiance
All went for nothing, he was forced to wed.
He takes his ancient wife and goes to bed.

   Now peradventure some may well suspect
A lack of care in me since I neglect
To tell of the rejoicings and display
Made at the feast upon their wedding-day.
I have but a short answer to let fall;
I say there was no joy or feast at all,
Nothing but heaviness of heart and sorrow.
He married her in private on the morrow
And all day long stayed hidden like an owl,
It was such torture that his wife looked foul.

   Great was the anguish churning in his head
When he and she were piloted to bed;
He wallowed back and forth in desperate style.
His wife lay still and wore a quiet smile;
At last she said, 'Dear husband, bless my soul!
Is this how knights treat wives upon the whole?
Are these the laws of good King Arthur's house?
Is all his knighthood so contemptuous?
I am your own beloved and your wife,
And I am she, indeed, that saved your life;
And certainly I never did you wrong.
Then why, this first of nights, so sad a song?

311

You're carrying on as if you were half-witted!
Say, for God's love, what sin have I committed?
I'll put things right if you will tell me how.'
   'Put right?' he cried. 'That never can be now!
Nothing can ever be put right again!
You're old, and so abominably plain,
So poor to start with, so low-bred to follow;
It's little wonder if I twist and wallow!
God, that my heart would burst within my breast!'
   'Is that,' said she, 'the cause of your unrest?'
   'Yes, certainly,' he said, 'and can you wonder?'
   'I could set right what you suppose a blunder,
That's if I cared to, in a day or two,
If I were shown more courtesy by you.
Just now,' she said, 'you spoke of gentle birth,
Such as descends from ancient wealth and worth.
If that's the claim you make for gentlemen
Such arrogance is hardly worth a hen.
Whoever loves to work for virtuous ends,
Public and private, and who most intends
To do what deeds of gentleness he can,
Take him to be the greatest gentleman.
Christ wills we take our gentleness from Him,
Not from a wealth of ancestry long dim,
Though they bequeath their whole establishment
By which we claim to be of high descent.
Our fathers cannot make us a bequest
Of all those virtues that became them best
And earned for them the name of gentleman,
But bade us follow them as best we can.
   'Thus the wise poet of the Florentines,
Dante by name, has written in these lines,
For such is the opinion Dante launches:
"Seldom arises by these slender branches
Prowess of men, for it is God, no less,
Wills us to claim of Him our gentleness."
For of our parents nothing can we claim
Save temporal things, and these may hurt and maim.

'But everyone knows this as well as I;
For if gentility were implanted by
The natural course of lineage down the line,
Public or not, it could not cease to shine
In doing the fair work of gentle deed.
No vice or villainy could then bear seed.

   'Take fire and carry it to the darkest house
Between this kingdom and the Caucasus,
And shut the doors on it and leave it there.
It will burn on, and it will burn as fair
As if ten thousand men were there to see,
For fire will keep its nature and degree,
I can assure you, sir, until it dies.

   'But gentleness, as you will recognize,
Is not annexed in nature to possessions,
Men fail in living up to their professions;
But fire never ceases to be fire.
God knows you'll often find, if you inquire,
Some lording full of villainy and shame.
If you would be esteemed for the mere name
Of having been by birth a gentleman
And stemming from some virtuous, noble clan,
And do not live yourself by gentle deed
Or take your fathers' noble code and creed,
You are no gentleman, though duke or earl.
Vice and bad manners are what make a churl.

   'Gentility is only the renown
For bounty that your fathers handed down,
Quite foreign to your person, not your own;
Gentility must come from God alone.
That we are gentle comes to us by grace
And by no means is it bequeathed with place.

   'Reflect how noble (says Valerius)
Was Tullius surnamed Hostilius,
Who rose from poverty to nobleness.
And read Boethius, Seneca no less,
Thus they express themselves and are agreed:
"Gentle is he that does a gentle deed."

And therefore, my dear husband, I conclude
That even if my ancestors were rude,
Yet God on high — and so I hope He will —
Can grant me grace to live in virtue still,
A gentlewoman only when beginning
To live in virtue and to shrink from sinning.

'As for my poverty which you reprove,
Almighty God Himself in whom we move,
Believe and have our being, chose a life
Of poverty, and every man or wife
And every child can see our Heavenly King
Would never stoop to choose a shameful thing.
No shame in poverty if the heart is gay,
As Seneca and all the learned say.
He who accepts his poverty unhurt
I'd say is rich although he lacked a shirt.
But truly poor are they who whine and fret
And covert what they cannot hope to get.
And he that having nothing covets not
Is rich, though you may think he is a sot.

'True poverty can find a song to sing.
Juvenal says a pleasant little thing:
"The poor can dance and sing in the relief
Of having nothing that will tempt a thief."
Though it be hateful, poverty is good,
A great incentive to a livelihood,
And a great help to our capacity
For wisdom, if accepted patiently.
Poverty is, though wanting in estate,
A kind of wealth that none calumniate.
Poverty often, when the heart is lowly,
Brings one to God and teaches what is holy,
Gives knowledge of oneself and even lends
A glass by which to see one's truest friends.
And since it's no offense, let me be plain;
Do not rebuke my poverty again.

'Lastly you taxed me, sir, with being old.
Yet even if you never had been told

By ancient books, you gentlemen engage
Yourselves in honor to respect old age.
To call an old man "father" shows good breeding,
And this could be supported from my reading.
    'You say I'm old and fouler than a fen.
You need not fear to be a cuckold, then.
Filth and old age, I'm sure you will agree,
Are powerful wardens upon chastity.
Nevertheless, well knowing your delights,
I shall fulfill your worldly appetites.
    'You have two choices; which one will you try?
To have me old and ugly till I die,
But still a loyal, true and humble wife
That never will displease you all her life,
Or would you rather I were young and pretty
And take your chance what happens in a city
Where friends will visit you because of me,
Yes, and in other places too, maybe.
Which would you have? The choice is all your own.'
    The knight thought long, and with a piteous groan
At last he said with all the care in life,
'My lady and my love, my dearest wife,
I leave the matter to your wise decision.
You make the choice yourself, for the provision
Of what may be agreeable and rich
In honor to us both, I don't care which;
Whatever pleases you suffices me.'
    'And have I won the mastery?' said she,
'Since I'm to choose and rule as I think fit?'
'Certainly, wife,' he answered her, 'that's it.'
'Kiss me,' she cried. 'No quarrels! On my oath
And word of honor you shall find me both,
That is, both fair and faithful as a wife;
May I go howling mad and take my life
Unless I prove to be as good and true
As ever wife was since the world was new!
And if to-morrow when the sun's above
I seem less fair than any lady-love,

Than any queen or empress east or west,
Do with my life and death as you think best.
Cast up the curtain, husband. Look at me!'
    And when indeed the knight had looked to see,
Lo, she was young and lovely, rich in charms.
In ecstasy he caught her in his arms,
His heart went bathing in a bath of blisses
And melted in a hundred thousand kisses,
And she responded in the fullest measure
With all that could delight or give him pleasure.
    So they lived ever after to the end
In perfect bliss; and may Christ Jesus send
Us husbands meek and young and fresh in bed,
And grace to overbid them when we wed.
And – Jesu hear my prayer! – cut short the lives
Of those who won't be governed by their wives;
And all old, angry niggards of their pence,
God send them soon a very pestilence!

The Friar's Tale

The Friar's Prologue

O UR worthy limiter the noble Friar
  Kept glancing with a lowering sort of ire
Towards the Summoner, but, to keep polite,
As yet had said no ugly word outright.
At last he turned towards the Wife of Bath,
'Madam,' he said, 'God be about your path!
You here have touched on many difficult rules
Debated, I assure you, in the Schools.
Much you advanced was excellent, I say;
But, Madam, as we ride along the way
We're only called upon to speak in game.
Let's leave the authorities, in Heaven's name,

To preachers and to schools for ordinands.
  'But if it meets the company's demands,
I'll talk about a summoner, for a game.
Lord knows, one can be certain from the name
A summoner isn't much to be commended.
I hope that none of you will be offended.
  'A summoner's one who runs about the nation
Dealing out summonses for fornication
And beaten up by every villager
At the town's end ...' 'Now, mind the manners, sir,'
Our Host called out, 'befitting your estate.
In company we do not want debate.
You tell your tale and let the Summoner be.'
'Nay,' said the Summoner, 'makes no odds to me.
Say what he likes, and when my turn's to come
I'll pay him back, by God! I'll strike him dumb!
I'll tell him what an honor it is, none higher,
To be a limiter, a flattering friar!
I'll tell him all about that job of his.'
  Our Host replied, 'Let's have no more of this.'
Then turning to the Friar, touched the spur
And said, 'Let's have your story, my dear sir.'

The Friar's Tale

IN my own district once there used to be
  A fine archdeacon, one of high degree,
Who boldly did the execution due
On fornication and on witchcraft too,
Bawdry, adultery and defamation,
Breaches of wills and contract, spoliation
Of church endowment, failure in the rents
And tithes and disregard of sacraments,
All these and many other kinds of crime
That need have no rehearsal at this time,
Usury, simony too. But he could boast
That lechery was what he punished most.

They had to sing for it if they were caught,
Like those who failed to pay the tithes they ought.
As for all such, if there was an informant,
Nothing could save them from pecunial torment.
For those whose tithes and offerings were small
Were made to sing the saddest song of all,
And ere the bishop caught them with his crook
They were all down in the archdeacon's book,
And he had jurisdiction, on inspection,
And powers to administer correction.

He had a summoner ready to his hand.
There was no slyer boy in all the land,
For he had subtly formed a gang of spies
Who taught him where his profit might arise,
And he would spare one lecher from his store
To teach the way to four-and-twenty more.
Though it may drive him mad as a March hare,
Our Summoner here, I mean, I will not spare
His harlotries. He has no jurisdiction
On friars and he cannot make infliction
Upon us, now or ever, or take dues
From friars ... 'Nor from women of the stews!'
The Summoner shouted, 'We have no control
On either lot.' 'The devil take your soul!'
Called out the Host, 'I say I won't have squalls.
On with your story, sir, and if it galls
The Summoner, spare him not, my worthy master! ...'

This treacherous thief (the Friar said) was pastor
To certain bawds that ate out of his hand,
Lures for a hawk, none such in all the land.
They told him all the secret things they drew
From sinners; their acquaintance was not new.
Each was his agent, say his private spy;
He drew large profits to himself thereby.
Even the archdeacon didn't always know
How much he got. He didn't have to show
A warrant when he chose to make things hot
For some obscure, uneducated sot,

For he could summon under threat of curse
And they were glad enough to fill his purse
Or give him banquets at the *Lamb and Flag*.

   And just as Judas kept a little bag
And was a thief, just such a thief was he.
His master got no more than half the fee.
To give the man his due and not to skimp,
He was a thief, a summoner, and a pimp.

   And he had wenches in his retinue,
So when the Reverend Robert or Sir Hugh
Or Jack or Ralph, whoever it was, drew near
And lay with them, they told it in his ear.
He and these wenches made a gang at it.
Then he would fetch forth a fictitious writ,
Summon them both before the Chapter-bench
And skin the man while letting off the wench,
Saying, 'Dear friend, I know you would prefer
Her name were struck from our black register;
Trouble yourself no further, my good man,
On her account. I'll help you all I can.'

   He knew so much of bribery and blackmail
I should be two years telling you the tale.
There is no sporting dog that's more expert
At knowing a wounded deer from one unhurt
Than was this summoner who could spot for sure
Lecher, adulterer or paramour.
Indeed on that his whole attention went
Because it was the source of all his rent.

   So it befell that on a certain day
This summoner rode forth to catch his prey,
A poor old fiddle of the widow-tribe
From whom, on a feigned charge, he hoped a bribe.
Now as he rode it happened that he saw
A gay young yeoman under a leafy shaw;
He bore a bow with arrows bright and keen
And wore a little jacket of bright green
And had a black-fringed hat upon his head.
'Hail, welcome and well met!' the summoner said.

'Welcome to you and all good lads,' said he,
'Whither away under the greenwood tree?'
Pursued the yeoman, 'Have you far to go?'
   The summoner paused a moment and said, 'No,
Just here, close by. In fact I'm only bent
On going for a ride, to raise a rent
That's owing to my lord, a little fee.'
'Why then you are a bailiff?' 'Yes,' said he.
He did not dare, for very filth and shame,
Say that he was a summoner, for the name.
   'Well, I'll be damned!' the yeoman said. 'Dear brother,
You say you are a bailiff? I'm another.
But I'm a stranger round about this part.
I'll beg acquaintance with you for a start,
And brotherhood, if that is fair to offer.
I have some gold and silver in my coffer
And should you chance to cross into our shire
All shall be yours, as much as you desire.'
'My word!' the summoner answered. 'Thanks a lot!'
The pair of them shook hands upon the spot,
Swore to be brothers to their dying day
And, chatting pleasantly, rode on their way.
   This summoner, always ready with a word,
As full of venom as a butcher-bird,
And sticking his nose into one thing or other
Went on, 'And where do you live at home, dear brother?
I might come calling there some other day.'
   The yeoman said in his soft-spoken way,
'O, far away up north; I'll tell you where.
I hope that some time I shall see you there.
Before we part I shall be so explicit
About my home I'm sure you'll never miss it.'
   'Brother,' the summoner said, 'I'd like to know
If you can teach me something as we go.
Since you're a bailiff just the same as me,
Tell me your subtler tricks. Now, seriously,
How can I win most money at the game?
Keep nothing back for conscience, or from shame.

Talk like a brother. How do you make out?'
   'Well, I break level, brother, just about.
I'll tell a truthful story; all in all
My wages are extremely tight and small.
My master's hard on me and difficult,
My job laborious and with poor result,
And so it's by extortion that I live.
I take whatever anyone will give.
At any rate by tricks and violences
From year to year I cover my expenses.
I can't say better, speaking truthfully.'
   The summoner said, 'It's just the same with me.
I'm ready to take anything, God wot,
Unless it is too heavy or too hot.
What I can get out of a little chat
In private – why should conscience bog at that?
Without extortion, how could I make a living?
My little jokes are hardly worth forgiving.
Bowels of pity, conscience, I have none.
Plague on these penance-fathers every one!
We make a pair, by God and by St James!
But, brother, what do you say to swapping names?'
   The summoner paused; the yeoman all the while
The summoner spoke had worn a little smile.
'Brother,' he answered, 'would you have me tell?
I am a fiend, my dwelling is in Hell.
I ride on business and have so far thriven
By taking anything that I am given.
That is the sum of all my revenue.
You seem to have the same objective too,
You're out for wealth, acquired no matter how,
And so with me. I'll go a-riding now
As far as the world's end in search of prey.'
   'Lord!' said the summoner. 'What did I hear you say?
I thought you were a yeoman, certainly.
You have the body of a man like me.
And have you, then, another shape as well
Appointed for your high estate in Hell?'

321

'No,' he replied, 'for Hell admits of none.
But when we like we can appropriate one,
Or rather make you think we have a shape;
Sometimes it's like a man, sometimes an ape,
Even an angel riding into bliss.
There's nothing very wonderful in this;
A lousy conjuror can trick your eye,
And he, God knows, has far less power than I.'

'But why,' pursued the summoner, 'track your game
In various shapes? Why don't you stay the same?'
'Just to appear,' he said, 'in such a way
As will enable us to snatch our prey.'

'But why do you have to go to all this bother?'
'For very many reasons, my dear brother;
You shall know all about it in good time.
The day is short and it is long past prime,
And yet I've taken nothing the whole day,
And I must think of business, if I may,
Rather than air my intellectual gift;
Besides, you lack the brains to catch my drift.
If I explained you wouldn't understand;
Yet since you ask why we're a busy band,
It's thus: at times we are God's instruments,
A means of forwarding divine events,
When He so pleases, that concern His creatures,
By various arts, disguised by various features.
We have no power without Him, that's a fact,
If it should please Him to oppose some act.
Sometimes, at our request, He gives us leave
To hurt the body, though we may not grieve
The soul. Take Job; his is a case in point.
At other times the two are not disjoint,
That is to say, the body and the soul.
Sometimes we are allowed to take control
Over a man and put his soul to test,
But not his body; all is for the best;
For every time a man withstands temptation
It is a partial cause of his salvation,

Though our intention is, when we beset him,
Not that he should be saved, but we should get him.
At times we slave for men without complaint
As on Archbishop Dunstan, now a saint;
Why, I was servant to an apostle once.'

   'Tell me,' the summoner said, '– I'm just a dunce –
But do you make new bodies as you go
Out of the elements?' The fiend said, 'No;
We just create illusions, or we raise
A corpse and use it; there are many ways.
And we can talk as trippingly and well
As to the Witch of Endor Samuel.
And yet some people say it wasn't he;
I have no use for your theology.

   'One thing I warn you of, it is no jape;
You soon will know for sure about our shape.
In any case, dear brother, you shall be
Where you shall have no need to learn of me,
And from your own experience declare
As much as from a professorial chair,
Better than even Vergil hereupon,
Or Dante either. Now let's hurry on,
For I intend to keep you company
Unless it chance that you abandon me.'

   'What?' said the summoner, 'Leave you on your own?
I am a yeoman, pretty widely known;
I wouldn't leave a brother on the shelf,
No, not if you were Lucifer himself!
I keep my word of honor to a brother,
And so I will to you. We bound each other
In brotherhood, that was the bargain made,
To work as one and go about our trade.
You take your share – whatever people give –
And I'll take mine, and that's our way to live.
If either should do better than the other,
Let him be true and share it with his brother.'

   'Agreed,' the devil answered. 'As you say.'
And on the word they trotted on their way.

Just at the entry of the very village
The summoner had it in his mind to pillage
They saw a farm-cart loaded up with hay.
There was a carter driving, but the way
Was deep and muddy and the cart stood still.
The carter lashed and shouted with a will,
'Hey, Brock! Hup, Scottie! Never mind for stones!
The foul fiend come and fetch you, flesh and bones,
As sure as you were foaled! Mud, ruts and rubble!
Lord, what a team! I've never known such trouble!
The devil take all, cart, horse and hay in one!'

   The summoner said, 'Now we shall have some fun!'
And, as if nothing were happening, he drew near
And whispered softly in the devil's ear:

   'Listen to that, dear brother, use your head!
Didn't you hear what the old carter said?
Take it at once, he gave them all to you,
His hay, his cart and his three horses too.'

   'Don't you believe it!' said the fiend. 'I heard,
But he meant nothing by it, take my word.
Go up and ask him if you don't trust me,
Or else keep quiet for a bit and see.'

   The carter thwacked his horses, jerked the rein,
And got them moving; as they took the strain,
'Hup, there!' he shouted. 'Jesus bless you, love,
And all His handiwork! Hey! Saints above!
Well tugged, old fellow, that's the stuff, Gray Boy!
God save you all, my darlings, send you joy!
That's lifted the old cart out of the slough!'

   'What did I tell you,' said the fiend, 'just now?
That ought to make it clear to you, dear brother,
The chap said one thing but he meant another.
So let's go on a bit. You mustn't scoff,
But here there's nothing I can carry off.'

   When they were out of town a little way
The summoner whispered to the fiend to say,
'There's an old fiddle here, an ancient wreck,
Dear brother, who would rather break her neck

Than lose a penny of her goods. Too bad,
She'll have to pay me twelve-pence. She'll be mad,
But if she doesn't pay she'll face the court.
And yet, God knows there's nothing to report,
She has no vices. But as you failed just now
To earn your keep, I'd like to show you how.'

The summoner battered at the widow's gate.
'Come out,' he said, 'you old inebriate!
I'll bet you've got a friar or priest inside!'

'Who's knocking? Bless us, Lord!' the widow cried,
'God save you, sir, and what is your sweet will?'

'Here!' said the summoner. 'I've a summons-bill.
On pain of excommunication, see
That you're at court, at the archdeacon's knee,
To-morrow morning. There are certain things
To answer for.' 'Christ Jesus, King of Kings,'
She said, 'have mercy! What am I to say?
I can't! I'm ill, and have been many a day.
I couldn't walk so far, nor even ride,
'Twould kill me. There's a pricking in my side.
Couldn't you write it down and save a journey,
And let me answer it through my attorney,
The charge I mean, whatever it may be?'

'Yes, if you pay at once,' he said. 'Let's see.
Twelve pence to me and I'll secure acquittal.
I get no profit from it – very little.
My master gets the profit and not me.
Come off it, I'm in haste. It's got to be.
Give me twelve pence. No time to wait, old fairy.'

'Twelve pence!' said she. 'O blessed Virgin Mary,
Help me and keep me clear of sin and dearth!
Why, if you were to offer me the earth
I couldn't! There's not twelve pence in my bag!
You know I'm nothing but a poor old hag,
Show kindness to a miserable wretch!'

'If I excuse you may the devil fetch
Me off! Though it should break you! Come along,
Pay up!' he said. 'But I've done nothing wrong!'

'You pay at once, or by the sweet St Anne,'
He said, 'I'll carry off your frying-pan
For debt, the new one, owed me since the day
You cuckolded your husband. Did I pay
For your correction then or did I not?'

'You lie!' she said. 'On my salvation! What?
Correction? Whether as widow or as wife
I've never had a summons in my life;
I never cuckolded my poor old man!
And as for you and for your frying-pan
The hairiest, blackest devil out of Hell
Carry you off and take the pan as well!'

Seeing her kneel and curse, the devil spoke:
'Now, Mother Mabel, is this all a joke,
Or do you really mean the things you say?'

'The devil,' she said, 'can carry him away
With pan and all unless he will repent!'
'No, you old cow, I have no such intent,'
The summoner said, 'there's no repentance due
For anything I ever had of you.
I'd strip you naked, smock and rag and clout!'

The devil said, 'What are you cross about,
Dear brother? You and this pan are mine by right.
You yet shall be in Hell with me to-night,
Where you'll know more about our mystery
Than any Doctor of Divinity.'

And on the word this foul fiend made a swoop
And dragged him, body and soul, to join the troupe
In Hell, where summoners have their special shelf.
And God, who in the image of Himself
Created man, guide us to Abraham's lap,
And make this Summoner here a decent chap!

My lords, I could have told you, never fear,
Had I the time to save this Summoner here,
Following texts from Christ and Paul and John
And many teachers who are dead and gone,
Of torments that are fit to terrorize
Your hearts, though tongue of man can scarce devise

Such things, or in a thousand winters tell
The pain of that accursed house of Hell.
Watch therefore, and pray Jesus of his grace
To keep us out of that accursed place,
And ward off Satan, tempting us from glory;
Ponder my words, reflect upon my story.
The lion's always on the watch for prey
To kill the innocent, if so he may;
And so dispose your heart that it withstand
The fiend who would enslave you in his band.
He may not tempt you, though, above your might,
For Christ will be your champion and your knight.
And Summoners, flee the sins that so beset you,
And learn repentance ere the devil get you.

The Summoner's Tale

The Summoner's Prologue

THE Summoner rose in wrath against the Friar
High in his stirrups and he quaked with ire.
He stood there trembling like an aspen leaf.
'I've only one desire,' he said, 'it's brief,
And one your courtesy will not deny;
Since you have heard this filthy friar lie
Let me refute him. I've a tale to tell!
This friar boasts his knowledge about Hell,
And if he does, God knows it's little wonder;
Friars and fiends are seldom far asunder.
Lord knows you must have often heard them tell
Of how a friar was ravished down to Hell
Once in a vision, taken there in spirit.
An angel led him up and down to ferret
Among the torments – various kinds of fire –
And yet he never saw a single friar,

Though he saw plenty of other kinds of folk
In pain enough. At last this friar spoke:
"Sir, are the friars in such a state of grace,"
He said, "none ever come into this place?"
"Why, yes," the angel answered, "many a million!"
And led him down to Lucifer's pavilion.
"Satan," the angel said, "has got a tail
As broad or broader than a carrack sail.
Hold up thy tail, thou Satan!" then said he,
"Show forth thine arse and let the friar see
The nest ordained for friars in this place!"
Ere the tail rose a furlong into space
From underneath it there began to drive,
Much as if bees were swarming from a hive,
Some twenty thousand friars in a rout
And swarmed all over Hell and round about,
And then came back as fast as they could run
And crept into his arse again, each one.
He clapped his tail on them and then lay still.
And after when the friar had looked his fill
On all the torments in that sorry place
His spirit was restored by Heaven's grace
Back to his body again and he awoke.
But all the same the terror made him choke,
So much the devil's arse was in his mind,
The natural heritage of all his kind.
God save you all except this cursed Friar,
For that is all the prologue I require.'

The Summoner's Tale

MY lords, there lies – in Yorkshire, as I guess –
A marshy district known as Holderness,
In which a friar, a limiter, went about
To preach his sermons and to beg, no doubt.
And on a certain day it so befell,
When he had preached in church, and cast his spell

With one main object, far above the rest,
To fire his congregation with a zest
For buying trentals,* and for Jesu's sake
To give the wherewithal for friars to make
Their holy houses where the Lord is dowered
With truest honor, not to be devoured
By those to whom there is no need to give
Like those endowed already, who can live,
Thanks be to God, in affluence and glory.
'Trentals,' he said, 'can fetch from Purgatory
The souls of all your friends, both old and young,
Yes, even when they're very quickly sung,
– Not that a priest is frivolous or gay
Because he only sings one mass a day –
Release the souls,' he thundered, 'from the pit,
Deliver them from the flesh-hook and the spit!
What agony to be clawed, to burn, to bake!
Be quick, exert yourselves, for Jesu's sake!'
  When he had finished all he had to say,
With *qui cum Patre** off he went his way.
When folk had put their pennies in the plate
He used to go away, he wouldn't wait.
With scrip and pointed staff uplifted high
He went from house to house to poke and pry
And beg a little meal and cheese, or corn.
His comrade had a staff was tipped with horn,
And bore a pair of ivory tablets, jointed,
Also a stylus elegantly pointed.
He always wrote the names down as he stood
Of those who gave him offerings or food
(Pretense of praying for them by and by).
  'Give us a bushel of barley, malt or rye,
A cookie, then, for God, a slice of cheese,
It's not for us to choose, but as you please;
A penny to say mass, or half a penny,
Some of your brawn perhaps – you haven't any? –
Well then, a bit of blanket, worthy dame,
Our well-beloved sister! There's your name,

It's down. Beef? Bacon? Anything you can find!'
    A sturdy varlet followed them behind,
The servant for their guests, who bore a sack,
And what they gave he carried on his back.
Once out of doors again and business done
He used to plane the names out, every one,
That he had written on his ivory tables.
He'd served them all with fairy-tales and fables....

    'No, there you lie, you Summoner!' said the Friar.
'Shut up! For Christ's sake be a little shyer
Of interruption,' said our Host, 'keep still!
Summoner, go on, spare nothing.' 'Nor I will.' ...

    On went this friar from house to house till he
Came up to one where he was wont to be
Better refreshed than anywhere in town.
The householder was sick and lying down;
Bedridden on a couch the fellow lay.
Deus hic! Well, Thomas, how are we to-day?'
The friar said, taking great pains to soften
His voice politely, 'God protect you! Often,
How often, I've sat upon this bench to steal
Your kindness, eaten many a merry meal!'
And from the bench he drove away the cat,
And laying down his pointed staff and hat,
His scrip as well, he settled softly down.
His comrade was off walking in the town
Together with the varlet, to get sight
Of where it was he meant to spend the night.

    'O my dear master,' said the sick old man,
'How have things been with you since March began?
Ain't seen you for a fortnight now or more.'

    'God knows,' he answered, 'I have labored sore
And more especially have said in care
Of your salvation many a precious prayer,
And for our other friends, but let that pass.
I went this morning to your Church for mass
And preached according to my simple wit;
It wasn't all on texts from Holy Writ,

For that's too hard for you as I suppose,
And I prefer to paraphrase or glose.
Glosing's a glorious thing, and anyway
"The letter killeth" as we clerics say.
And so I taught them to be charitable
And spend their goods where it is reasonable;
And there I saw your wife – Ah, where is she?'
  'Out in the yard I think, or ought to be,'
The fellow said; 'she'll come, she can't be far.'
  'Why, sir, you're welcome, by St John you are!'
The woman said, 'I hope you're keeping sprightly?'
Up from his bench the friar rose politely
Embracing her – the clasp was somewhat narrow –
And kissed her sweetly, chirping like a sparrow
As his lips parted. 'Ma'am,' he said, 'I'm fine.
Your servant, Ma'am,' he said, 'in all that's mine.
Thanks be to God that gave you soul and life
I haven't seen a prettier little wife
In all the church to-day, upon my word!'
  'Well, God amend defects!' the woman purred.
'At any rate you're welcome, I'll be bound.'
  'My warmest thanks! That's what I've always found.
If I may trespass – you're so very kind –
On your good nature, if you wouldn't mind,
I want to talk to Thomas here; you know
These curates are so negligent and slow
At groping consciences with tenderness.
I study how to preach and to confess,
Earnestly read St Peter and St Paul
And walk about to fish and make a haul
Of christian souls, pay Christ his proper rent,
And if I spread His word I am content.'
  'Now, my dear master, by your leave,' said she,
'Scold the man well, for by the Trinity,
He is as irritable as an ant,
Though he has everything a man can want.
I try to keep him warm at night, I squeeze him,
Put my leg over him, or arm, to please him,

And all he does is grunt, like boar in sty!
I get no other sport of him, not I.
No way of pleasing him at all, I promise.'

'O Thomas, *je vous dis,* O Thomas, Thomas!
That is the devil's work and must be chidden.
Anger's a thing by Heavenly God forbidden;
I mean to speak of that, a word or so.'

'Now, master,' said the wife, 'before I go,
What would you like for dinner? What would suit?'
'Well, Ma'am,' he answered, *'je vous dis sans doute,*
If I could have a little chicken-liver
And some of your soft bread – the merest shiver –
And then a pig's head roasted – but, do you see?
I won't have any creature killed for me –
It would be homely and sufficient fare.
The sustenance I take is very spare;
You see, my spirit draws its nourishment
Out of the Bible, and my body's spent
In pains and prayers; my stomach is destroyed.

'However, Ma'am, you mustn't be annoyed
To hear me speak as frankly as I do,
For these are things I tell to very few.'

'Before I leave you, sir, you ought to know,'
She said, 'my baby died two weeks ago,
Just after you left town on visitation.'

'I know. I saw his death by revelation,'
Replied the friar, 'in our dormitory.
I saw the little fellow borne to glory,
I dare say it was less than half an hour
After his death indeed. To God the power!
Our sexton and our infirmarian,
They saw it too, both friars boy and man
These fifty years, thank God. They now are free
To walk alone, they've reached their jubilee.*
I rose at once, in fact the entire place
Rose, and the tears were trickling down my face.
There was no noise, no clattering bells were rung,
But a *Te Deum* – nothing else – was sung,

332

Save that I made an act of adoration
To Christ, to thank Him for His revelation.
For I assure you both, believe me well,
Our orisons are more effectual
And we see more of Christ's most secret things
Than common people do, or even kings.
We live in poverty and abstinence
But common folk in riches and expense
On food and drink and other foul delight;
But we contemn all worldly appetite.

'Dives and Lazarus lived differently,
And different their guerdon had to be.
Whoever prays must fast, he must keep clean.
Fatten his soul and make his body lean.
We follow the Apostle; clothes and food
Suffice us though they may be rough and rude.
Our purity and fasting have sufficed
To make our prayers acceptable to Christ.

'Moses had fasted forty days and nights
Before Almighty God, upon the heights
Of Sinai, came down to speak with him,
And with an empty stomach, frail of limb,
Moses received the law Jehovah drew
With his own finger; and Elijah too
When in Mount Horeb, ere he could have speech
With that Almighty Lord who is the leech
Of life, had fasted long in contemplation.

'Aaron no less, under whose domination
The temple was, and other Levites too,
When they approached the temple to renew
Their services and supplications, they
Refrained from drinking – drinking, that's to say,
That might have made them drunk – attending there
In abstinence, in watching and in prayer
Lest they should die. Take heed of what I say;
Unless the priest is sober who would pray
For you – but there! I've said enough of it.

'Jesus our Lord, it says in Holy Writ,

333

Fasted and prayed, and patterned our desires,
And so we mendicants, we simple friars
Have wedded poverty and continence,
Charity, humbleness and penitence,
And persecution too for righteousness;
Pure, merciful, austere, but quick to bless
Though weeping often. Therefore our desires
– I'm speaking of ourselves, mendicant friars –
Are more acceptable to God, more able
Than yours, with all your feasts upon the table.

    'I speak the truth; gluttony was the vice
That first flung Adam out of Paradise;
And man was chaste in Eden, I may mention.

    'But listen to me, Thomas, pay attention.
Though there's no text exactly, I suppose,
Yet in a manner of speaking if I glose
A little, you will see our Lord referred
Especially to friars in the word
"Blessed are the poor in spirit." Think and look,
Study the gospels, search the Holy Book,
And see if it be liker our profession
Than theirs who swim in riches and posssesion.
Fie on their pomp! Fie on their gluttony!
Their ignorance is a disgrace to see.

    'Jovinian makes a good comparison,
"Fat as a whale and waddling like a swan,"
They stink of wine like bottles in a bar;
How reverent their supplications are!
When they say prayers for souls their psalm of David
Is just a "Burp! *Cor meum eructavit!*"*
Who follows on the gospel, tracks the spoor
Of Christ, but we the humble, chaste and poor,
The doers of the word, not hearers only?
And as a hawk springs up into the lonely
Regions of heaven, so the prayer aspires
Of charitable, chaste and busy friars,
Takes flight and enters in at God's two ears.
O Thomas, Thomas! Let me say with tears

And by that patron who is called St Ives,
Where were your hope to be as one that thrives
If you were not our brother? Day and night
Our Chapter prays the Lord to send you might,
Strengthen your body, girdle it and belt it!'
'God knows,' the fellow said, 'I haven't felt it.
So help me Christ I've spent a lot in hire
These last few years on various kinds of friar,
Aye, many a pound; and yet I'm none the better.
I've poured it out. I'm very near a debtor.
Farewell my gold, it's gone; no more to go!'
    'O Thomas!' said the Friar. 'Did you so?
What need to seek out "various kinds of friar"?
Who, with a perfect doctor, could require
To seek out other doctors in the town?
Your own inconstancy has let you down.
Do you suppose our convent, and I too,
Are insufficient then to pray for you?
Thomas, that joke's not good. Your faith is brittle.
You're ill because you've given us too little.
"Ah! give that convent half a quarter of oats!"
"Ah! give that convent four and twenty groats!"
"Ah! give that friar a penny and let him go!"
No, Thomas, Thomas, it should not be so!
What is a farthing worth if split in twelve?
An undivided thing is (if you delve
Into your wits) stronger than when it's scattered.
Thomas, by me you never shall be flattered.
You're trying to get our work for nothing, eh?
What does Almighty God who made us say?
"The laborer is worthy of his hire."
Thomas, you know it's not that I desire
Your treasure for myself; it should be spent,
Seeing our convent is so diligent
In prayer for you, to build the church of Christ.
Thomas! If you would learn or be enticed
To learn what good there is in building churches,
St Thomas' life may help in your researches,

The saint of India. There you lie in ire,
The devil having set your heart on fire,
And chide this foolish, innocent woman here,
Your wife, so meek, so patient, so sincere.
So, Thomas, please let this be understood;
No wrangling with your wife! It's for your good.
And take this thought away to fill your head
Touching this matter; wisely was it said:
"Then be not as a lion in thy house,
A terror to thy household, tyrannous,
Nor such that thine acquaintance flees away."
I charge you, Thomas, once again and say,
Beware of her that in your bosom sleeps;
Beware the serpent that so slyly creeps
Amidst the grass and stings with subtlety.
Beware, my son, and listen patiently,
For twenty thousand men have lost their lives
For wrangling with their lovers and their wives.
And since you have so holy and meek a wife
What, Thomas, is the need for all this strife?
No serpent is so cruel, truth to tell,
If one should tread upon his tail, so fell
As women who have given way to ire.
Vengeance is then the sum of their desire.
Ire is a sin, one of the deadly seven,
Abominable unto God in Heaven,
And a destruction to yourself, none quicker.
Every illiterate parson, every vicar
Can tell that ire engenders homicide.
For ire is the executor of pride.
Were I to say what ire can bring in sorrow
To man my tale would last until tomorrow.
So day and night I pray as best I can
God send no power to an angry man!
Great harm can come of it, great misery,
When angry men are set in high degree.
'Once on a time an angry potentate,
Seneca says, bore rule over a state.

A certain day two knights went riding out
And fortune willed that it should come about
That one of them returned, the other not.
The knight was brought to judgment on the spot;
This judge gave sentence: "You have killed your friend;
You are condemned to death and that's the end."
And to another knight was standing by
He turned and said, "Go, lead him out to die."
And so it happened as they went along
To the appointed place, towards the throng
There came the knight that was reported dead.
So it seemed best that both of them be led
Together back before the judge again.
"My lord," they said, "the knight has not been slain;
His friend is guiltless. As you see, they thrive."
"You all shall die," said he, "as I'm alive!
You first, the second, you, and you the third!"
And turning to the first he said this word;
"I have condemned you. You must therefore die."
Then to the next, "You too, and this is why:
Your comrade clearly owes his death to you."
Then to the third he turned and said, "You too;
You had my orders; they were not fulfilled."
And so it was the three of them were killed.

   'An angry man and drunken was Cambyses,
Who took great joy in showing off his vices.
A knight, it happened, in his company,
Given to virtue and morality,
In private conference with him began:
"A lord is lost if he's a vicious man,
And drunkenness is filthy to record
Of any man, especially a lord.
Many the eye and ear that takes good care
To spy on lords, they can't be certain where.
For God's love be more temperate in your drink,
For wine will rob you of your power to think
And incapacitate your members too."

   ' "You'll see," said he, "the opposite is true,

And prove it by your own experience
That wine has no such power of offense.
There is no wine so strong as to deny
Strength to my hand or foot or sight of eye."
'And out of spite he drank as much, nay, more
A hundred times than he had drunk before.
And right away this angry, cursed wretch
Gave an immediate command to fetch
This noble's son, and there he made him stand;
Then snatching up a bow into his hand
Drew string to ear, and aiming it with care
He shot him with an arrow then and there.
"Now have I got a steady hand or not?
Now have my mental powers gone to rot?"
The tyrant said, "Has wine destroyed my sight?"

'Why should I tell the answer of the knight?
His son was slain, there is no more to say.
Dealing with lords be careful in your play;
You sing *Placebo!* I shall if I can,
Except when talking to some poor old man.
To tell their vices to the poor is well,
But not to lords, though they should go to Hell.

'Cyrus the Persian was an evil-liver
And given to anger; he destroyed the river
Gyson in which his horse was drowned, upon
His expedition to take Babylon.
That river in his rage was so diminished
Women could wade it by the time he'd finished.

'Solomon teaches us as no one can:
"Make thou no friendship with an angry man;
And with a furious man take not thy way,
Lest thou repent it"; there's no more to say.

'Leave anger, Thomas; brother, have a care!
You'll find me just. I'm like a joiner's square.
That devil's knife, O draw it from your heart!
It is your anger causes you to smart.
Make your confession to me if you can.'

'No, by St Simon,' said the ailing man,

'The curate came and shrived me here to-day.
I told him everything I had to say.
There's no more need to speak of it,' said he,
'Unless I care to, from humility.'

'Then give me of your gold to make our cloister,'
Said he, 'for many a mussel, many an oyster,
When other men eat well and fill their cup,
Has been our food, to build our cloister up.
And yet we've hardly finished the foundation.
There's not a tile as yet or tesselation
Upon the pavement that we hope to own,
And forty pound is owing still for stone.
'Now, Thomas, help, for Him that harrowed Hell,
For otherwise we shall be forced to sell
Our books, and if you lacked our predication
The world would quickly fall to desolation.
To cheat it of our sermons and bereave
The world of us, dear Thomas, by your leave,
Were worse than to bereave it of the sun.
Who teaches and who works as we have done?
And for a long, long time,' he said, 'because
There have been friars since Elijah was;
Elisha too was one, the books record,
In charity with us, I thank our Lord.
Now Thomas, help, for holy charity!'
And down at once he went upon his knee.

The ailing man was nearly mad with ire;
He would have very gladly burnt the friar,
Him and his lying speech and false profession.
'I'll give you what I have in my possession,
Such as it is,' he said, 'I have none other.
You said a moment back I was your brother?'
'Believe it,' said the friar, 'and none better;
I brought your wife our letter – our sealed letter!'

'Well now,' he said, 'there's something I can give
Your holy convent, if I am to live.
And you shall have it in your hand to own
On one condition and on one alone,

339

That you divide it equally, dear brother,
And every friar to have as much as other.
But swear by your profession to the thing,
And without fraudulence or cavilling.'

'I swear it by my faith!' the friar said,
Clasping the hand of the poor man in bed.
'My hand on it! In me shall be no lack.'

'Well, then, reach down your hand along my back,'
The sick man said, 'and if you grope behind,
Beneath my buttocks you are sure to find
Something I've hidden there for secrecy.'

'Ah!' thought the friar, 'that's the thing for me!'
And down he launched his hand and searched the cleft
In hope of finding what he had been left.
When the sick man could feel him here and there
Groping about his fundament with care,
Into that friar's hand he blew a fart.
There never was a farm-horse drawing cart
That farted with a more prodigious sound.

Mad as a lion then the friar spun round,
'You treacherous lout!' he cried, 'God's bones and blight!
You did it on purpose, It was done for spite!
You shall pay dearly for that fart, I say!'

The sick man's servants, hearing the affray,
Came leaping in and chased away the friar,
And off he went still spluttering with ire
To find his comrade where he kept his goods.
He looked like a wild boar out of the woods,
Gnashing his teeth, he was so furious.
He strode along towards the manor-house
Where lived a man of honor and possession
Who used to seek the friar in confession.
This worthy man was the manorial lord;
As he was sitting eating at his board
In came the friar in a towering rage
Almost past speech for anger by that stage,
But in the end 'God bless you, sir,' said he.
The lord stared back. 'Hey, *benedicite!*

It's Friar John! What sort of world is this?
It's plain to see that something's gone amiss.
You look as if the wood were full of thieves;
Sit down and tell me what it is that grieves
You so! I'll settle it for you if I can.'

'I've had the greatest insult,' said the man.
'Down in your town to-day – God give you joy –
No guttersnipe in all the world, no boy
But would be shocked at it, no serf at tillage,
At what I've had to suffer in your village.
It's an abomination, *most* unpleasant;
What shocks me most of all, this hoary peasant
Even blasphemed our holy convent too!'

'Now, master,' said the lord, 'I beg of you –'
'No master, sir,' he said, 'your servitor!
Although the Schools did me that honor, sir;
But still God wishes not that men should call
Us "Rabbi" either here in your large hall
Or in the market.' 'Never mind,' said he,
'Tell me your trouble.' 'Sir, there was done to me,
And to my Order too, an odious wrong;
Per consequens to all that may belong
To Holy Church itself. May God amend it.'

'Sir,' said the lord, 'you know the way to end it.
Keep calm, you're my confessor; I know your worth.
You are the salt and savor of the earth.
For love of God be patient and unfold
The matter of your grief.' So then he told
The story (you have heard it) with a will.

The lady of the house sat very still
Till she had heard the friar's whole tirade.
'Mother of God,' she said, 'O blessed Maid!
And is there nothing else? Now tell me true.'

'Madam,' he answered, 'May I hear your view?'
'My view?' she said. 'God help us! What's the need?
I say a churl has done a churlish deed.
What should I say? May God deny him ease!
His poor sick head is full of vanities.

I think he must have had some kind of fit.'
  'Madam,' said he, 'I'll pay him out for it,
By God I will! There are within my reach
Several ways; for instance I can preach,
I can defame him! I won't be derided
Or bidden divide what cannot be divided
In equal parts – God damn his ignorance!'
  The lord had sat as if he were in trance,
Rolling in heart the problem up and down,
How the imagination of a clown
Had hit on his conundrum for the friar.
'I never before heard such a thing transpire;
I think the devil put it in his mind.
In all arithmetic you couldn't find
Until to-day so tricky an equation.
How could one set about a demonstration
Where every man alike should have his part
Both of the sound and savor of a fart?
Proud churl! O nice distinction! Damn his nerve!'
He then went on more gravely to observe,
'Whoever heard of such a thing till now!
"To every man alike?" Good Lord, but how?
It is impossible, it cannot be!
Aha, nice churl! God send him misery!
The rumbling of a fart or any sound
Is only air reverberating round,
What's more, diminishingly, bit by bit.
Upon my word! No one could have the wit
To see it was divided equally.
To think a churl, a churl of mine, could be
So shrewd, and to my own confessor too!
He's certainly demoniac in my view!
Now eat your food and leave the churl alone
And let the devil hang him for his own!'
  Now the lord's squire was standing by and heard
The tale as he was carving, word for word,
And saw the problem you have heard defined.
'My lord,' he said, 'I hope you will not mind,

But for a piece of cloth to make a gown,
I'd tell the friar — but he mustn't frown —
How such a fart could equally be shared
Between him and his convent, if I cared."

His lord replied, 'Well, tell us then, go on,
And you shall have your gown-cloth, by St John.'

'Well, when the weather, sir,' he said, 'is fair,
When there's no wind or movement in the air,
Then have a cart-wheel brought into this hall,
But see the spokes are fitted — twelve in all,
A cartwheel has twelve spokes — then, by and by,
Bring me twelve friars. You will ask me why?
Well, thirteen make a convent, as I guess.
And this confessor here, for worthiness,
Shall bring the number to thirteen, my lord.
Then they shall all kneel down with one accord;
To each spoke's end a friar, I propose,
Shall very seriously lay his nose.
Your excellent confessor, whom God save,
Shall put his nose right up under the nave.
And then the churl, with belly stiff and taut
As drum or taber, hither shall be brought,
Set on the wheel thus taken from the cart
Above the nave, and made to let a fart.
Then you will see, as sure as I shall live,
And by a proof that is demonstrative,
That equally the sound of it will wend,
Together with the stink, to the spokes' end,
Save that this worthy friar, your confessor,
Being of greater honor, they of lesser,
Shall have the first-fruits, as is only right.
A noble custom, in which friars unite,
Is that a worthy man should first be served;
And certainly it will be well-deserved.
To-day his preaching did us so much good,
Being beneath the pulpit where he stood,
That I'd allow him, if it fell to me,
First smell of every fart, say up to three,

And so would all his convent I am sure,
His bearing is so holy, fair and pure.'
    The lord and lady – all except the friar –
Thought Jacky's answer all they could desire,
As wise as Euclid or as Ptolemy.
As for the churl, it was his subtlety,
His wit, they said, to think of such a crack.
'He is no fool, he's no demoniac!'
And Jacky has acquired a new gown.
My tale is done; we've almost come to town.

[GROUP E]

The Clerk's Tale

The Clerk's Prologue

'YOU, sir, from Oxford!' said the Host. 'God's life!
    As coy and quiet as a virgin-wife
Newly espoused and sitting mum at table!
You haven't said a word since we left stable.
Studying, I suppose? On wisdom's wing?
Says Solomon, "There's a time for everything."
    'For goodness' sake cheer up, show animation!
This is no time for abstruse meditation.
Tell us a lively tale in Heaven's name;
For when a man has entered on a game
He's bound to keep the rules, it's by consent.
But don't you preach as friars do in Lent,
Dragging up all our sins to make us weep,
Nor tell a tale to send us all to sleep.
    'Let it be brisk adventure, stuff that nourishes,
And not too much of your rhetorical flourishes.
Keep the "high style" until occasion brings
A use for it, like when they write to kings,

And for the present put things plainly, pray,
So we can follow all you have to say.'

    This worthy cleric left the land of nod
And said benignly, 'Sir, I kiss the rod!
Our company is under your control
And I am all obedience heart and soul,
That is, as far as reason will allow.

    'I heard the story I shall tell you now
In Padua, from a learned man now dead,
Of proven worth in all he did and said.
Yes, he is dead and nailed up in his chest,
And I pray God his spirit may have rest.

    'Francis Petrarch,* the poet laureate,
They called him, whose sweet rhetoric of late
Illumined Italy with poesy,
As Lynian* did with his philosophy
And law, and other special kinds of learning.
Death that allows no lingering or returning
In, as it were, the twinkling of an eye
Has slain them both; and we must also die.

    'But, to return to this distinguished man
From whom I learnt the tale, as I began,
Let me say first he starts it by inditing
A preface in the highest style of writing,
Ere coming to the body of his tale,
Describing Piedmont, the Saluzzo vale,
And the high Apennines that one may see
Bounding the lands of western Lombardy;
And he is most particular to tell
Of Monte Viso, where, from a little well,
The river Po springs from its tiny source.
Eastwards it runs, increasing on its course,
Towards the Aemilian Way; Ferrara past,
It reaches Venice and the sea at last,
Which is not only far too long to tell
But, as I think, irrelevant as well,
Except to set the tale and engineer it
A frame-work. This is it, if you will hear it.'

The Clerk's Tale

PART I

Upon the western shores of Italy
  Where Monte Viso lifts into the cold,
There lies a plain of rich fertility
With many a town and tower to behold,
Built by their forefathers in days of old,
And other lovely things to see in legion.
Saluzzo it is called, this splendid region.

There was a marquis once who ruled that land,
As had his ancestors in days gone by.
His vassals were obedient at his hand
Ready to serve, the lowly and the high.
Honored and dreaded, under fortune's eye
He long had lived and found the living pleasant,
Beloved alike by nobleman and peasant.

He was, moreover, speaking of descent,
The noblest-born of all in Lombardy,
Handsome and young and strong; in him were blent
High honor and a gentle courtesy.
He was discreet in his authority,
Though in some things he was indeed to blame,
As you shall hear, and Walter was his name.

I blame his failure in consideration
Of what the distant future might provide.
He always fed his present inclination,
Hawking and hunting round the countryside.
As to more serious cares, he let them slide,
And worst of all, whatever might miscarry,
He could not be prevailed upon to marry.

This was the only point that really stung them,
And so one day a deputation went
To wait on him. The wisest man among them,
Or else the least unwilling to consent
To give the marquis their admonishment,
The ablest there to touch on such a head,
Boldly addressed the marquis thus and said:

'My noble lord, your great humanity
Gives us assurance; we are therefore bold
To speak on any point of urgency
Or heavy care of which you should be told.
Then, sir, let not your clemency withhold
A hearing to our pitiful petition;
Do not disdain my voice or our position.

'Though what I ask concerns me no more nearly
Than any of your subjects in this place,
Yet forasmuch as you have loved me dearly
And ever shown the favors of your grace,
I dare the better beg in such a case
For gentle audience; here is our request,
And you, my lord, must do as you think best.

'We love you well, sir, are indeed rejoiced
In all you do or ever did, and we
Scarce can imagine thoughts that could be voiced
To lap us round in more felicity
Save one thing only, would that it might be!
Did you but choose, my lord, to take a wife,
What sovereign comfort to your country's life!

'O bow your neck under that blessed yoke!
It is a kingdom, not a slavery;
Espousal, wedlock, it is called. Invoke
Your wisdom, ponder carefully and see
How variously days pass; the seasons flee
Away in sleeping, waking, roaming, riding.
Time passes on and there is no abiding.

'Still in the flower of your youth's delights
Age creeps upon you, silent as a stone.
Death menaces all ages and he smites
The high and low, the known and the unknown;
We see for certain, are obliged to own
That we must die, but we are ignorant all
Of when the hour's to come, the blow to fall.

'Incline to our petition for protection,
Hear us that never crossed your least behest,
And we, with your consent, will make election
Immediately and choose a wife possessed
Of gentlest quality and birth, the best
In all the land, beseeming to her place,
An honor both to God and to your Grace.

'Deliver us from anxious fears and rid
Our hearts of care, for blessed Jesu's sake;
For if it so befell – which God forbid! –
Your line should end, then might not fortune rake
Some strange successor in to come and take
Your heritage? Should we not all miscarry?
Therefore we beg you speedily to marry.'

Their humble prayer and their imploring features
Made much impression on his clemency
And he replied, 'My people, fellow-creatures,
Married's a thing I never thought to be.
I go rejoicing in my liberty,
And that and marriage seldom go together;
Where I was free, am I to take the tether?

'Yet, since your offer is sincerely meant,
And since I trust you now as in the past,
I freely will admit myself content
To humor you and take a wife at last.
But as for the suggestion you should cast
About to find me a bride, I must remit
That duty; kindly say no more of it.

'God knows it's true that children in the main
Are much unlike their elders gone before,
Natural goodness comes of God, no strain
Of blood can give it, no, nor ancestor;
I trust in God's good bounty; say no more.
My marriage, my condition, rank and ease
I lay on Him. Do He as He may please.

'Leave me alone to choose myself a wife,
That is my burden, my prerogative.
But I command you, charge you on your life,
Whoever I shall choose, you are to give
All honor to her, long as she may live,
In word and deed, here and elsewhere, no less
Than to an emperor's daughter or princess.

'And over this you furthermore shall swear
Never to grumble, never to check or strive
Against my choice, if I am to impair
My personal liberty that you may thrive.
Where I have set my heart I mean to wive;
If you withhold consent as to this latter
I beg you'll speak no more upon the matter.'

With heart's goodwill they gave him their assent
To this demand, not one that made objection,
But begged the princely favor ere they went
That he would name a day for the election
Of his espoused, and quickly, for a section
Among his folk were yet uneasy, dreading
The marquis had no real thought of wedding.

He granted them a day of their own choosing
When he would wed in sober certainty;
He said he did so not to seem refusing
Their reasonable request, and reverently
In grave obedience then they bent the knee
Thanking him one and all, and were content,
Having achieved their aim, and home they went.

And thereupon he bade his ministers
To make such preparations as were fit
Against a feast, giving his officers
And squires such orders as he pleased for it,
And they obeyed him, setting all their wit
With diligence, the greatest and the least,
To make provision for a solemn feast.

PART II

Not far from where the noble palace stood
In which this marquis set about his wedding
There was a pretty village near a wood
Where the poor folk, each in his little steading,
Tended their animals with food and bedding
And took what sustenance they could from toil,
According to the bounty of the soil.

Among these poorer folk there dwelt a man
Who was esteemed the poorest of them all;
Yet there are times when God in Heaven can
Send grace into a little ox's stall.
Janicula the village used to call
This poor old man; his daughter was a pearl.
Griselda was the name of this young girl.

But in the virtuous beauty of her heart
She was among the loveliest man could ask,
For being poorly bred, no sensual part
Had learnt to use her beauty as a mask.
More often from the well than from the cask
She drank, and loving virtue, sought to please
By honest labor, not by idle ease.

And though as yet a girl of tender age,
Yet in the breast of her virginity
There was a ripeness, serious and sage.

With fostering love and reverent constancy
Her poor old father in his poverty
She tended, spun her wheel and watched his sheep
At pasture, never idle save asleep.

When she came homeward she would often bring
Roots, herbs and other grasses to the croft;
These she would shred and seethe for flavoring,
Then make her bed that was in nothing soft.
And thus she kept her father's heart aloft
With all the obedience, all the diligence
By which a child can show her reverence.

Griselda, though among his poorest creatures,
Walter had often seen, for riding by,
Hunting perhaps, a something in her features
Caught his regard, not that he sought to try
The frivolous glance of wantonness; his eye
Fell on her with a serious awareness
And he would often ponder on her fairness.

Her womanliness was what his heart commended,
Her goodness too, far passing the condition
Of one so young, was beautifully blended
In looks and deeds. A vulgar intuition
Lacks insight into virtue; his position
Taught him to recognize it and decide,
Were he to marry, she should be his bride.

The day appointed for his wedding came
But no one knew what woman it should be,
In wonder at which his people would exclaim,
Talking among themselves in privacy,
'When will the marquis quit his vanity
And take a wife? Alas to see him thus!
Why does he try to fool himself and us?'

Nevertheless the marquis bade prepare
Brooches and rings, all for Griselda, lit
With jewels, gold and lapis; he took care

Her wedding-garment should be made to fit,
But by another girl they measured it
Who was of equal stature; gems were sewn
On it to grace a wedding like his own.

And as the morning opened on the day
Appointed when the wedding was to be,
They decked the palace out in full array,
The hall, the chambers, each in its degree;
The store-rooms, bulging with a quantity
Of delicate viands, held in plenteous strength
Italy's best from all its breadth and length.

The royal marquis in his richest dress
With lords and ladies in a company
Invited to the banquet, and no less
His household officers and soldiery,
Rode off with many a sound of minstrelsy
Towards the little thorp I spoke about
And by the shortest road, in sumptuous rout.

How could the innocent Griselda tell
That all this pomp was leveled at her head?
She had gone off for water to the well
And having drawn it, home she quickly sped,
For she had heard the marquis was to wed;
She knew it was the day and hoped she might
Be present as he passed and see the sight.

She thought, 'I'll stand among the other girls,
My own companions, by our door and see
The marchioness, the marquis and his earls.
I'll hurry home as quickly as can be
And finish off the work that's there for me
So that I can have leisure then to wait
And watch her riding to the castle gate.'

She reached the threshold with her water-pot
And as she did the marquis called her name.
She, putting down her vessel on the spot

Beside the cattle-stall, returned and came
Before him, falling on her knees, the same
Serious-looking girl; she knelt quite still
And waited quietly to hear his will.

The thoughtful marquis, speaking with an air
Of sober gravity, said thus to her:
'Tell me, Griselda, is your father there?'
In all humility, without demur,
She answered, 'He is here and ready, sir.'
She rose at once and of her own accord
Fetched out her father to his overlord.

He took the poor old fellow by the hand,
Leading him off to speak with him apart.
'Janicula, I can no more withstand,
No, nor conceal, the pleasures of my heart.
If you consent, accepting from the start
Whatever follows, I will take to wife
Your daughter and will love her all my life.

'You love me as I know and would obey,
Being my liege-man born and faithful too;
Whatever pleases me I dare to say
May well succeed in also pleasing you.
Yet in this point I specially pursue
Tell me, I beg you, can my purpose draw
Consent to take me for your son-in-law?'

Wholly astounded at the news he heard
The old man turned deep red and stood there quaking,
So troubled he could hardly say a word,
Except 'My lord, my will is in your making;
What you desire in any undertaking
Let me not hinder; I am bound to do,
My dear, dear master, what best pleases you.'

The marquis answered softly, 'None the less
In your own cottage you and I and she
Must have a conference. Why? You cannot guess?

I have to ask her if her will may be
To marry and submit herself to me.
This must be done while you are by to hear,
I will not speak unless I have you near.'

While they were in the chamber and about
The treaty, which you presently shall hear,
The throng pressed round their dwelling-place without
And wondered at its decency and cheer,
How well she tended on her father dear.
But she, Griseld, might wonder even more,
For such a sight she'd never seen before.

Nor is it strange Griselda was astounded
To see so great a guest in such a place,
She was not used to being so surrounded
By noble visitors. How pale her face ...
But let me keep my story up to pace;
These are the words in which her lord conveyed
His will to this benign, true-hearted maid:

'Griselda, I would have you understand
As pleasing to your father and to me
That I should marry you, and here's my hand
If, as I may conjecture, you agree.
But I would rather ask you first,' said he,
'Since all is done in such a hasty way,
Will you consent or pause before you say?'

'I warn you to be ready to obey
My lightest whim and pleasure; you must show
A willing heart, ungrudging night or day,
Whether I please to offer joy or woe.
When I say "Yes" you never shall say "No"
Either by word or frowning a defiance.
Swear this and I will swear to our alliance.'

In wonder at these words, quaking for dread,
She answered, 'Lord, unworthy though I be
Of so much honor, so unmerited,

If it seems good to you, it is to me.
And here I promise never willingly
To disobey in deed or thought or breath
Though I should die, and yet I fear my death.'

'That is enough, Griselda mine!' said he.
He left the chamber then with sober tread
And reached the door; and after him came she.
And to the throng of people there he said:
'Here stands the wife it is my choice to wed.
Give her your reverence and love, I pray,
Whoever loves me. There's no more to say.'

And that she might not take the smallest bit
Of her old gear into his house, he bad
His women strip her there, and I admit
Those ladies of the court were scarcely glad
To touch the rags in which the girl was clad.
Yet the bright beauty of her natural glow
Was clothed anew at last from top to toe.

They combed her hair that fell but rudely tressed
With slender hands as if preparatory
To coronation, and a crown was pressed
Upon her head with gems of changeful glory.
Why should I let her raiment stay my story?
She stood transfigured in her gorgeous dress
Scarce recognizable for loveliness.

The marquis then espoused her with a ring
Brought for the purpose; on a horse he set her,
It was a nobly-pacing snow-white thing.
And to the palace next with those that met her,
Leading the way with joyful heart he let her
Be brought in triumph, and the day had end
In revel till they saw the sun descend.

Shortly, to let my story quicken pace,
I say this young, new marchioness so stood
In favor with the Lord and Heaven's grace,

It could not seem by any likelihood
That she was born and bred in servitude,
As in a cottage or an oxen-stall,
But rather nourished in an emperor's hall.

To all that looked on her she grew so dear,
So much to be revered, where she was born
Those who had watched her childhood year by year
Could hardly credit it, and dared have sworn
That she had never labored in the corn
Nor was Janicula's child, for by her feature
Fancy would think she was some other creature.

Virtuous ever, as had long been known,
She had increased to such an excellence
Of grace she was as bounty on a throne,
Wise, and so lovely in her eloquence,
So grave and so benign, she charmed the sense
And gathered every heart in her embrace,
They loved her all that looked upon her face.

Nor only was Griselda thus renowned
Within Saluzzo, for her bounteous name
Was published forth in all the region round.
If one said well another said the same;
Indeed her goodness had so wide a fame,
Men, women too, the younger and the older,
Went to Saluzzo only to behold her.

And thus in humble, nay, in royal kind,
Walter espoused a love as fortunate
As it was fair. God's peace was in his mind
And he enjoyed the outward gifts of fate;
And in that he had seen in low estate
The hidden grace, men held him to have been
A prudent man, and that is seldom seen.

Nor was it only that by natural wit
She could accomplish all a woman should
In homely ways, for, were there call for it,

She also could advance the public good;
There was no rancor, no discordant mood
In all that country that she did not ease
Or use her grace and wisdom to appease.

She, in her husband's absence, did not cease
Her labors; if the nobles of the land
Fell into enmity she made their peace.
So wise and ripe the words at her command,
Her heart so equitable and her hand
So just, they thought that Heaven had sent her down
To right all wrongs and to protect the town.

And it was not long after, to her joy,
Griselda bore a daughter fine and fair,
And though she would have rather borne a boy,
Walter was glad and so his people were,
For though it was a girl, perchance an heir
Might yet be born to them and likely so,
Seeing she was not barren. Time would show.

PART III

IT happened, as it often does in life,
While yet the child was sucking at her breast
The marquis, in obsession for his wife,
Longed to expose her constancy to test.
He could not throw the thought away or rest,
Having a marvelous passion to assay her.
Needless, God knows, to frighten and dismay her.

He had assayed her faith enough before
And ever found her good; what was the need
Of heaping trial on her, more and more?
Though some may praise the subtlety, indeed
For my part I should say it could succeed
Only in evil; what could be the gain
In putting her to needless fear and pain?

357

But this was how he fed his prepossession;
He came alone one night to where she lay
With troubled features and a stern expression
And said, 'Griseld, do you recall the day
I came and took you from your poor array
And raised you to the height of nobleness?
You've not forgotten that, or so I guess.

'I say, Griseld, this present dignity
To which I raised you cannot have, I know,
Made you forgetful of your debt to me
Who took you up from what was poor and low,
For all the little wealth that you could show.
Take heed of every word I say to you;
No one is there to hear it but us two.

'You may remember your arrival here
Into this house, it's not so long ago;
And though I love you much and hold you dear,
My noblemen are far from doing so.
They say it is a scandal and a show
That they should serve you, lifted from the tillage
As you have been, born in a little village.

'And now you've borne your daughter, all the more
No doubt they murmur phrases such as these.
But I desire, as I did before,
To live my life among them and in ease.
I cannot then ignore contingencies
And must dispose your daughter as is best,
Not as I wish to, but as they suggest.

'But still God knows it's painful to me too;
Yet without your full knowledge and consent
I will do nothing, but it is for you
To acquiesce and show no discontent.
Summon your patience, show that they were meant,
Those promises you gave me to obey,
Down in your village on our wedding-day.'

Apparently unmoved as she received
What he had said, no change in her expression
Or tone of voice, Griselda unaggrieved
Replied, 'My child and I are your possession
And at your pleasure; on my heart's profession
We are all yours and you may spare or kill
What is your own. Do therefore as you will.

'Nor is there anything, as God may save
My soul, that pleasing you displeases me,
Nor is there anything that I could crave
To have, or dread to lose, but you,' said she.
'This is my heart's will and shall ever be;
This may no length of time, no death deface;
My heart will never turn or change its place.'

If he were gladdened at her mild reply
There was no sign upon his face to show,
But gravely and with unrelenting eye
He gazed at her. At last he turned to go.
Soon after this, within a day or so,
He told a man in secret what he held
Was needful and he sent him to Griseld.

He was a sort of secret agent, one
That had been ever faithful in pursuing
Important tasks. When wickedness is done
Such men are very useful in the doing.
He loved and feared his master, and reviewing
What was commanded of him, made his way
With silent stalk to where Griselda lay.

'Madam,' the fellow said, 'I must be pardoned
For doing that to which I am constrained;
You are too wise to let your heart be hardened;
You know a lord's command must be sustained
And not refused, although it be complained
Against and wept for. Servants must obey,
And so will I. There is no more to say.

'It is commanded that I take this child.'
He said no more but grabbed the innocent
Despitefully, his countenance as wild
As if he would have slain it ere he went.
Griselda had to suffer and consent,
And like a lamb she lay there, meek and still,
And let the cruel fellow do his will.

He was a man of ominous ill-fame,
In voice and feature ominous, as are such,
And ominous the hour at which he came.
Alas, her daughter that she loved so much
Would, as she thought, be murdered at his touch.
Nevertheless she wept not nor lamented;
It was her husband's will and she consented.

She found her voice at last and she began
Humbly imploring not to be denied
This mercy, as he was a gentleman,
To let her kiss the child before it died;
She took it to her breast with terrified
And stricken face, and lulled it in her loss;
She kissed it then and signed it with the cross,

Saying with love, 'Farewell, O sacrificed
And blessed child that I shall never see;
Look, I have marked thee with the cross of Christ.
He is thy father, may He comfort thee,
Who died, for sake of us, upon a tree;
Thy little soul I offer in His sight
Since thou shalt die, for sake of me, to-night.'

And had there been a nurse with her, God knows
She would have thought it pitiful to see;
Well might a mother then have wept her woes.
Yet she was grave, and gazing steadfastly
As one who suffers all adversity
In meek submission, turned with sorrow-laden
Spirit and said, 'Take back your little maiden.

'Go now,' she said, 'and do as you are bidden.
But one thing let me beg you of your grace;
Bury the little body, be it hidden,
Unless my lord forbade it, in some place
That beasts and birds of prey can never trace.'
Yet not a word in answer would he say;
He took the little child and went his way,

Reporting to the marquis once again
What she had said, how looked, if reconciled,
As briefly point by point he made all plain
And having done he gave him up the child.
And though some touch of tenderness beguiled
His master, yet he held his purpose still
As lords will do that mean to have their will.

He bade the fellow secretly to take
The child and wrap the softest winding round
Her little form and carefully to make
A chest to bear it in, and then he bound
The man on pain of death that not a sound
Of his intention should be uttered, dumb
On whither he was going or whence come.

But to Bologna, to the marquis' sister,
The Countess of Panaro, he must go,
Taking the child, and he must there enlist her
To help him in this matter and bestow
All fostering care, so that the child might grow
In gentle grace, but above all to hide
Whose child it was, whatever should betide.

The man went off and did as he was bidden.
Now let us watch the marquis as he ranged
In quick imagination for some hidden
Sign in his wife whether she were estranged;
Was there a chance word showing she had changed
Towards him? But he still could never find
Her anything but serious and kind,

As glad, as humble and as quick to serve,
And in her love as she was wont to be;
In everything the same, she did not swerve,
And of her daughter not a word said she.
There was no sign of that adversity
To see upon her; and her daughter's name
She never used in earnest or in game.

PART IV

FOUR years went by in this unaltered state
Before Griselda was with child once more,
And then she bore a boy as delicate
In grace and beauty as the child before.
The marquis being told set greatest store
On it, nor only he but all the county,
And all gave thanks and honor to God's bounty.

When it was two years old, weaned from the breast
And taken from its nurse, there came a day
When Walter yet again was moved to test
The patience of his wife in the same way.
O needless, needless was the test, I say!
But married men too often use no measure
That have some patient creature at their pleasure.

'Wife,' said the marquis, 'as I said at first,
My people take it ill that we were married.
Now that my son is born they think the worst;
Never were things so bad, for I am harried
By murmurings and rumors that are carried
About my ears; I feel a deadly smart
That has indeed almost destroyed my heart.

'For now they say, "When Walter's reign is done
Old Janicle's descendants will succeed
And be our masters, either that or none."'

Such is the common talk, it is indeed.
Murmurs like that a ruler has to heed,
And certainly I dread all such opinions,
Though secretly advanced, in my dominions.

'I mean to live in quiet if I may,
And so am utterly disposed in mind
To serve the brother in the self-same way
As I have served his sister. I designed
To give this warning lest you were inclined
To do some outrage in your violent grief;
I beg you to be patient then, in brief.'

'I long have said,' she answered, 'Oh, believe me,
Nothing I will nor yet would have unwilled,
But as it pleases you. It does not grieve me
At all, though son and daughter both were killed
At your commandment; let it be fulfilled.
In my two children I have had no part
But sickness first, then pain and grief of heart.

'You are our sovereign, do with what is yours
Just as you please and do not bid me frame
Advice for you; for at my father's doors
I left my clothing. Was it not the same
To leave my will and freedom when I came?
I took your clothing and I therefore pray
Your pleasure may be done. I will obey.

'And surely had I had the prescience
To know your will before you told it me
I had performed it without negligence.
But knowing what your pleasure is to be,
I hold to it with firmest constancy.
For if I knew my death itself would ease you,
Then I would die, and gladly die, to please you.

'For death can never make comparison
Beside your love.' And when the marquis saw
Her faithfulness he could not look upon

Her face and dropped his eyes in wondering awe,
Thinking, 'What patience to endure the law
Of my caprices!' and he left the room
Happy at heart, but set his face in gloom.

The ugly officer as brutally
As he had snatched her daughter, or with more
Brutality if more in man could be,
Seized on her son, so beautiful, and tore
Him from her arms; she patient as before
Gave him no sign of suffering in her loss
But kissed her son and signed him with the cross.

But yet she begged the fellow, if he might,
To close the little body in a grave.
His tender limbs so delicate to sight
She sought in her extremity to save
From birds and beasts, but not a sign he gave
And snatched the child with careless cruelty,
But bore it to Bologna tenderly.

The marquis wondered ever more and more
At so much patience in her misery;
Had he not known for certain long before
How perfectly she loved her children, he
Would have supposed some cunning devilry
Of malice, some heart's cruelty or base
Indifference beneath her constant face.

But well the marquis knew it was no mask,
For she had ever loved her children best,
Next to himself. Now, I would like to ask
Of women, had he made sufficient test?
Could stubborn husband fancy or suggest
More that would prove a steadfast wifeliness
To one continuing stubborn to excess?

But there are folk in such a state of mind
That, if they finally resolve to take
Some certain course to which they feel inclined,

Cannot hold back, but fettered to their stake,
Hold to their purposes and cannot slake
Their fevered wills. So too this marquis nursed
His purposes, to test her as at first.

And so he waited for a word or glance
To show her change of heart, but there was none,
No variation in her countenance
Could he discover; face and heart were one.
And as she aged the love in her begun
Continued even truer, made addition,
If that could be, in love and true submission.

Therefore there seemed to be between these two
One undivided will; if Walter pressed
For something, it became her joy to do;
And God be thanked all happened for the best.
And she gave proof that in whatever test
A wife, as of herself, in nothing should
Direct her will but as her husband would.

Walter's ill-fame began to mount and spread;
His cruel soul had led him to embark
For having wed a pauper, people said,
On murdering both his children in the dark.
Such was the common murmur and remark.
No wonder if it was; by what they heard
About it, murder was the only word.

And so the love his people felt of yore
Turned into hatred; scandal and ill-fame
Are things a man may well be hated for;
To be called murderer is a hateful name.
Yet he in game or earnest with the same
Cruel device drove on to what he sought;
To test her further was his only thought.

Now when his daughter was some twelve years old
He sent to Rome, long cunningly apprised
Of his intentions, and the court was told

That such and such a bull should be devised
That his fell purpose might be realized,
And that the Pope, to set all minds at rest,
Should bid him wed again as he thought best.

I say he ordered them to counterfeit
A papal bull declaring approbation
Of a divorce, for Walter then could meet
Objection with a papal dispensation
And calm the rancor and the indignation
Between his people and him. They framed the bull
And published the whole forgery in full.

The common people, and no wonder, held
Or else supposed that things were even so.
But when these tidings came to poor Griseld
I deem her heart was weighted down with woe.
But she, and now no less than long ago,
Was ready, humble creature, faithfully
To meet misfortune and adversity.

And still she waited on his will and pleasure
To whom she had been given, heart and soul,
As to her one unfailing worldly treasure.
Yet to be brief about it and control
My tale, the marquis now to reach his goal
Devised a letter that declared his aim,
And to Bologna secretly it came.

It was for Lord Panaro, for the earl
Who had espoused his sister, and requested
That he would send him home his boy and girl
In public state and openly invested
With every honor, but it still protested
That upon no account should he declare,
Even if questioned, whose the children were,

But say the maid was shortly to espouse
The Marquis of Saluzzo; and thereto
The earl agreed. As day began to rouse

He started on the journey and he drew
Towards Saluzzo with a retinue
Of many lords in rich array to guide
This maiden and the brother at her side.

All in her wedding-dress and fresh as heaven
She rode in pearl and gold without alloy,
Her brother too, a little lad of seven,
Looked freshly, in the tunic of a boy;
So with great splendor, every face in joy,
They shaped their journey, riding all the way;
And thus they neared Saluzzo day by day.

PART V

MEANWHILE, according to his cruel bent
The marquis sought to test his wife yet more
And by the uttermost experiment
To prove her spirit to the very core,
Whether she still were steadfast as before;
And so in open audience one day
And in a blustering voice he chose to say:

'It was agreeable enough, forsooth,
To marry you, Griselda, in the flower
Of your obedient love and simple truth,
And not for lineage or worldly dower;
But now I know in very truth that power,
If one reflects, is nothing much to praise;
It is a servitude in many ways.

'I may not do as any plowman may;
My subjects are constraining me to take
Another wife, they clamor day by day.
Even the Pope has thought it fit to slake
Their rancor by consenting, you need make
No doubt of that; indeed I have to say
My second wife is now upon her way.

'Strengthen your heart to give her up your place.
As for the dowry that you brought of old,
Take it again, I grant it as a grace;
Go home, rejoin your father in his fold.
No one can count upon his luck to hold,
And I enjoin you to endure the smart
Of fortune's buffets with an even heart.'

She answered patiently without pretense:
'My lord, I know as I have always done
That, set against your high magnificence,
My poverty makes no comparison.
It cannot be denied, and I for one
Was never worthy, never in my life,
To be your chambermaid, much less your wife.

'And in this house whose lady you have made me,
As God's my witness whom I love and fear,
And as His power may gladden me and aid me,
I never thought myself the mistress here,
Rather a servant, humble and sincere,
To your high honor; so I shall think forever
Of you, above all creatures whatsoever.

'That you so long, of your benignity,
Have held me high in honor and display,
Whereas I was not worthy so to be,
I thank my God and you; and now I pray
Revoke it, for there is no more to say.
Gladly I'll seek my father and will live
My life with him, whatever life may give.

'For I was fostered there when I was small,
Only a child, and there I'll live and die
A widow clean in body, heart and all;
I gave my maidenhead to you, and I
Am still your faithful wife, I do not lie.
And God forbid a wife to one so great
Should take another man to be her mate.

'Touching your second wife, may God in grace
Grant you both joy and long prosperity,
For I will gladly yield her up my place
That once was such a happiness to me.
But since it pleases you, my lord,' said she,
'In whom was formerly my whole heart's rest,
Then I will go when you shall think it best.

'But as you proffer me what first I brought,
Such dowry as I had, it's in my mind
It was my wretched clothing and worth nought,
And would indeed be hard for me to find.
O blessed God, how noble and how kind
You seemed in speech, in countenance, in carriage,
That day, the day on which we made our marriage!

'It's truly said, at least I find it true
For the effect of it is proved in me,
"A love grown old is not the love once new."
And yet whatever the adversity,
Though it were death, my lord, it cannot be
That ever I should repent, though I depart,
For having wholly given you my heart.

'My lord, you know that in my father's place
You stripped me of my rags and in their stead
Gave me rich garments, as an act of grace.
I brought you nothing else it may be said
But faith and nakedness and maidenhead.
Here I return your garments and restore
My wedding ring as well, forevermore.

'And the remainder of the gems you lent
Are in your chamber I can safely say.
Naked out of my father's house I went
And naked I return again to-day;
Gladly I'll do your pleasure, if I may.
But yet I hope you will not make a mock
Of me or send me forth without a smock.

'So infamous a thing you could not do
As let the womb in which your children lay
Be seen in nakedness, bare to the view
Of all your people, let me not I pray
Go naked as a worm upon the way.
Bethink yourself, my own dear lord, because
I was your wife, unworthy though I was.

'Therefore in guerdon of my maidenhead
Which, hither brought, returns with me no more,
Vouchsafe a payment, give to me instead
Just such a simple smock as once I wore
To hide the womb of one that heretofore
Has been your wife; and here at last I leave you
And bid farewell, dear lord, lest I should grieve you.'

'The smock,' he said, 'you have upon your back
You may retain; remove it to your stall.'
Yet as he spoke his voice began to crack
For pity, and he turned and left the hall.
She stripped her garments in the sight of all
And in her smock, head bare and feet unshod,
Home to her father and his house she trod.

Folk followed weeping as she passed them by,
They railed on fate for all that had occurred.
Her eyes withheld their weeping and were dry
And at this time she did not speak a word.
The news soon reached her father; when he heard
He cursed the day and hour of his birth
That fashioned him a man to live on earth.

He, never doubt it, though so old and poor,
Had ever been suspicious of the match,
Had always thought it never could endure,
In that the marquis, having had the snatch
Of his desires, would feel disgrace attach
To his estate in such a low alliance,
And when he could would set it at defiance.

At her approach he hastened forth to meet her,
Led by the sound of many a beholder
That wept to see her pass, and he to greet her
Brought her old cloak and cast it on her shoulder
And wept. It fitted not, for it was older
By many a day than was her wedding-dress;
The cloth was coarsely woven, comfortless.

Thus with her father for a certain space
This flower of love and wifely patience stayed.
Never a word or look upon her face
In front of others or alone conveyed
A hint that she had suffered, or betrayed
Any remembrance of her former glory;
Her countenance told nothing of her story.

And that's no wonder; in her high estate
Her spirit had a full humility,
No tender mouth for food, no delicate
Heart's hungering after royal brilliancy
Or show of pomp; benignly, patiently,
She had lived wise in honor, void of pride,
Meek and unchanging at her husband's side.

They speak of Job and his humility,
For clerics when they wish to can endite
Its praises nobly, and especially,
In men – they praise few women when they write;
Yet none can reach a humbleness as white
As women can, nor can be half so true
As women are, or else it's something new.

PART VI

Now from Bologna he of whom I spoke,
The earl, arrived. The greater and the less
Got wind of it and all the common folk

Buzzed with the news a second marchioness
Was being brought in all the loftiness
Of pomp and splendor. Such a sight to see
Had never been known in all west Lombardy.

The marquis, who had planned and knew it all,
Before the earl had fully reached his place,
Sent down for poor Griselda in her stall;
And she with humble heart and happy face
Came at his bidding, all without a trace
Of swelling thought, and went upon her knees
And greeted him with reverence and at ease.

'Griseld,' said he, 'my will is firmly set.
This maiden hither brought to be my bride
To-morrow shall as royally be met
As possible with all I can provide
That's in my house. My servants, side by side
According to their rank, shall wait upon her
As may be best arranged in joy and honor.

'I have no woman of sufficient skill
To decorate the chambers as I hold
They should be decorated. If you will
I should be glad to see it all controlled
By you who know me and my tastes of old.
And though your dress is not a thing of beauty
I hope at least that you will do your duty.'

'Not only, lord, would I be glad,' said she,
'To do your will; I long and shall endeavor
To serve and please you in my own degree
And not to faint in service, now or ever.
For neither grief or happiness can sever
My love from me. My heart can never rest
Save in the ceaseless will to love you best.'

And she began upon the decorations;
There were the boards to set, the beds to make.
All she could do in many occupations

She did, and begged the maids for goodness' sake
To hurry and to sweep and dust and shake,
While she, most serviceable of them all,
Went garnishing the chambers and the hall.

The earl arrived, beginning to alight
With the two children early in the day,
And all the people ran to see the sight
Of so much opulence and rich array.
And soon among them there were those to say
That Walter was no fool, and though obsessed
To change his wife, it might be for the best.

'For she is lovelier,' they all agreed,
'And younger than Griselda. Put the case
That fruit will fall to them; a fairer breed
Will issue from such lineage and grace.'
Her brother had so beautiful a face
It caught them with delight, opinion changed
And now applauded what their lord arranged.

'O stormy people, frivolous and fickle,
Void of true judgment, turning like a vane,
Whom every novelty and rumor tickle,
How like the moon you are to wax and wane,
Clapping your praises, shouting your disdain,
False judges, dear at a penny as a rule,
Who trusts to your opinion is a fool.'

So said the serious people of the city
Who watched the throng go gazing up and down
Glad merely for the novelty, the pretty
New lady that had come to grace the town.
But let me leave the pleasure-seeking clown
And turn to my Griselda, in the press
Of all her labors, in her steadfastness.

Busy in all, she worked, disposed and settled,
Labored and strove to cater and adorn,
Nor did she seem at all abashed or nettled

Although her clothes were coarse and somewhat torn,
But with a face as cheerful as the morn
Went to the gate with all her retinue
To greet the marchioness, and then withdrew.

She met the guests so cheerfully and greeted them
With so much skill according to their rank
That none could find a fault in how she treated them
And all were wondering whom they had to thank,
For how could such a pauper, to be frank,
Know all the rules of honor and degree?
They praised her prudence as a rarity.

And in the meanwhile ceaselessly she still
Praised the young bride and praised her brother too
With so much heart, with such benign goodwill
That no one could have given them better due.
And in the end when all the retinue
Sat down to meat, Walter began to call
Griselda who was busy in his hall.

'Griseld,' he said to her as if in jest,
'How do you like the beauty of my wife?'
'Indeed, my lord,' she said, 'I must protest
I never saw a lovelier in my life.
God give her joy and may there be no strife
Between you, and I pray that He may send
Your fill of happiness to your lives' end!

'One thing I beg of you, and warn you too,
Never to goad her, never put on trial
This tender girl as I have known you do;
For she was fostered preciously, a vial
More delicate. I think the self-denial
Adversity might force on her would be
Harder for her to suffer than for me.'

When Walter saw this patience in Griseld,
Her happy face, no malice there at all,
And thought of his offenses long upheld

To test her, ever constant as a wall,
Grave, innocent and ever at his call,
The stubborn marquis could no more repress
His pity for such wifely steadfastness.

'It is enough,' he said, 'Griselda mine!
Have no more fears, let not your heart be sore.
Your faith and gentleness as far outshine
All other faith as you were tested more
In wealth and want than any wife before.
Dear wife, I know your steadfastness by this.'
He took her up into his arms to kiss.

She, lost in wonder, did not seem to grasp
Or even hear the words he uttered thus,
But as a sleeper breaking from the clasp
Of an amazement, woke incredulous.
'Griseld,' said he, 'by Him that died for us
You are my wife and I have none but you,
Nor ever had as God may judge me true!

'This is your daughter whom you so commended
As wife for me; the other on my oath
Shall be my heir as I have long intended,
They are the children of your body, both.
Bologna nourished them and fed their growth
In secret; take them back and never say
Your children have been lost or snatched away.

'Let those that otherwise have talked of me
Know that I did this, be it bad or good,
Neither in malice nor in cruelty
But for the trial of your womanhood.
What! Slay my children? God forbid I should!
Rather I kept them privately apart
Till I had proved the purpose of your heart.'

On hearing this Griselda fell in swoon
In piteous joy, but made recovery
And called her children to her and they soon

Were folded in her arms. How tenderly
She kissed them as the salt tears falling free
Bathed them and glistened on their face and hair;
How like a mother stood Griselda there!

And Oh how pitiful it was to see
Her fainting and to hear her humble tone,
'All thanks to you, my dearest lord,' said she,
'For you have saved my children, you alone!
Were I to die this moment I have known
Your love and have found favor in your sight,
And death were nothing, though I died to-night.

'O dear, O tender ones, so long away,
Your sorrowing mother steadfastly had thought
That some foul vermin, hound or beast of prey
Had eaten you. But God in mercy brought
You back to me and your kind father sought
In tender love to keep you safe and sound.'
She suddenly swooned again and fell to ground.

Though she had fainted, sadly, clingingly
She held her children in that first embrace,
And it was difficult for skill to free
Them from her arms, and touching to unlace.
O many a tear on many a pitying face
Ran down among those standing at her side,
Scarce able in her presence to abide.

Walter caressed her, loosed her from her grief,
And up she rose bewildered from her trance,
While all the rest in joy at her relief
Made much of her and cleared her countenance;
And Walter showed such loving vigilance
It was a dainty thing to see the air
Of new-found happiness between the pair.

The ladies round her, when the moment came,
Led her towards her chamber; there the old
Poor rags she wore, though never worn in shame,

They stripped and set on her a gown of gold;
A coronet of jewels manifold
They crowned her with and led her into hall
There to receive the homage of them all.

Thus to a piteous day a blissful close,
And every man and woman, as they might,
Gave themselves up to revelry; there rose
The stars, and all the welkin shone with light.
Greater the glad solemnities that night,
Greater the joy in feasting and defray
In treasure than upon their wedding-day.

For many a year in high prosperity
These two lived on in concord to the close;
Their daughter too they married worthily
And richly to a lord, best among those
In Italy. They also found repose
For old Janicula whom Walter kept
Safe at his court till soul from body crept.

Their son succeeded to the inheritance
After his father's day in peace and rest;
He married happily but did not chance
To put his wife to such a searching test.
This world of ours, it has to be confessed,
Is not so sturdy as it was of old.
Hear how my author ends the tale he told:

'This story does not mean it would be good
For wives to ape Griseld's humility,
It would be unendurable they should.
But everybody in their own degree
Should be as perfect in their constancy
As was Griselda.' That is why Petrarch chose
To tell her story in his noble prose.

For since a woman showed such patience to
A mortal man, how much the more we ought
To take in patience all that God may do.

Reason He has to test what He has wrought,
Yet never tempts the souls that He has bought
Above what they are able, and St James
Tells us He tests us daily, and reclaims.

He will permit, to exercise our virtue,
The sharper scourges of adversity
To lash us often, not that they may hurt you,
Nor yet to test the will, for certainly
No one can know our frailty more than He
Who knew them ere our birth, and all is best;
Then let our virtues learn to suffer test.

But one word more, my lords, before I go.
It isn't very easy nowadays
To find Griseldas round the town, you know.
And if you try imposing these assays,
What gold they have is mixed with such allays
Of brass, that, though the coin looks right perhaps,
When you begin to bend the thing it snaps.

So, from affection for the Wife of Bath,
Whose life and all her sect may God maintain
In high authority upon their path
– And pity else – I sing you this refrain
With lusty heart, to gladden you again,
Dropping the note of earnest emphasis.
So listen to my song, it goes like this:

*Chaucer's Envoy to the Clerk's Tale**

GRISELDA and her patience both are dead
And buried in some far Italian vale.
So let it then in open court be said,
'Husbands, be not so hardy as to assail
The patience of your wives in hope to find
Griseldas, for you certainly will fail.

Chaucer's Envoy to the Clerk's Tale

O noble wives, in highest prudence bred,
Allow no such humility to nail
Your tongues, or give a scholar cause to shed
Such light on you as this astounding tale
Sheds on Griselda, patient still and kind,
Lest Chichevache* engulf you like a whale.

Imitate Echo, she that never fled
In silence, but returns you hail for hail,
Never let innocence besot your head,
But take the helm yourselves and trim the sail,
And print this lesson firmly in your mind
For common profit; it can never stale.

Arch-wives, stand up, defend your board and bed!
Stronger than camels as you are, prevail!
Don't swallow insults, offer them instead.
And all you slender little wives and frail,
Be fierce as Indian tigers, since designed
To rattle like a windmill in a gale.

Never revere them, never be in dread,
For though your husband wears a coat of mail,
Your shafts of crabbed eloquence will thread
His armor through and drub him like a flail,
Voice your suspicions of him! Guilt will bind
Him down, he'll couch as quiet as a quail.

If you are beautiful, advance your tread,
Show yourself off to people, blaze the trail!
If you are ugly, spend and make a spread,
Get friends, they'll do the business of a male;
Dance like a linden-leaf if so inclined,
Leave him to weep and wring his hands and wail!

The Merchant's Tale

The Merchant's Prologue

'WEEPING and wailing, care and other sorrow,
  I know them well enough by eve and morrow,'
The Merchant said; 'like others I suppose
That have been married, that's the way it goes;
I know too well that's how it goes with me.
I have a wife, the worst that there could be;
If she were coupled to a fiend from Hell
She'd be a match for him as I can tell.
Why single out one vice or why recall
Her soaring malice? She's a shrew in all.
There's a wide difference I'm bound to say
Between Griselda's patience and the way
My wife behaves; her studied cruelty
Surpasses everything. If I were free,
Never again, never again the snare!
We married men, our life is grief and care.
Try it who will, whoever it is I promise
He'll find I've spoken truly, by St Thomas,
For most of us – I do not say for all,
And God forbid that such a thing befall.

'Ah, my good Host, I have been wedded now
These two months past, no more than that I vow,
Yet I believe no bachelor alive,
Not if you were to take a knife and rive
Him to the heart I say, could ever tell
A hint of half the agony and Hell
I get from my intolerable wife!'
  Our Host replied, 'The Lord protect your life!
But since you know so much about the art
Of marriage, let me beg you to impart.'
  'With pleasure,' he said, 'but on the personal score
I'm so heart-scalded I shall say no more.'

The Merchant's Tale

THERE was a knight one time of good renown
In Lombardy, Pavia was the town.
He'd lived there very prosperously for more
Than sixty years and was a bachelor,
Though always taking bodily delight
On women, such as pleased his appetite,
As do these foolish worldings, never fear.
   Now when this knight had passed his sixtieth year
– Whether it was for dotage or a surge
Of holiness, who knows? – he felt an urge
So violent to be a wedded man
That day and night his eager fancies ran
On how to single out the perfect bride,
Praying the Lord he might not be denied
Once to have knowledge of that blissful life
There is between a husband and his wife,
And live under the holy bond and tether
In which God first bound woman and man together
'No other life,' he said, 'is worth a bean;
For wedlock is so easy and so clean
It is a very paradise on earth.'
Thus said this aging knight, so full of worth.
   And certainly, as sure as God is King,
To take a wife is a most glorious thing,
Especially if a man is old and hoary;
Then she's the fruit of all his wealth and glory.
It's then he ought to take her, young and fair,
One upon whom he might beget an heir,
And lead a life of rapture, far above
What bachelors are pleased to call 'free love';
They moon about singing their silly song
Either when something happens to go wrong
Or they are somehow thwarted. One can see
Their love is only childish vanity.

And it's no more than right it should be so
If these free lovers are consumed with woe;
They build on brittle ground, so all is ready
For brittle love, though they expect a steady.
Their liberty is that of bird or beast,
They've no restraint, no discipline at least,
Whereas a married man achieves a state
Of bliss that's orderly and fortunate.
Under the yoke of matrimony bowed,
The heart, in bliss abounding, sings aloud.
For who is so obedient as a wife?
Who is so true, so careful for his life
Whether in health or sickness as a mate?
For weal or woe she tends upon his state,
Never forsakes him in her love or tires
Though he lie bedridden till he expires.

And yet some writers say this isn't so;
One such was Theophrastus long ago.
Who cares if Theophrastus was a liar?
'Don't take a wife,' he said, 'from a desire
To make economies and spare expense.
A faithful servant shows more diligence
In guarding your possessions than a wife,
For she claims half you have throughout her life;
And if you're sick, as God may give me joy,
Your friends, even an honest serving-boy,
Do more than she, who's watching for a way
To corner your possessions night and day.
And if you take a wife into your bed
You're very likely to be cuckolded.'

Opinions such as these and hundreds worse
This fellow wrote, God lay him under curse!
But take no heed of all such vanity,
Defy foul Theophrastus and hear me.

A wife is verily the gift of God.
All other kinds of gift, the fruitful sod
Of land, fair pastures, movables in store
Rents – they're the gifts of fortune, nothing more,

That pass as does a shadow on a wall.
   Still, if I must speak plainly, after all
A wife does last some time, and time may lapse
A good deal slower than one likes, perhaps.
   Marriage is a momentous sacrament,
Bachelordom contemptible, and spent
In helpless desolation and remorse
– I'm speaking of the laity, of course.
I don't say this for nothing; listen why.
Woman was made to be a man's ally.
When God created Adam flesh and bone
And saw him belly-naked and alone,
He of His endless goodness thus began:
'Let us now make a help-meet for this man
Like to himself.' And He created Eve.
Here lies the proof of what we all believe,
That woman is man's helper, his resort,
His earthly paradise and his disport.
So pliant and so virtuous is she
They cannot but abide in unity.
One flesh they are; one flesh as I suppose
Has but a single heart in joys and woes.
   A wife! Saint Mary, what a benediction!
How can a man be subject to affliction
Who has a wife? Indeed I cannot say.
There is a bliss between them such as may
No tongue tell forth, such as no heart can judge.
If he be poor she helps her man to drudge,
Sets guard upon his goods and checks the waste;
All that her husband likes is to her taste,
She never once says 'no' when he says 'yes.'
'Do this,' says he; 'already done,' she says.
O blissful state of wedlock, no way vicious
But virtuous and merry, nay, delicious,
And so commended and approved withal
That any man who's worth a leek should fall
Down on his knees in gratitude for life
To God for having given him a wife,

Or else pray God that He vouchsafe to send
A wife to him, to last him till the end.

   Then he can count upon security
And not be tricked, as far as I can see,
Provided that he works by her advice;
Then he can hold his head up. And how nice,
How truthful, how discreet in her replies
A woman is! To do as do the wise
Do as she says and you'll be happy then.

   Jacob, as I have heard from learned men,
Did as Rebecca said; she bid him deck
– She was his mother – skins about his neck
And so he won his father's benison.

   Take Judith, in the story further on,
She saved God's people wisely; them she kept
By slaying Holofernes while he slept.

   Take Abigail, what good advice she gave!
It saved her husband Nabal from the grave.
Take Esther too whose wisdom brought relief
To all God's people, saved them from their grief
And made Ahasuerus grant promotion
To Mordecai for his true devotion.

   None so superlative in their degree,
Says Seneca, as humble wives can be.
'The tongue of wife,' so Cato was to say it,
'Commands the husband; suffer and obey it.'
And yet she will obey by courtesy.
A wife is guardian of your husbandry;
Well may a man in sickness wail and weep
Who has no wife to nurse him and to keep
His house for him; do wisely then and search
A wife and love her as Christ loves His Church.
For if you love yourself you love your wife,
For no one hates his flesh, nay all his life
He fosters it, and so I bid you wive
And cherish her or you will never thrive.
Husband and wife, whatever the worldly say
In ribald jest, are on the straight, sure way.

They are so knit no accident or strife
Harms them, particularly not the wife.

So January thought, of whom I told,
Deeply considering as he grew old
The life of lusty joy and virtuous quiet
That marriage offers in its honey-diet.
And so one day he sent for all his friends
To tell them how he meant to gain his ends.

With serious face he spoke, and solemn tongue.
'My friends,' he said, 'I am no longer young;
God knows I'm on the threshold of the grave.
I ought to think I have a soul to save.

'My body I have foolishly expended;
Blessed be God, that still can be amended.
I have resolved to be a wedded man,
And that at once in all the haste I can
To some fair virgin, one of tender years.
Prepare yourselves to help as overseers
Against my wedding, for I will not wait.
I for my own part will investigate,
And soon, to find a tender girl, if any
Be fit to marry me. Since you are many
You may discern more readily than I
Where it would most befit me to ally.

'But, my dear friends, you may as well be told
The woman must on no account be old,
Certainly under twenty, and demure.
Flesh should be young though fish should be mature;
As pike, not pickerel, makes the tastier meal,
Old beef is not so good as tender veal.
I'll have no woman thirty years of age;
That's only fodder, bean-straw for a cage.
God knows these ancient widows know their trade,
They are as tricky as the Boat of Wade*
And can be irritating when they try;
I'd never have a moment's peace, say I.
Subtle is the scholar taught in several schools;
Women are taught in many, they're no fools,

Half-scholars one might say; but when they're young
A man can still control them with his tongue
And guide them should their duty seem too lax
Just as a man may model in warm wax.
So let me sum the matter in a clause;
I will have no old woman, for this cause.
For were I so unlucky as to marry
Where I could take no pleasure, I'd miscarry,
I should commit adultery and slide
Straight downwards to the devil when I died.
I could beget no child on her to greet me,
Yet I had rather that the dogs should eat me
Than that my fine inheritance should fall
Into strange hands, that let me tell you all.

'I'm not a fool, I know the reason why
People should wed, though I could specify
Many who prate of it, but I engage
They know about as little as my page
Touching the reasons one should take a wife.
A man unable to be chaste in life
Should take a wife in holy dedication
And for the sake of lawful procreation
Of children, to the honor of God above,
Not as a paramour or lady-love,
But to curb lechery, which he should eschew,
Paying his debt whenever it falls due,
And each a willing helper to the other
In trouble, or like sister to a brother
And live a life of holy chastity;
But, by your leave, sirs, that would not suit me.
For, God be thanked for it, I still can claim
My limbs are strong, sufficient for the game,
And can do all that's proper to a man;
I'm the best judge myself of what I can.
I may seem hoary, but I'm like a tree
That blossoms white before the fruit can be;
Blossoming trees are neither dry nor dead
And I am only hoary on my head.

My heart and all my members are as green
As laurel is, all the year round, I mean.
And now you are informed of my intention
I beg you to agree without dissension.'

Various men gave various examples
Of classic marriages, convincing samples;
Some praised it certainly, some reprehended,
But at the last, to get the matter ended,
As altercation happens every day
Among good friends who mean to say their say.
An argument was presently begun
Between two friends of his, Placebo one,
Justinus, as I recollect, the other.

Placebo said, 'Dear January, dear brother,
You have no need, my lord, it must appear,
To take advice from anybody here,
Save that your sapience after meditation
Would prudently resist the inclination
To set aside the word of Solomon,
For this is what he said for everyone:
"Do all things by advice," his saying went,
"And then you'll have no reason to repent."
Though that may be what Solomon commends,
Dear lord, my brother, nay my best of friends,
As surely as the Lord may give me rest
I think your own opinion is the best.
Take it from me – if I can find the phrase –
You know I've been a courtier all my days,
God knows unworthily, I make admission,
Yet I have stood in quite a high position
And among lords of very great estate;
But I have never joined in a debate
With them, or offered contradiction. Why?
Well, obviously, my lord knows more than I,
And what he says I hold as firm and stable;
I echo it as far as I am able.
No counselor is such a fool as he
That, serving on a lord of high degree,

Dares to presume or even thinks it fit
To be superior to him in wit.
Lords are no fools, believe me ... May I say
That you have also shown yourself to-day
A man of lofty views, an eloquent,
A holy-minded man, and I consent
To all you said. It should be written down.
A speech like that – there isn't one in town,
No, nor all Italy, able to supply it!
Christ holds himself more than rewarded by it.
In anyone at all advanced in age
It shows a lively spirit to engage
In taking a young wife. Ah, Lord of grace!
You've pinned your heart up in a jolly place;
Follow your inclination; I protest
Whatever you decide on will be best.'

    Justinus who sat silent, having heard
Placebo speaking, then took up the word.
'Brother,' he said, 'be patient with me, pray;
You spoke your mind, now hear what I would say.
Seneca gave a lot of sound advice;
He says it's always better to think twice
Before you give away estates or pelf.
And therefore if you should advise yourself
In giving property away or land,
If it's important you should understand
Who is to get your goods, how much the more
You ought to think things over well before
You give away your body. If I may
I'd like to warn you; it is no child's play
Choosing a wife. It needs consideration,
In fact it asks a long investigation.

    'Is she discreet and sober? Or a drinker?
Or arrogant? Or shrewish like a tinker?
A scolder? Or extravagant? Too clannish?
Too poor? Too rich? Unnaturally mannish?
Although we know there isn't to be found
In all the world one that will trot quite sound,

Whether it's man or beast, the way we'd like it,
It were sufficient bargain, could we strike it,
In marrying a woman if she had
More good among her qualities than bad.
  'But all this asks some leisure to review;
God knows that many is the tear I too
Have wept in secret since I had a wife.
Praise whoso will the married state of life
I find it a routine, a synthesis
Of cost and care, and wholly bare of bliss.
And yet the neighbors round about, by God,
Especially the women – in a squad –
Congratulate me that I chose to wive
The constantest, the meekest soul alive.
I know where the shoe pinches; but for you,
Why, you must please yourself in what you do.
You're old enough – that's not what I disparage –
To think before you enter into marriage,
Especially if your wife is young and fair.
By Him that made earth, water, fire and air,
The youngest man in this distinguished rout
Will find it quite a task – you need not doubt –
To keep his woman to himself; and you
Will only please one for a year or two
– That is to say, please to the point of fervence.
Wives ask a lot in matters of observance.
I beg you not to take it the wrong way.'
'So that,' said January, 'is what you'd say!
Straw for your Seneca and your aphorisms,
Chop-logic and pedantic catechisms,
Weeds in a basket! Wiser men than you,
As you have heard, take quite another view
Of my proposal. What would you reply,
Placebo?' 'Curses on the man, say I,
Who seeks to offer an impediment,'
Said he; and so by general consent
His friends then rose, declaring it was good
That he should marry when and where he would.

Busy imaginations, strange invention
And soaring fantasy obsessed the attention
Of January's soul about his wedding.
Came many a lovely form and feature shedding
A rapture through his fancies night by night.
As who should take a mirror polished bright
And set it in the common market-place,
And watch the many figures pause and pace
Across his looking-glass; in such a way
Old January allowed his thoughts to play
Mirroring all the girls that lived nearby,
Still undetermined where his thought should lie.
For were there one with beauty in her face
Another, scarce less lovely, stood in grace
With people, seemed benign, a tender dove,
So the voice went, sober and fit for love;
Others were rich, but had a tarnished name.

At last, and half in earnest, half in game,
He fixed on one, and setting her apart,
He banished all the others from his heart.
He chose her on his own authority,
For love is always blind and cannot see,
And when he lay in bed at night his thought
Pictured her in his heart, for he was caught
By her fresh beauty and her age so tender;
Her little waist, her arms so long and slender,
Her sage deportment and her gentle birth,
Her womanliness and pensive way in mirth.
He, condescending on her thus, was fettered;
He felt his choice could never have been bettered,
For January, reaching his own conclusion,
Supposed the wits of others in confusion
If they opposed him; other choice would be
Impossible. Such was his fantasy.

He sent his friends a very strong request
Begging the pleasure – would they do their best? –
Of an immediate visit. In his belief
They needn't be kept long; he would be brief,

For there was no more need to cast around;
He was resolved, the lady had been found.

Placebo came and so did all the rest,
And January began with the request
That none should offer any argument
Against the purpose 'which was his intent,
Pleasing to God Almighty, and,' said he,
'The very ground of his prosperity.'

He said there was a maiden in the town
Whose beauty was indeed of great renown;
Her rank was not so great, to tell the truth,
But still she had her beauty and her youth;
She was the girl he wanted for his wife,
To lead a life of ease, a holy life.
And he thanked God he'd have her all alone
And nobody should part him from his own.
He begged them then to labor in his need
And help to make his enterprise succeed,
For then, he said, his mind would be at rest
'With nothing to annoy me or molest,
But for one thing which pricks my conscience still,
So listen to me kindly if you will.

'I've often,' he continued, 'heard ere this
That none may have two perfect kinds of bliss,
Bliss in this world, I mean, and bliss in Heaven;
Though he keep clear of sin – the deadly seven
And all the branches of their dreadful tree –
Yet there's so perfect a felicity
In marriage, so much pleasure, so few tears,
That I keep fearing, though advanced in years,
I shall be leading such a happy life
Of delicate ease, without a hint of strife,
That I shall have my heaven here in earth,
And may not that cost more than it is worth?
Penance and pain are paid for heavenly treasures,
So how should I, if lapped in all the pleasures
Of wedded life, attain to joys supernal
And enter into bliss with Christ Eternal?

That is my terror. Have you a suggestion,
My worthy brothers, to resolve the question?'
    Justinus, who despised this nonsense, said,
Jesting as ever, what was in his head;
And wishing not to spin things out in chatter
Used no authorities to support the matter.
'If there's no obstacle,' he said, 'but this,
God by some mighty miracle of His
May show you mercy as He is wont to do,
And long before they come to bury you
May cause you to bewail your married life
In which you say there never can be strife.
And God forbid that there should not be sent
A special grace that husbands may repent,
And sent more often than to single men.
This, sir, would be my own conclusion, then;
Never despair! You still may go to glory,
For she perhaps may prove your purgatory,
God's means of grace, as one might say, God's whip
To send your soul to Heaven with a skip
And swifter than an arrow from the bow!
    'I hope to God that you will shortly know
There's no such paramount felicity
In marriage, nor is ever like to be,
As to disqualify you for salvation,
Provided you observe some moderation,
Tempering down the passions of your wife
With some restriction of your amorous life,
Keeping yourself, of course, from other sin.
My tale is done – but there! My wits are thin.
But do not be afraid, for that's the moral.'
    (Let us wade out, however, from this quarrel;
The Wife of Bath, if you can understand
Those views of hers on marriage now in hand,
Declared them well, and may they not distress you.)
    And so Justinus said, 'Farewell, God bless you!'
He took his leave of January his brother
And they had no more speech with one another.

And when his friends saw that it needs must be
They made a careful marriage-treaty. She,
The girl agreed upon, whose name was May,
And with the smallest possible delay,
Was to be married to this January.

    And I assume there is no need to tarry
Over the marriage contracts, bond and writ,
Possessions, land, and all the rest of it,
Or make you listen to her rich array,
But finally there came the happy day
And off at last to church the couple went
There to receive the holy sacrament.

    Out came the priest, with stole about his neck,
And bade her be like Sarah at the beck
Of Abraham in wisdom, truth and grace,
Said all the prayers were proper to the case,
Then signed them with the cross and bade God bless
Them both, and made all sure in holiness.

    Thus they were wedded in solemnity,
And at the wedding-banquet he and she
Sat with their worthier guests upon the dais.
Joy and delight filled the entire place,
Stringed instruments, victuals of every kind,
The dantiest all Italy could find.
Music broke forth as with the sound of Zion,
Not Orpheus nor the Theban king Amphion
Ever achieved so sweet a melody.

    At every course there came loud minstrelsy
And Joab's trumpets never took the ear
So forcefully as this, nor half so clear
Those of Theodamas when Thebes stood out.
Bacchus himself was pouring wine about
And Venus smiled on everyone in sight,
For January had become her knight
And wished to try his courage in the carriage
Of his new liberty combined with marriage.
Armed with a fire-brand she danced about
Before the bride and all the happy rout;

And certainly I'll go as far as this
And say that Hymen, God of wedded bliss,
Never beheld so happy a wedded man.

Hold thou thy peace, O poet Martian,
Give us no more thy marital doxology
For Mercury on wedding with Philology!
Silence the song the Muses would have sung,
Thine is too small a pen, too weak a tongue,
To signalize this wedding or engage
To tell how tender youth and stooping age
Were married, joys that none may write about!
Try it yourself and you will soon find out
If I'm a liar or not in such a case.

For there sat May with so benign a face
That but to see her was a fairy-tale.
Queen Esther's eye could never so assail
Ahasuerus, never looked so meek;
Of so much loveliness I dare not speak,
Yet thus much of her beauty I will say
That she was like the brightest morn of May
With every grace and pleasure in her glance.

Old January sat ravished in a trance
And every time he gazed upon her face
His heart began to menace her and race;
He longed to strain her to him with the ardor
That Paris showed for Helen, aye, and harder.
And yet he felt strong qualms of pity stir
To think he soon must do offense to her,
That very night, and murmured, 'Tender creature!
Alas, God grant you may endure the nature
Of my desires, they are so sharp and hot.
I am aghast lest you sustain them not.
God hinder me from doing all I might!
But O I wish to God that it were night,
And the night last forever! Oh, how slow ...
Why don't these people hurry up and go?'

So he began to dedicate his labors
To getting rid politely of his neighbors,

And to detaching them from food supplies.
At last their reason told them they should rise;
They danced and drank and, left to their devices,
They went from room to room to scatter spices
About the house. Joy rose in every man
Except in one, a squire called Damian,
Who carved for January every day.

He was so ravished by the sight of May
That in mad anguish of desire he could
Almost have died or fainted where he stood,
So sorely Venus burnt him with the brand
Which, as she danced, she carried in her hand.
And hastily the boy went off to bed;
No more of him at present need be said.
I leave him there to weep and to complain
Till fresh young May have pity on his pain.

O perilous fire, breeding in the bedding!
O household traitor proffering faith, but heading
For treacherous service of the blackest hue,
Sly viper in the bosom, heart untrue,
God shield us all from your acquaintanceship!
O January drunk upon the lip
Of marriage in your pleasures, Damian,
Your very squire, born your serving-man,
Even now is meditating villainy.
O God unmask your household enemy!
Over the world no pestilence can roam
That is as foul as foe within the home.

The sun had traced his arc with golden finger
Across the sky, caring no more to linger
On the horizon in that latitude.
Night with her mantle which is dark and rude
Had overspread the hemisphere about,
And gone were all the merry-making rout
Of January's guests, with hearty thanks,
And homeward each convivially spanks
There to take up such business as will keep
Him happy till it should be time for sleep.

Soon after this the restive January
Demanded bed; no longer would he tarry
Except to quaff a cordial for the fire
That claret laced with spice can lend desire;
For he had many potions, drugs as fine
As those that monk, accursed Constantine,
Has numbered in his book *De Coitu*.
He drank them all; not one did he eschew,
And to his private friends who lingered on
He said, 'For God's love, hurry and be gone,
Empty the house politely if you can.'
And presently they did so to a man.
A toast was drunk, the curtains back were thrown;
The bride was borne to bed as still as stone.
And when the priest had blessed the wedding-bed
The room was emptied and the guests were sped.

Fast in the arms of January lay
His mate, his paradise, his fresh young May.
He lulled her, sought to kiss away her trouble;
The bristles of his beard were thick as stubble,
Much like a dog-fish skin, and sharp as briars,
Being newly shaved to sweeten his desires.
He rubbed his chin against her tender cheek
And said, 'Alas, alas that I should seek
To trespass – yet I must – and to offend
My spouse, ere the time ripens to descend.
Nevertheless consider this,' said he,
'No workman, whatsoever he may be,
Can do his work both well and in a flurry;
This shall be done in perfect ease, no hurry.
It's of no consequence how long we play,
We are in holy wedlock, and we may.
O blessed be the yoke that we are in
For nothing we can do will count as sin.
A man is not a sinner with his wife,
He cannot hurt himself with his own knife;
We have the law's permission thus to play.'
And so he labored till the break of day,

Then took a sop of claret-sodden toast,
Sat up in bed as rigid as a post,
And started singing very loud and clear.
He kissed his wife and gave a wanton leer,
Feeling a coltish rage towards his darling
And chattering in the jargon of a starling.
The slack of skin about his neck was shaking
As thus he fell a-chanting and corn-craking.

God knows what May was thinking in her heart
Seeing him sit there in his shirt apart,
Wearing his night-cap, with his scrawny throat.
She didn't think his games were worth a groat.

At last he said, 'I think I'll take a rest;
Now day has come a little sleep were best.'
And down he lay and slept till half-past eight;
Then he woke up, and seeing it was late,
Old January arose; but fresh young May
Kept her apartment until the fourth day
As women will, they do it for the best.
For every laborer must have time to rest,
For otherwise he can't keep laboring;
And that is true of every living thing,
Be it a fish, a bird, a beast, or man.

Now I will speak of woeful Damian
Languishing in his love, as will appear.
I should address him thus, if he could hear:
'O silly Damian! Alas, alas!
Answer my question; in your present pass
How are you going to tell her of your woe?
She's absolutely bound to answer no,
And if you speak, she's certain to betray you;
I can say nothing. Heaven help and stay you!'

Sick-hearted Damian in Venus' fire
Is so consumed, he's dying with desire,
And so he took his courage in his hand
To end a grief he could no longer stand
And with a pen that he contrived to borrow
He wrote a letter pouring out his sorrow

After the fashion of a song or lay
Indited to his lady, dazzling May,
And wrapped it in a purse of silk apart
To hang inside his shirt, upon his heart.

The moon that at the noon-tide of the day
When January married lovely May,
Had stood in *Taurus,* in the second degree,
Had glided into *Cancer* now, and she,
This exquisite young lady, she of whom
I speak, beautiful May, had kept her room
As is the custom among nobles all.
A bride of course should never eat in hall
Till four days afterwards, or three at least,
But when they're over, let her go and feast.

On the fourth day, from noon to noon complete,
And when high mass was over, in his seat
Sat January in his hall with May,
As fresh and bright as is a summer's day.
And it so happened that this good old man
Remembered Damian, and thus began:
'Where's Damian? Saints above! How can it be
That Damian isn't here to wait on me?
Is he still sick? What's happened? Is he up?'

The squires standing there to fill his cup
Excused him on the grounds that he was ill,
He was in bed, unfit for duty still;
No other reason could have kept him back.

'I'm sorry for it. What a sharp attack!
And he's a gentleman to tell the truth,'
The old man said, 'and if he died, poor youth,
It were a pity; he's a lad of worth.
I don't know anyone of equal birth
Who's so discreet, so manly and so able;
Thrifty and serviceable too at table.
As soon as possible after meat to-day
I'll visit him myself; and so shall May.
We'll give him all the comfort that we can.'

Then everybody blessed the kind old man

So eager in his bounty and good breeding
To offer anything that might be needing
To comfort a sick squire; a gentle deed.
　'Madam,' said January, 'take good heed
That after meat you and your women all,
When you have sought your room and left the hall,
Go up and have a look at Damian
And entertain him; he's a gentleman.
And tell him too that I shall do my best
To visit him myself, after my rest.
Now hurry on, be quick, and I shall bide me
Here, until you return to sleep beside me.'
And on the word he rose and gave a call
To fetch a squire (the marshal of the hall)
And gave him some instructions. Fresh young May
With all her women took the shortest way
To Damian's room an sat beside his bed;
A warmth of comfort was in all she said,
Benignity and beauty in her glance.
And Damian when at last he saw his chance
Secretly took his purse and *billet-doux*
Couched in the sweetest phrases that he knew
And put it in her hand with nothing more
Than a long sigh as deep as to the core,
But in a whisper he contrived to say,
'Mercy, my darling, don't give me away,
I should be killed if this were ever known.'
The purse slid from his bosom to her own
And off she went. You'll get no more of me.
　Back to old January then went she;
He was reclining on his bed by this.
He drew her to his arms with many a kiss,
Then settled back to sleep at once; and so
The girl pretended that she had to go
Where everybody has to go at times.
There, after memorizing Damian's rhymes,
She tore them into pieces and she cast
Them softly down the privy-drain at last.

Who fell into a study then but May?
And down beside old January she lay;
He slept until awoken by his cough.
He begged her then to strip her garments off
And said he would enjoy a little play;
Garments were always getting in the way.
And she obeyed whether she would or no.
Lest I offend prim people I will go
No further into what he did, or tell
Whether she thought it paradise or hell.
I leave them working thus as I suppose
Till it was evensong, and then they rose.

Whether by destiny or accident,
By starry influence or natural bent,
Or whether some constellation held its state
In heaven to make the hour fortunate
For giving *billet-doux* and lending wing
To Venus – there's a time for everything,
The learned say – and get a lady's love,
I cannot tell. But God who sits above
And knows that every action has a cause,
Let Him give judgment. I can only pause
And wonder; this at least is true of May
That such was the impression made that day
And such her pity for that sick young man
She could not rid her heart of Damian
Or of the wish to see his troubles ended.
'Whoever else,' she thought, 'may be offended,
I do not care; but I can promise this,
To love him more than anyone there is,
Though he mayn't have a shirt. I will be kind.'
Pity flows swiftly in a noble mind.

Here you can see what bounty may be sought
And found in women who take careful thought.
Some female tyrants – many I have known –
Are pitiless, their hearts are made of stone
And would have rather let him die the death
Than yield their grace or favor by a breath,

And they exult in showing cruel pride,
Calmly indifferent to homicide.

Soft May felt pity, you must understand.
She wrote a letter in her own fair hand
In which she granted him her very grace.
There needed nothing but the time and place
To grant the satisfactions he desired;
He was to have whatever he required.

So when she saw occasion one fine day
To visit him, off went the lovely May
And thrust this letter down with subtle skill
Under his pillow, read it if he will.
She took him by the hand and squeezed it hard,
But secretly, for she was on her guard,
Bade him get well, then went without demur
To January who had called for her.

Then up rose happy Damian on the morrow;
Gone was all trace of malady and sorrow.
He preens himself and prunes and combs his curls
To take the fancy of his queen of girls.
To January his master in addition
He was a very spaniel in submission,
And was so pleasant in his general drift
(Craft's all that matters if you have the gift),
That people spoke him well in every way,
But above all he stood in grace with May.
Thus I leave Damian, busy with his needs,
And turn once more to how my tale proceeds.

Some writers argue that felicity
Wholly consists in pleasure; certainly
This noble January, as best he might
In all that was befitting to a knight,
Had planned to live deliciously in pleasure;
His house and all his finery and treasure
Were fashioned to his rank as are a king's,
And among other of his handsome things
He had a garden, walled about with stone;
So fair a garden never was there known.

For out of doubt I verily suppose
That he who wrote the *Romance of the Rose*
Could not have pictured such magnificence;
Priapus never had the eloquence,
Though he be god of gardens, to re-tell
The beauty of this garden and the well
Under a laurel, standing ever-green.
Many a time King Pluto and his Queen
Proserpina and all her fairy rout
Disported and made melody about
That well and held their dances, I am told.

    This January, so noble, and so old,
Found walking in it such felicity
That no one was allowed to have the key
Except himself, and for its little wicket
He had a silver latch-key to unclick it
Or lock it up, and when his thought was set
Upon the need to pay his wife her debt
In summer season, thither would he go
With May his wife when there was none to know,
And anything they had not done in bed
There in the garden was performed instead,
So in this manner many a merry day
Was spent by January and lovely May.
But worldly joys, alas, may not endure
For January or anyone, be sure.

    Changeable Fortune, O unstable Chance,
Thine is the scorpion's treacherous advance!
Thy head all flattery, about to sting,
Thy tail a death, and death by poisoning.
O brittle joy, O venom sweet and strange,
O monster that so subtly canst arrange
Thy gifts and color them with all the dyes
Of durability to catch the wise
And foolish too! Say, why hast thou deceived
Old January, thy friend as he believed?
Thou hast bereft him of his sight, his eye
Is dark and in his grief he longs to die.

Alas this noble January, he
So generous once in his prosperity
Went blind; quite suddenly he lost his sight.
Pitiful loss! He wept it day and night,
While fell suspicion fired his melancholy
Thinking his wife might fall into some folly.
His heart burned hot; he had been nothing loth,
Nay glad, if one had come to slay them both.
For neither on his death nor in his life
Was she to be the mistress or the wife
Of any other, but in weeds of state,
True as a turtle that has lost her mate,
She was to live, the garments on her back
A widow's, never anything but black.

But in the end, after a month or two,
His sorrows cooled a little, it is true,
For when he saw there was no remedy
He took in patience his adversity,
Save that the ineradicable sting
Of jealousy embittered everything,
For so outrageous are the thoughts it rouses
That neither when at home or in the houses
Of his acquaintance, no, nor anywhere
Would he allow his wife to take the air
Unless his hand were on her day and night.

Ah, how she wept, fresh as she was, and bright,
Who loved her Damian, and with so benign
A love that sudden death was her design
Unless she could enjoy him; so at first
She wept and waited for her heart to burst.

And Damian too, upon the other part,
Became in turn so sorrowful of heart
That none was ever like him; night and day
There never was a chance to speak to May
As to his purpose, no, nor anything near it,
Unless old January was there to hear it,
Holding her hand and never letting go.

Nevertheless by writing to and fro

And private signals Damian knew her mind
And she was well aware what he designed.

O January, what might it thee avail
Though thou couldst see as far as ship can sail?
As well be blind and be deceived as be
Deceived as others are that still can see.
Consider Argus with his hundred eyes
Poring and prying, yet for all these spies
He was deceived, and many more I know,
God wot, who sagely think they are not so.
Least said is soonest mended; say no more.

Now this fresh May of whom I spoke before
Took some warm wax and fashioned an impression
Of that same key in January's possession
Into the garden, where he often went.
Damian who knew exactly what she meant
Secretly forged a counterfeited key.
That's all there is to say, but presently
A wonder will befall, if you will wait,
Thanks to this key and to the wicket-gate.

O noble Ovid, that was truly spoken
When you affirmed there was no cunning token
Or trickery, however long or hot,
That lovers could not find. For did they not
When Pyramus and Thisbe, I recall,
Though strictly watched, held converse through a wall?
Who could have thought of such a trick as that
But lovers? To return to what we're at,
Our present purpose, on the eighth of June
Old January felt himself in tune,
Egged on by her, to pass the time in play
Down in his garden all alone with May.

The morning shone on them and thus said he:
'Rise up, my wife, my love, my lady free!
The turtle's voice is heard, my dove, my pet.
Winter is gone with all its rain and wet;
Come out with me, bright-eyes, my columbine,
O how far fairer are thy breasts than wine!

Our garden is enclosed and walled about;
White spouse, come forth to me; ah, never doubt
But I am wounded to the heart, dear wife,
For love of you, unspotted in your life
As well I know. Come forth to take our pleasures,
Wife of my choice and treasure of my treasures!'

He got these lewd old words out of a book.
And May at once gave Damian a look
Signaling he should go before and wait;
So Damian ran on, unlocked the gate
And darted in as swiftly as a bird,
And, so as to be neither seen nor heard,
He crouched beneath the bushes on his own.

And then this January, blind as stone,
Came hand in hand with May, but unattended,
And down into the garden they descended
And having entered clapped the wicket to.

'Now wife,' he said, 'none's here but I and you,
And you are she, the creature I best love.
For by the Lord that sits in Heaven above
Believe me I would die upon the knife
Rather than hurt you, truest, dearest wife.
Remember how I chose you, for God's sake;
Not covetously nor in hope to make,
But only for the love I had to you.
And though I may be old and sightless too,
Be true to me and I will tell you why.

Three things for certain you shall win thereby:
First, love of Christ; next, honor to yourself;
Last, your inheritance, my lands and pelf,
Towers and towns; draw the agreement up,
They're yours, it shall be signed before we sup.
But first, as God may bring my soul to bliss,
I pray you seal the covenant with a kiss.
And though I may be jealous, blame me not;
You are so deeply printed in my thought
That when I meditate your loveliness
And my dislikeable old age, I guess

That howsoever, were it death to me,
I could not bear to lose your company,
For very love; I say it with no doubt.
Now kiss me, wife, and let us roam about.'

Fresh-hearted May on hearing what he said
Benignly answered him with drooping head,
But first and foremost she began to weep.
'Indeed,' she said, 'I have a soul to keep
No less than you, and then there is my honor
Which for a wife is like a flower upon her.
I put it in your hands for good or ill
When the priest bound my body to your will,
So let me answer of my own accord
If you will give me leave, beloved lord;
I pray to God that never dawn the day
– Or let me die as foully as I may –
When I shall do my family that shame,
Or bring so much dishonor on my name,
As to be false. And if my love grow slack,
Take me and strip me, sew me in a sack
And drop me in the nearest lake to drown.
I am no common woman of the town,
I am of gentle birth, I keep aloof.
So why speak thus to me, for what reproof
Have I deserved? It's men that are untrue
And women, women ever blamed anew.
I think it a pretense that men profess;
They hide behind a charge of faithlessness.'

And as she spoke she saw a short way off
Young Damian in his bush. She gave a cough
And signaled with a finger quickly where
He was to climb into a tree – a pear
Heavily charged with fruit, and up he went
Perfectly understanding what she meant,
Or any other signal I may state
Better than January could, her mate.
For she had written to him, never doubt it,
Telling him all and how to set about it.

And there I leave him sitting, by your pardon,
While May and January roamed the garden.

    Bright was the day and blue the firmament,
Down fell the golden flood that Phoebus sent
To gladden every flower with his beams;
He was in *Gemini* at the time, it seems,
And but a little from his declination
In *Cancer,* which is Jupiter's exaltation.
And so it happened through the golden tide
Into the garden from the further side
Came Pluto who is king of Fairyland
And many a lady of his elfin band
Behind his queen, the lady Proserpine,
And one behind another in a line.
– If you consult your Claudian you may read
How she was gathering flowers in a mead
And how he fetched her in his grisly cart –
The King of Faery sat him down apart
Upon a little bench of turfy green
And then he turned and thus addressed his queen:

    'Dear wife,' he said, 'what no one can gainsay
And what experience shows us every day
Are the foul treacheries women do to men.
Ten thousand tales, and multiply by ten,
Record your notable untruth and lightness.
O Solomon in thy wisdom, wealth and brightness,
Replete in sapience as in worldly glory,
How memorable are thy words and story
To every creature capable of reason!
Of man's true bounty and of woman's treason
Thou saidst, "Among a thousand found I one,
And yet among all women found I none."

    'So said the king who knew your wickedness;
And Jesus son of Sirach,* as I guess,
Seldom says much of you in reverence –
Wild fire and a corruptive pestilence
Fall down upon you all to burn and blight!
Do you not see that honorable knight

Who, being blind and old and unobservant,
Is to be cuckolded by his own servant?
Look, there he sits, that lecher in the tree!
Now will I grant it of my majesty
To this blind, old and estimable knight
That he shall instantly receive his sight
Whenever his wife begins her villainy.
He shall know all about her harlotry
Both in rebuke of her and others too.'

    'So that,' the queen replied, 'is what you'll do!
Now, by my grandsire's soul, though she is young
I'll put a ready answer on her tongue
And every woman's after, for her sake.
Though taken in their guilt they yet shall make
A bold-faced explanation to excuse them
And bear down all who venture to accuse them;
For lack of answer none of them shall die.
Though a man saw things with his very eye
We'll face it out, we women, and be bold
To weep and swear, insinuate and scold
As long as men are gullible as geese.

    'What do I care for your authorities?
I'm well aware this Jew, this Solomon
Found many women fools as he went on,
But if he never found a woman true,
God knows that there are many men who do,
Who find them faithful, virtuous and good.
Witness all those in christian sisterhood
Who proved their constancy by martyrdom.
And Roman history has mentioned some,
Aye many, women of exceeding truth.
Now keep your temper, sir, though he, forsooth,
Said there were no good women, if you can.
Consider the opinion of this man.
He meant it thus that sovereign constancy
Is God's alone who sits in Trinity.
Hey! God knows Solomon is only one;
Why do you make so much of Solomon?

What though he built God's temple in the story?
What though he were so rich, so high in glory?
He also made a temple for false gods;
Nothing is worse than that! So what's the odds?
Fair as you plaster him with whitewash, sir,
He was a lecher and idolater,
And in his latter days forsook the Lord;
And if God never had (as books record)
Forgiven him because He loved his father,
Solomon would have lost his kingdom rather
Than worship Him. And all your spite, say I.
Against us isn't worth a butterfly.
I am a woman and I needs must speak
Or swell until I burst. I won't be meek!
And since he said that we were wrangleresses,
As ever I may hope to flaunt my tresses,
I will not spare for manners or politeness
To rail at one who rails at woman's lightness.'

    'Madam,' he said, 'be angry now no more;
I give it up. But seeing that I swore
Upon my oath to grant him sight again,
I'll stand by what I said, I tell you plain.
I am a king; it fits me not to lie.'
'And I'm the Queen of Fairyland, say I!
Her answer she shall have, I undertake.
Let us have no more words, for goodness' sake.
Indeed I don't intend to be contrary.'

    Now let us turn again to January
Who walked the garden with his pretty May
And sang more merrily than a popinjay,
'I love you best, and ever shall, my sweet!'
So long among the paths had strayed their feet
That they at last had reached the very tree
Where Damian sat in waiting merrily,
High in his leafy bower of fresh green.
And fresh young May, so shiningly serene,
Began to sigh and said, 'Alas, my side
Is hurting me; whatever may betide

I must have just one pear that I can see
Or I shall die! I long so terribly
To eat a little pear, it looks so green.
O help me for the love of Heaven's Queen!
I warn you that a woman in my plight
May often feel so great an appetite
For fruit that she may die to go without.'
   'Alas,' he said, 'there's nobody about
Able to climb. Alas, alas,' said he,
'That I am blind.' 'No matter, sir,' said she,
'For if you would consent – there's nothing in it –
To hold the pear-tree in your arms a minute
(I know you have no confidence in me),
Then I could climb up well enough,' said she,
'If I could set my foot upon your back.'
   'Of course,' he said, 'why, you shall never lack
For that, or my heart's blood to do you good.'
And down he stooped; upon his back she stood,
Catching a branch, and with a spring she thence
– Ladies, I beg you not to take offense,
I can't embellish, I'm a simple man –
Went up into the tree, and Damian
Pulled up her smock at once and in he thrust.
   And when King Pluto saw this shameful lust
He gave back sight to January once more
And made him see far better than before.
Never was man more taken with delight
Than January when he received his sight,
And his first thought was to behold his love.
He cast his eyes into the tree above
Only to see that Damian had addressed
His wife in ways that cannot be expressed,
Unless I use a very vulgar word.
He gave a roaring cry, as might be heard
From stricken mothers when their babies die.
'Help! Out upon you!' he began to cry.
'Strong Madam Strumpet! What are you up to there?'
'What ails you, sir?' said she, 'what makes you swear?

Have patience, use the reason in your mind,
I've helped you back to sight when you were blind!
Upon my soul I'm telling you no lies;
They told me if I wished to heal your eyes
Nothing could cure them better than for me
To struggle with a fellow in a tree.
God knows it was a kindness that I meant.'
'Struggle!' he said. 'I saw you! In it went!
A shameful death to both of you! What lies!
I saw him have you, saw it with these eyes,
And if I didn't, hang me by the neck!'

   'Why then,' she said, 'my medicine's gone to wreck,
For certainly if you could really see
You'd never say such words as those to me;
You have some glimpses, but no perfect sight.'
'I see,' he said, 'as well as ever I might,
Thanks be to God. I got the clearest view
Of what it was he seemed to do to you.'

   'You're hazy, hazy, my good sir,' said she;
'That's all I get for helping you to see.
Alas,' she said, 'that ever I was so kind!'

   'Dear wife,' said January, 'never mind,
Come down, dear heart, and if I've slandered you
God knows I'm punished for it. Come down, do!
Yet by my father's soul it seemed to me
That Damian there had had you in the tree
And that your smock was pulled up to his chest.'

   'Well, you must think as it may please you best,'
She said, 'but sir, reflect; when one awakes
No one can see quite clearly and it takes
A little time, one's dazzled by the blaze
Until one has recovered from the daze.
Just so a man who has been blind for long
Cannot expect his sight to be so strong
At first, or see as well as those may do
Who've had their sight back for a day or two.
Until your sight has settled down a bit
You may be frequently deceived by it.

Be careful then, for by our heavenly King
Many a man feels sure he's seen a thing
Which was quite different really, he may fudge it;
Misapprehend a thing and you'll misjudge it.'
   And on the word she jumped down from the tree.
And January – who so glad as he? –
Kissed her and clasped her in his arms – how often! –
And stroked her breast caressingly to soften
Her indignation. To his palace then
He led her home. Be happy, gentlemen,
That finishes my tale of January;
God and his Mother guard us, blessed Mary!

Epilogue to the Merchant's Tale

'HEY!' said our Host. 'Hey, Lord a-mercy, sir!
   Well, God preserve me from a wife like her.
Just think what stratagems and subtleties
There are in women, busy little bees
They are, deceiving us poor foolish men!
They wriggle here and there and back again
To dodge the truth; the Merchant's tale has shown it.
And it's a fact, and I'm obliged to own it,
I have a wife, although she's poor enough;
A blabbing shrewish tongue she has, and rough.
Apart from that she has a heap more vices.
No matter, let it go, for that suffices.
But, d'ye know what? – you mustn't tell the wife –
I bitterly regret I'm tied for life.
Were I to reckon up her every vice
I should seem too fastidious at the price.
'Cause why? Because she'd hear of it, no doubt,
Reported by some person in this rout,
By whom it's hardly necessary to say;
In things like that women can find a way.
And anyhow my brains would hardly run
To telling you, and so my story's done.'

[GROUP F]

The Squire's Tale

The Squire's Prologue

'SQUIRE, come up and if you feel disposed
Say something about love – it is supposed
You know as much of that as any man.'
'O no, sir,' he replied, 'but what I can
I'll do with all my heart. I won't rebel
Against your pleasure; I've a tale to tell.
Have me excused if I should speak amiss,
My will is good and, look, my tale is this.'

The Squire's Tale

PART I

AT Tzarev in the land of Tartary
There dwelt a king at war with Muscovy,
Which brought the death of many a doughty man.
This noble king was known as Cambuskan*
And in his time enjoyed such great renown
That nowhere in that region up or down
Was one so excellent in everything;
Nothing he lacked belonging to a king.

As to the faith in which he had been born
He kept such loyalties as he had sworn,
Then he was powerful and wise and brave,
Compassionate and just, and if he gave
His word he kept it, being honorable,
The same to all, benevolent, and stable
As is a circle's center; and in fight
As emulous as any squire or knight,

Young, personable, fresh and fortunate,
Maintaining such a kingliness of state
There never was his match in mortal man.

This noble king, this Tartar Cambuskan,
Begat two sons on Elpheta his wife.
The elder bore the name of Algarsyf,
The other son, the younger, Cambalo.
He had another child, a daughter though,
Youngest of all; her name was Canace.
To tell her beauty is too much for me,
Lying beyond what tongue of mine can sing;
I dare not undertake so high a thing.
My English too is insufficient for it,
It asks a rhetorician to explore it,
A poet in the colors of that art,
To give a fair account of every part.
I am none such, I speak as best I can.

Now it so happened that when Cambuskan
Had borne his diadem for twenty years,
As was his usual custom it appears
He had the feast of his nativity
Proclaimed throughout the land of Tartary.
It was the Ides of March, in the new year;
Phoebus the sun shone happily and clear
For he was near his point of exaltation
In face of Mars, and there he held his station
In *Aries,* and that's a sultry sign.
Cheerful the weather, vigorous and benign,
And all the birds against the sunny sheen,
What with the season and the early green,
Sang the loud canticles of their affection,
For, as it seemed, at last they had protection
Against the sword of winter, keen and cold.

This noble Cambuskan of whom I told
Sat on his dais in a royal robe,
High on his throne with diadem and globe,
And there held feast in all his power enfurled,
And there was nothing like it in the world.

If I should pause to tell of his array
The task would occupy a summer's day,
Nor is there any need I should enforce
Attention to his banquet, course on course,
Or number the quaint dishes they put on,
The heron-chick, the richly roasted swan,
For in that country veteran knights report
There are some meats esteemed the daintiest sort
Though in this country their esteem is small,
But there is none who could report it all,
So let me not delay you – it is prime
Of day, it would be fruitless loss of time.

Let me retrace my footsteps to their source.
It happened, close upon the second course,
As the king sat with his nobility
Listening to instruments of minstrelsy
That made delicious music in the hall,
Suddenly at the door in sight of all
There came a knight upon a steed of brass
Bearing a mirror, broad and made of glass.
Upon his thumb he had a golden ring
And at his side a naked sword a-swing,
And up he rode and reached the royal table.
In all that hall not one of them was able
To speak a word for wonder at this knight;
They waited, young and old, and watched the sight.

This stranger-knight so suddenly presented,
Bare-headed, armed and richly ornamented,
Saluted king and queen and nobles all
In order as they sat about the hall
With such deep reverence and comely grace,
Not only in his speech but in his face,
That Gawain,* ever courteous, ever bland,
Though he were come again from fairyland
A greater courtesy could not have shown.
And thus before high table and the throne
He gave his message in a manly voice
In his own language with a perfect choice

Of phrase, faultless in syllable or letter;
And, that his story might appear the better,
Gesture and word were fitted each to each
As taught to those that learn the art of speech,
And though I lack his talent to beguile
And cannot climb over so tall a stile,
I say as to their general content
The words I use amount to what he meant,
So far as I can trust my memory.

'The King of India and of Araby
Who is my sovereign lord, this solemn day
Salutes your Majesty as best he may
And sends you here in honor of your feast
Through me who am your servant, though the least,
This steed of brass that easily may run,
Within the natural circuit of the sun,
That is to say in four and twenty hours,
Wherever you may wish, in drought or showers,
And bear your body to whatever place
Your heart desires at a gentle pace
And without hurt to you through foul or fair.
If you should wish to fly, and mount the air
As does an eagle when it seeks to soar,
This very steed will bear you as before
In perfect safety on your chosen track,
Though you should fall asleep upon his back,
And when you twist this pin return again.

'He that devised it had a cunning brain;
He watched through many a change of constellation
Ere finding one to suit his operation,
And he knew many a magic seal and spell.

'This mirror that I have in hand as well
Is such that those who look in it may see
The coming shadow of adversity
Upon yourself and kingdom, it will show
You plainly who is friend and who is foe.
More than all this, if any lady bright
Has set on any man her heart's delight,

If he be false she shall perceive his shady
And treacherous conduct and the other lady
So openly, nothing will hide his treason.
And so, against this lusty summer season,
This mirror and this ring are sent by me,
As you behold, to Lady Canace
Your excellent and lovely daughter here.

'The virtue of the ring, as will appear,
Stands in this point; if she be not averse
To wear it on her thumb or in her purse,
There is no bird that flies beneath the reach
Of heaven but she will understand its speech
And know its meaning openly and plain
And in its language answer it again.
Of every rooted grass that grows on earth
She shall have knowledge too and test its worth
In sickness or on wounds however wide.

'This naked sword here hanging at my side
Retains the property to cut and bite
The armor of whatever man you smite,
Though it were thicker than a branching oak;
And when a man is wounded by its stroke
Nothing can heal him till the sword is laid
In mercy flat upon the wound it made,
Where he was hurt. This is as much to say
Lay the blade flat, turning the edge away,
And stroke the wound, and you will see it close;
This is the very truth in sober prose.
While it is in your hold it cannot fail.'

The stranger-knight, thus having told his tale,
Rode out of hall, dismounted and had done.
His steed of brass that glittered like the sun
Stood in the courtyard still as any stone.
They gave the knight a chamber of his own,
Unarmed and feasted him, and in a while
His gifts were carried forth in royal style,
That is to say the mirror and the sword,
And brought to the high tower under ward

Of certain officers appointed for it.
    As for the ring, in solemn pomp they bore it
To Canace herself who sat at table.
But I assure you all it is no fable
That horse of brass could not be raised or slewed
But stood its ground as if it had been glued.
It was of no avail to drive or bully,
Use windlass, engine, artifice or pulley;
And why? Because they didn't know the dodge.
And so they were obliged to let it lodge
Below until the knight had shown them how
To shift him; you shall hear it, but not now.
    Great was the crowd that swarmed about in force
To gaze upon the stationary horse.
It was as tall, as broad, and of a length
Just as proportionable to its strength
As any courser bred in Lombardy,
Quick-eyed, as horsely as a horse can be,
Like an Apulian steed, as highly bred.
And I assure you that from tail to head
Nothing could be improved by art or nature,
So they supposed at least who saw the creature.
But yet the wonder nothing could surpass
Was how it went if it were made of brass.
Some thought it came from fairyland's dominions.
    Various men gave various opinions,
As many heads, so many fallacies.
They murmured round it like a swarm of bees
And guessed according to their fantasy,
Or quoted snatches of old poetry
Saying it was like Pegasus of old,
The fabled horse that flew on wings of gold,
Or it was Sinon's horse by whose employ
The Greeks had brought destruction upon Troy,
As one may read in those old epic tales.
Said one of them, 'My spirit fairly quails
To think there may be men-of-arms within it
Plotting to take our town this very minute.

It would be well if such a thing were known.'
Another, whispering to his friend alone,
Muttered, 'He's wrong. More like some apparition
Or trick-illusion made by a magician,
Like what these jugglers do at feasts of state.'

Thus they kept up the jangle of debate
As the illiterate are wont to do
When subtler things are offered to their view
Than their unletteredness can comprehend;
They reach the wrong conclusions in the end.

Some wondered at the mirror and its power
(It had been taken to the master-tower)
And how such things could be foreseen in it.
Another said that such a thing could fit
Quite naturally through the redirection
Of angles by the laws of light-reflection,
And said there was another such in Rome.
Then they referred to many a learned tome
By Aristotle and by Alhazen
And Witelo and other learned men*
Who when alive had written down directives
For use of cunning mirrors and perspectives,
As anyone can tell who has explored
These authors. Others wondered at the sword
That had the power to pierce through anything,
And spoke of Telephus the Mysian king,
And of Achilles and his marvelous spear,
Able to heal no less than it could sear,
Exactly like this sword that at a word
Could wound a man or heal him, as you heard.

They spoke of sundry ways of hardening metal
By various ointments, and they tried to settle
The times and methods for this mystery,
Which are unknown, at any rate to me.

And then they spoke about the magic ring
Given to Canace, a marvelous thing,
Concluding thus: 'None such, as one supposes,
Was ever known; but Solomon and Moses

Were said to have been cunning in that art.'
Thus people spoke in little groups apart;
And others said how strange it was to learn
That glass is made out of the ash of fern,
Though bearing no resemblances to glass;
But being used to this they let it pass,
The argument declined, they ceased to wonder,
Like those who speculate on what makes thunder,
Ebb, flood or mist, how gossamer is blown,
Or anything until the cause is known.
And so they guessed and judged as they were able
Until the king began to rise from table.

Phoebus was over the meridian line;
It was the hour of the ascending sign
Of royal *Leo* with his Aldiran,*
And this great Tartar king, this Cambuskan,
Rose from the board in all his majesty.
Before him went a blare of minstrelsy
Until he reached the presence-room surrounded
By divers instruments, and these were sounded
So sweetly it was heaven to those that listened.
Children of Venus glided there and glistened
In happy dance, for she was mounted high
In *Piscis*, and looked down with friendly eye.

The noble king was seated on his throne;
The stranger-knight was fetched and he alone
Was chosen forth to dance with Canace.
Great was the reveling and jollity,
It went beyond all dull imagination;
Only a man who knows the exaltation
Of serving love, a man as fresh as May,
A gamesome one, could tell of their array.

For who could paint the circling of their dances,
So foreign to us, or the countenances
So subtle-smooth in their dissimulations
For fear of jealousy's insinuations?
No one but Launcelot and he is dead.
Pass over then and leave them there to tread

Their long delight, beyond all words of mine.
So on they danced till it was time to dine.

The steward bids men hurry with the spices
And fetch the wine, the minstrelsy entices,
The ushers and the squires in a pack
Run off and bring the wines and spices back.
They ate and drank, and having left the table
They sought the temple as was reasonable.
The service done, they feasted all day long.
Why should I tell you what they served the throng?
Everyone knows that at a royal feast
There's plenty for the greatest and the least,
And delicacies more than I would know.

His supper done, the king proposed to go
And see this horse of brass with all his rout
Of lords and ladies standing round about.

Such the amazement at this brazen horse,
Not since the siege of Troy had run its course,
At which another horse amazed her men,
Had there been such astonishment as then.
The king at last put question to the knight
As to this courser's properties and might,
Begging him to explain the beast's control.

This horse began to dance and caracole
Under its master's hand that held the rein;
He answered, 'Sir, there's nothing to explain
But this; if you would ride it far or near,
Just twirl this pin that's standing in its ear,
As when we are alone I soon can show,
Then name the country where you wish to go,
Or else the place, wherever you would ride,
And having reached it, if you so decide,
Bid him descend and twirl another pin,
For all the mechanism lies therein,
And down he'll go to carry out your will
And having reached the ground will stand stock-still.
Whatever then the world may do or say
He cannot thence be dragged or borne away.

'To make him move or seek some other place
Twirl this pin and he'll vanish into space
And disappear completely out of sight,
Yet will return to you by day or night
If you should please to summon him again
After a manner that I shall explain
To you alone, and that without delay;
Ride when you will, there is no more to say.'

    The knight informed the king as he had said,
And when he had it firmly in his head
How to control the beast in everything
How blithe, how happy was this doughty king!
And he returned to revel as before.
Then they took off the bridle that it wore
And laid it with his treasures in the tower.
The horse then vanished, but beyond my power
To tell you how, you get no more from me.
And thus I leave in joy and jollity
This Cambuskan, feasting with all his train
Till dawn of day had almost sprung again.

PART II

THE nourisher of all digestion, sleep,
  Began to wink upon them, 'Drinking deep,'
He said, 'and heavy toil for slumber call,'
And with a yawning mouth he kissed them all,
Saying, 'To bed, to bed, it is the hour
Of my dominion, blood is in its power.
Cherish your blood,' he whispered, 'nature's friend.'

    They thanked him yawningly and in the end
By twos and threes they wandered off to rest
As sleep ordained, they took it for the best.
What dreams they had shall not be told for me;
Their heads were full of the fumosity
That causes dreams which are of no account.
And so they lay and slept until the fount

Of day filled heaven, all but Canace;
For she was temperate and womanly
And having kissed her father had departed
And sought her rest before the evening started.
She had no wish to pale her lovely cheek
Or greet the morrow colorless and bleak.

    She slept her beauty-sleep and then awoke,
And at her waking, in her heart there spoke
Such joy about her glass and magic ring
That twenty times she felt her color spring.
She had dreamed visions from the deep impression
Made by the magic glass, her new possession.

    So ere the sun began its upward glide
She called the waiting-woman at her side
And told her that it was her wish to rise.

    Like all old women, glad to be as wise
As are their mistresses, the crone replied,
'What, madam, do you mean to go outside
This early? Everyone is still asleep.'
'I will arise,' she said, 'I cannot keep
In bed or sleep, I want to walk about.'

    Her woman called the servants in a rout
And up they got – some ten or twelve there were –
And up rose Canace as fresh and fair,
As bright and ruddy as the early sun
When by some four degrees it has begun
To rise into the *Ram*. It was no higher
When she was ready; forth at her desire
She lightly stepped, and gowned to greet the May,
Sweet season of delight, to walk and play.
Some five or six were with her, and, content,
Forth by an alley through the park she went.

    There was a mist that glided from the earth
And gave the sun a huge and ruddy girth,
And yet it was so beautiful a sight
That all their hearts were lifted in delight,
What with the season and the dawn-light springing
And noise of all the birds in heaven singing;

For instantly she knew what they were saying
And understood the meaning in their maying.

    The knot and gist of every tale that's told,
If lingered out till all desire be cold
In those that listen and the moment's past,
Savors the less the longer it may last
By fulsomeness of its prolixity,
And for that reason as it seems to me
I ought to reach that knot of which I'm talking
And make an end, and quickly, of her walking.

    Amidst a tree so parched it seemed of chalk
Where Canace came dallying in her walk
Above her head a falcon sat on high.
This bird began so piteously to cry
That all the woods re-echoed her distress.
And she had scourged herself with pitiless
Beating of both her wings; a crimson flood
Poured down and painted all the tree with blood,
As ever and again with scream and shriek
She bent and tore her body with her beak.
There is no tiger, no, nor cruel beast
That dwells in wood or forest, west or east,
But would have wept if weep indeed it could
In pity of her, shrieking as she stood.
And never yet has been a man to tell
– If only I could describe a falcon well! –
Of such another bird, as fair to see
Both in its plumage and nobility
Of form and attribute, or find her twin.

    It seemed this falcon was a peregrine
From foreign country; bleeding there she stood,
Fainting from time to time from loss of blood,
Till she had nearly fallen from the tree

    This beautiful king's daughter, Canace,
That on her finger bore the curious ring
By which she understood whatever thing
Birds in their language said, and which could teach
Her how to answer in their natural speech,

Had understood the words the falcon said;
The pity of it almost struck her dead.

  Up to the tree she hastened at her cries
And looking with compassion in her eyes
Held out her lap towards it, knowing well
The bird was like to faint, and if she fell
For lack of blood, she would be there at hand
Below the branches. Long she seemed to stand
And wait, and then at last began to talk,
As you shall hear, and thus addressed the hawk.

  'What is the cause, if you are free to tell,
That puts you to the furious pain of Hell?'
Said Canace to the poor bird above.
'Is it for grief in death, or loss of love?
For as I think these have the greatest part
Among the sorrows of a noble heart.
Other misfortunes one may well contemn,
The way is open for avenging them,
So that it must be either love or loss
That is occasion for your cruel cross,
For none, I see, has hunted you to-day.
God's love, have pity on yourself, or say
How I can help you. Neither east nor west
Was ever bird or beast so sore distressed
That ever I saw, or in such piteous plight;
It kills my heart to witness such a sight.
I feel such great compassion, come to me,
Come down for love of God and leave the tree,
For as I am the daughter of a king,
If I knew verily the cause and spring
Of your misfortunes, were it in my power,
I would make all things well this very hour.
Great God of nature, help me so to do!
I shall find herbs enough and salves for you
To heal your wounds, and quickly if you will.'

   The falcon gave a shriek more piteous still
Than any yet and fell to earth; she lay
Stone-still for she had fainted dead away,

Till, lifted up by Canace and taken
Into her lap, the bird began to waken,
And being recovered had the strength to talk,
Answering in the language of a hawk:
   'That pity is swift to course in noble heart,
Feeling the likeness of another's smart,
Is daily proved, as anyone can see,
Both by experience and authority,
For gentleness of birth and breeding shows
Itself in gentleness; you feel my woes
As I can see, and sure it is a fashion
Well fitting a princess to show compassion
As you have done, my lovely Canace,
In true and womanly benignity
That nature planted in your disposition.
And in no hope to better my condition
But to obey your generosity,
Also that others may be warned by me,
As lions may take warning when a pup*
Is punished, I will therefore take it up
And make a full confession of my woe
While yet there is the time before I go.'
   And ever while the falcon said her say
The other wept as she would melt away
Until the falcon bade her to be still
And sighing spoke according to her will.
   'Where I was bred – alas, the cruel day! –
And fostered in a rock of marble gray
So tenderly that nothing troubled me,
I never knew the word adversity
Till I could wing aloft into the sky.
   'There was a tercelet* that lived nearby
Who seemed the very well of gentle breeding;
Yet he was filled with treachery, exceeding
In all that's false. He wore the humble cloak
And color of true faith in all he spoke,
An eagerness to please me and to serve.
Who could imagine such a hawk would swerve?

Dyed in the grain they were, those treacherous powers!
Just as a serpent hides itself in flowers
Ready to strike and waits the moment fit,
Just so this god of love, this hypocrite,
Kept up all ceremonious obligations,
The sweet observances and protestations
That make the music of a gentle love.

   'But as a sepulcher is white above
The rotting corpse within, as we are told,
Just so this hypocrite blew hot and cold
And in this way pursued his treacherous bent;
None knew, unless the devil, what he meant.

   'So long I heard his weeping and complaining,
So long beheld the service he was feigning,
My heart, too foolish-pitiful to sound him,
All innocent of the treachery that crowned him,
Fearing his death, for so it seemed to me,
Believed his oaths, believed him trustworthy,
And granted him my love, on this condition,
That my good name, my honor and position
In public and in private had no hurt;
That is to say according to desert
In him my heart and thought were his forever,
But otherwise God knows, and he knew, never.
I took his heart exchanging it for mine.

   'How true the saying in the ancient line,
"Thieves' thoughts are not the thoughts of honest men,"
For seeing things had gone so far by then,
That I had fully granted him my love
In such a way as I have told above
And had as freely given my heart as he
Had sworn his own was given up to me,
Straightway this tiger with his double heart
Fell on his knees and played the humble part
With such devout and bashful reverence
He seemed a noble lover, one whose sense
Was ravished, one would think, for very joy.

   'Not Jason, no, nor Paris, Prince of Troy

– Did I say Jason? Sure, no other man
Since Lamech was, Lamech who first began,
So it is said, the game of loving two,
Has ever since the world itself was new
Thought or contrived the twenty thousandth part
Of counterfeited sophistry and art
As did my love. None fit to tie his shoe
Where there was double-faced deceit to do,
Not one to pay the thanks he paid to me!
And yet his manner was a heaven to see
For any woman, be she ne'er so wise,
Painted and trim and barbered to the eyes
Both in his words and in his countenance.

'I loved him, then, for his obedient glance
And for the truth I judged was in his heart,
So that at any time he felt the smart
Of pain, were it so little as a breath,
And I was told, it seemed the twist of death
Tore at my heart. And so it grew to this,
My will became the instrument of his,
That is to say my will obeyed his mood
In everything as far as reason would
Within the bounds of honor; nearer, nearer
We grew together, none so dear, none dearer
Then he, God knows, and none shall ever be!

'This lasted for two years perhaps, or three,
And I supposed nothing of him but good.
But at its final ending thus it stood:
As fortune willed, he had to leave the land
In which I lived. Ah, never make demand
Of what I felt in sorrow, ask no question,
I cannot picture it, for no suggestion
Would paint the truth, but this I boldly say,
I knew the pain of death that fatal day,
Such was my grief because he had to go.

'He took his leave with such a world of woe
So sorrowfully, that I felt assured
His feelings were no less than I endured

428

Hearing him speak, seeing his change of hue.
I was so certain he was wholly true,
So certain he would come to me again
And very soon, if ever truth were plain.

'And there were reasons too for him to go,
Reasons of honor; it is often so.
I made a virtue of necessity
And took it well, knowing it had to be.
I sought to hide my sorrow, as in fitness
I should, and took his hand – St John my witness! –
And said, "Lo, I am yours, and though we sever,
Be such as I have been and shall be ever."

'What he replied I need not now rehearse;
For who could have said better, or done worse?
For what he said was well enough, and soon
The thing was done. Ah, "long should be the spoon
At supper with the devil!" so they say.

'And so at last he went upon his way
And forth he flew, whither it seemed him best.
Yet later, when he had a mind to rest,
I think he must have had the text in mind
That "everything according to its kind
Seeks its own pleasure," so they say, I guess.
Man by his nature seeks new-fangledness,
As do those birds that people keep in cages;
One cares for them day-long and one engages
To get them straw as fair and soft as silk
And gifts of sugar, honey, bread and milk,
Yet on the instant that the slide is up
The foot will spurn away the proffered cup
And to the woods they fly for worms to eat,
Such is their longing for new-fangled meat,
The love for novelty their natures gave them;
No royalty of blood has power to save them.

'So with this tercelet falcon, woe the day!
Although of gentle birth, though fresh and gay,
Handsome, adoring, good in everything,
One day he saw a kite upon the wing

And suddenly he felt a love so hot
For this same kite that mine was clean forgot,
And thus he broke his faith in foul delight
And thus my love is servant to a kite
And I am lost and there's no remedy!'
    She ceased and with a scream of agony
She swooned away in her protectress' arms.
Great the lamenting for her falcon's harms
That Canace and all her ladies made,
Not knowing how to soothe her or persuade.
    Canace bore her homeward in her lap;
In softest plasters she began to wrap
The falcon's wounds that her own beak had torn,
And Canace went delving eve and morn
For herbs out of the ground; new salves she made
From precious grasses of the finest shade
To heal her hawk, indeed both day and night
She lavished on her all the care she might.
    Beside her bed she made a little mew
To house the falcon, hung with velvet blue*
Within, to signify fair faith that's seen
In women, and the mew was painted green
Without, with pictures of these treacherous fowls
Like tytyfers and tercelets and owls,
And there were magpies painted too, to chide
Them spitefully, to chatter and deride.
    Thus I leave Canace to nurse her hawk
And of her ring at present I will talk
No more, till I return to make it plain
How the poor falcon got her love again
Repentant, as the tale I tell will show,
Through the good offices of Cambalo,
Son of the king of whom I have made mention.
But for the moment it is my intention
To tell adventures and the feats of war,
Such marvels as you never heard before.
    First I will tell you about Cambuskan
And all the cities that he overran;

Then I shall speak of Algarsyf his son
And next of Theodora whom he won
To wife, and of the perils he must pass
On her account, helped by the steed of brass.
And after of another Cambalo
Who fought her brothers in the lists and so
At last won Canace by might and main.
And where I stopped I shall begin again.

PART III

A POLLO whirled his chariot on high
  Up through the house of Mercury, the sly –

Words of the Franklin to the Squire and of the Host to the Franklin

'F AITH, Squire, you have acquitted yourself well;
  There's wit and gentle breeding, I can tell!'
The Franklin said. 'Considering your youth,
You speak most feelingly, and that's the truth;
I praise you, sir, and judge there's no one here
Will equal you in eloquence, or near,
If you should live. God prosper all that's in you
And may your talents flourish and continue!
It's all so dainty, it delighted me.
  'I have a son, and by the Trinity
I'd rather than have twenty pounds' worth land,
Though it should fall right now into my hand,
That he should prove a man of such discretion
As you have shown. A plague upon possession!
What use is property if you're a dunce?
I've spoken to him sharply more than once
And shall again. He doesn't like advice,
All he can do is squander and play dice

And lose his money, at his present stage.
He'd rather romp and chatter with a page
Than entertain a serious conversation
Or learn to be a gentleman. Vocation –'

'Straw for your gentle breeding,' said the Host.
'Come, Franklin! Lord, you know as well as most
That each must tell a tale or two at least
Or break his word and miss the final feast.'

'I know it well,' the Franklin answered back.
'Please do not lay me open to attack
Just for a word or two to this young man.'

'Well, no more words, and tell us if you can
Some story of your own.' 'Glad to obey,
Since it's your wish; here's what I have to say.
Nothing could move me to oppose your will
Save in so far as I may lack the skill;
I hope you may take pleasure in my stuff,
And if you do I'll know it's good enough.'

The Franklin's Tale

The Franklin's Prologue

O F old the noble Bretons in their days
Delighted in adventures and made lays
In rhyme, according to their early tongue,
Which to the sound of instruments were sung,
Or read in silence for their own delight.
And I remember one, if I am right,
Which I will render you as best I can.

But, sirs, I'm not a cultivated man,
And so from the beginning I beseech
You to excuse me for untutored speech.
They never taught me rhetoric I fear,
So what I have to say is bare and clear.

I haven't slept on Mount Parnassus, no,
Nor studied Marcus Tullius Cithero.*
I can't give coloring to my words – indeed
Such colors as I know adorn the mead,
Or else are those they use in dyes or paint.
'Colors of rhetoric' to me seem quaint,
I have no feeling for such things; but still
Here is my story, listen if you will.

The Franklin's Tale

IN Brittany, or as it then was called,
Armorica, there was a knight enthralled
To love, who served his lady with his best
In many a toilsome enterprise and quest,
Suffering much for her ere she was won.
  She was among the loveliest under sun
And came from kindred of so high a kind
He scarce had the temerity of mind
To tell her of his longing and distress.
But in the end she saw his worthiness
And felt such pity for the pains he suffered,
Especially for the meek obedience offered,
That privately she fell into accord
And took him for her husband and her lord
– The lordship husbands have upon their wives.
And to enhance the bliss of both their lives
He freely gave his promise as a knight
That he would never darken her delight
By exercising his authority
Against her will or showing jealousy,
But would obey in all with simple trust
As any lover of a lady must;
Save that his sovereignty in name upon her
He should preserve, lest it should shame his honor.
  She thanked him, and with great humility
Replied, 'Sir, since you show a courtesy

So fair in proffering me so free a rein,
God grant there never be betwixt us twain
Through any fault of mine dispute or strife.
Sir, I will be your true and humble wife,
Accept my truth of heart, or break, my breast!'
Thus were they both in quiet and at rest.

    For there's one thing, my lords, it's safe to say;
Lovers must each be ready to obey
The other, if they would long keep company.
Love will not be constrained by mastery;
When mastery comes the god of love anon
Stretches his wings and farewell! he is gone.
Love is a thing as any spirit free;
Women by nature long for liberty
And not to be constrained or made a thrall,
And so do men, if I may speak for all.

    Whoever's the most patient under love
Has the advantage and will rise above
The other; patience is a conquering virtue.
The learned say that if it not desert you
It vanquishes what force can never reach;
Why answer back at every angry speech?
No, learn forbearance or, I'll tell you what,
You will be taught it, whether you will or not.
No one alive – it needs no arguing –
But sometimes says or does a wrongful thing;
Rage, sickness, influence of some malign
Star-constellation, temper, woe or wine
Spur us to wrongful words or make us trip.
One should not seek revenge for every slip,
And temperance from the times must take her schooling
In those that are to learn the art of ruling.

    And so this wise and honorable knight
Promised forbearance to her that he might
Live the more easily, and she as kind
Promised there never would be fault to find
In her. Thus in this humble, wise accord
She took a servant when she took a lord,

A lord in marriage in a love renewed
By service, lordship set in servitude;
In servitude? Why no, but far above,
Since he had both his lady and his love,
His lady certainly, his wife no less,
To which the law of love will answer 'yes.'

So in the happiness that they had planned
He took his wife home to his native land
With joyful ease and reached his castle there
By Penmarch Point, not far from Finisterre,
And there they lived in amity unharried.

Who can recount, unless he has been married,
The ease, the prosperous joys of man and wife?
A year or more they lived their blissful life
Until it chanced the knight that I have thus
Described and who was called Arveragus
Of Caer-rhud, planned to spend a year or so
In Britain (no, not Brittany), to go
And seek high deeds of arms and reputation
In honor; that was all his inclination.
He stayed two years, at least the book says thus.

Now I will pause about Arveragus
And turn to speak of Dorigen his wife
Who loved her husband as her own heart's life.

She wept his absence, sighed for him and pined,
As noble wives will do when so inclined;
She mourned, lay wakeful, fasted and lamented,
Strained by a passion that could be contented
Only by him, and set the world at naught.
Her friends who knew the burden of her thought
Brought her such consolations as they might;
They preached to her, they told her day and night,
'You'll kill yourself for nothing.' Such relief
And comfort as is possible to grief
They fuss about to find, and finding, press
Upon her to relieve her heaviness.

Slow is the process, it is widely known,
By which a carver carves his thought in stone,

Yet cuts at last the figure he intended;
And slowly too, thus soothed and thus befriended,
Her soul received the print of consolation
Through hope and reason, and her long prostration
Turned to recovery, she ceased to languish;
She couldn't be always suffering such anguish.

Besides Arveragus as it befell
Sent letters to her saying all was well
And that he shortly would be home again;
Only for that her heart had died of pain.

Her friends, seeing her grief began to ease,
Begged her for heaven's sake, and on their knees,
To come and roam about with them and play,
And drive her darker fantasies away;
And finally she granted their request
And clearly saw it would be for the best.

Her husband's castle fronted on the sea
And she would often walk in company
High on the ramparts, wandering at large.
Many a ship she saw and many a barge
Sailing such courses as they chose to go;
But these made part and parcel of her woe
And she would often say, 'Alas for me,
Is there no ship, so many as I see,
To bring me home my lord? For then my heart
Would find a cure to soothe its bitter smart.'

At other times she used to sit and think
With eyes cast downward to the water's brink
And then her heart endured a thousand shocks
To see such jagged, black and grisly rocks,
So that she scarce could stand upon her feet.
Then she would refuge in some green retreat,
Lie on a lawn, and looking out to sea
With long, cold sighs, would murmur piteously:

'Eternal God that by thy providence
Guidest the world in wise omnipotence,
They say of Thee that Thou hast nothing made
In vain; but, Lord, these fiendish rocks are laid

In what would rather seem a foul confusion
Of work than the creation and conclusion
Of One so perfect, God the wise and stable;
Why madest Thou thy work unreasonable?
These rocks can foster neither man nor beast
Nor bird, to north or south, to west or east;
They are a menace, useless, to my mind.
Lord, seest Thou not how they destroy mankind?
A hundred thousand bodies dead and rotten
Have met their death on them, though now forgotten;
Thy fairest work, wrecked on a rocky shelf,
Mankind, made in the image of Thyself.
It seemed that then Thou hadst great charity
Towards mankind; how therefore may it be
That Thou hast fashioned means as these to harm them
That do no good, but injure and alarm them?
    'I know it pleases scholars to protest
In argument that all is for the best,
Though what their reasons are I do not know.
    'But O Thou God that madest wind to blow,
Preserve my husband, that is my petition!
I leave the learned to their disquisition.
But would to God these rocks so black, so grim,
Were sunk in Hell itself for sake of him!
They are enough to kill my heart with fear.'
Thus she would speak with many a piteous tear.

    Her friends could see it gave her no relief
To roam the shore, but added to her grief,
And so they sought amusement somewhere else.
They led her by the water-ways and wells
And many another scene of loveliness;
They danced, they played backgammon, they played chess,
    And so one sunny morning, as they'd planned,
They went into a garden near at hand
Where they had staged a picnic and supplied
Victuals enough and other things beside,
And there they lingered out the happy day.
    It was the morning of the sixth of May

437

And May had painted with her softest showers
A gardenful of leafiness and flowers;
The hand of man with such a cunning craft
Had decked this garden out in pleach and graft,
There never was a garden of such price
Unless indeed it were in Paradise.
The scent of flowers and the freshening sight
Would surely have made any heart feel light
That ever was born, save under the duress
Of sickness or a very deep distress;
Pleasure and beauty met in every glance.

    And after dinner they began to dance
And there was singing; Dorigen alone
Made her continual complaint and moan
For never among the dancers came to view
Her husband, he that was her lover too.
Nevertheless she had to pass the day
In hope, and let her sorrows slide away.

    Now in this dance, among the other men,
There danced a squire before Dorigen,
Fresher and jollier in his array,
In my opinion, than the month of May.
He sang and danced better than any man
There is or has been since the world began.
He was, what's more, if I could but contrive
To picture him, the handsomest man alive,
Young, strong and wealthy, mettlesome, discreet,
And popular as any you could meet;
And shortly, if I am to tell the truth,
All unbeknown to Dorigen, this youth
– A lusty squire and servant in the game
Of Venus, and Aurelius was his name –
Had loved her best of any for two years
And longer so it chanced, but still his fears
Had never let him bring the matter up;
He drank his draught of penance without cup.*

    He had despaired of her and dared not say
More of his passion than he might convey

In general terms, by saying that he burned
With love but that his love was not returned;
On all such themes he fashioned many a phrase,
Wrote songs, complaints, roundels and virelays
Saying his griefs were more than he dared tell,
He languished as a fury did in Hell,
And he must die, he said, as Echo did
For young Narcissus and the love she hid.
But in no other way, as said above,
Had he the courage to confess his love,
Save that perhaps from time to time at dances,
Where youth pays love's observances, his glances
It well may be would linger on her face
Beseechingly, as is the common case;
But she was unaware of what he meant.

    Nevertheless it happened, ere they went
Out of the garden, since he lived nearby
And was of good position, standing high
In honor and had known her from of old,
They fell in speech and he at last grew bold
And drew towards the purpose in his head.
Taking his opportunity he said:
"Madam, by God's green earth and all its treasure,
Had I imagined it could give you pleasure
That day, on which your lord Arveragus
Went over sea, then I, Aurelius
Would have gone too, and never come again.
I know the service of my love is vain,
My recompense is but a bursting heart.

    'Madam, have pity on the pain and smart
Of love; a word from you can slay or save.
Would God your little feet stood on my grave!
There is no time to say what I would say;
Have mercy, sweetheart, cast me not away.'

    She looked at him with closer scrutiny
And answered, 'Are you saying this to me?
Can you intend it? Never,' she said, 'till now
Had I suspected that – what you avow.

But by the Lord that gave me soul and life
I never mean to prove a faithless wife
In word or deed if I can compass it.
I will be his to whom I have been knit.
Take that for final answer, as for me.'
　But after that she added playfully,
'And yet, Aurelius, by the Lord above
I might perhaps vouchsafe to be your love,
Since I perceive you groan so piteously.
Look; on the day the coasts of Brittany
Are stone by stone cleared of these hateful rocks
By you, so that no ship or vessel docks
In danger, when, I say, you clear the coast
So clean there's not a single stone to boast,
I'll love you more than any man on earth;
Accept my word in truth for all it's worth.'
　'Is there no other way than this?' said he.
　'No, by the Lord,' she said, 'that fashioned me.
For it will never happen, that I know;
So clear your heart of fancies, let them go.
How can a man find daintiness in life
Who goes about to love another's wife,
That can enjoy her body when he pleases?'
　Aurelius sighed again. The long uneases
Of lovers' woe returned on hearing this
And he replied with sorrowing emphasis,
'Madam, it is impossible to do,
So I must die a horrible death, for you.'
And on the word he turned and went away.
　Her other many friends came up to play
And wander with her through the leafy walk
Of alleys pleached, but of her lover's talk
They did not know. Revels began anew,
On till the dazzling sun had lost its hue
For the horizon reft it of its light;
This is as much to say that it was night.
So they went home delighted, all in joy
Except, alas, Aurelius, wretched boy.

He sought his house, a sigh at every breath,
And could see no way of avoiding death.
Within himself he felt his heart turn cold
And falling on his knees began to hold
His hands to heaven and the upper air
In raving madness, and he said a prayer.
Excessive suffering had turned his head,
He knew not what he spoke, but this he said,
With pleading heart and pitiful, to one
And all the gods, beginning with the sun:

'Apollo, God and Governor, whose power
Tends over every plant and herb and flower
And tree, appointing unto each by reason
Of thy celestial course, his time and season,
According as thy arc is low or high,
Lord Phoebus, in thy mercy cast an eye
On sad Aurelius, wretched and forlorn.
Look on me, Lord! My lady-love has sworn
To prove my death, though for no fault in me,
Unless, O Lord, in thy benignity
Thou pity a dying heart; for well I know,
Shouldest thou please, Lord Phoebus, to bestow
Thy mercy, thou canst help me best of all
Except my lady; listen to my call,
Vouchsafe to hear me, Lord, if I expound
A means of help and how it may be found.

'Thy blissful sister, Luna the Serene,
Chief goddess of the ocean and its queen,
Though Neptune have therein his deity,
Is over him and empress of the sea.
Thou knowest, Lord, that just as her desire
Is to be lit and quickened by thy fire,
For busily she follows after thee,
Just so the natural longing of the sea
Follows on her and so is bound to do;
She is its goddess and the rivers' too.

'And so, Lord Phoebus, this is my request,
Do me this miracle – or burst, my breast! –

That even now at thy next opposition
Which is to be in *Leo,* thou petition
Thy sister to bring floods so much increased
That they shall rise five fathom at the least
Above the highest rock that now appears
In Brittany, and let this last two years.
Then to my lady I can safely say,
"Keep truth with me, the rocks are all away."

'Lord Phoebus, do this miracle for me now!
Beg her to go no faster, Lord, than thou;
I say, beseech thy sister that she go
No faster than thyself two years or so,
Then she will be at full, and so will stay,
And the spring floods continue night and day.
And should she not vouchsafe in such a way
The granting of my lady, then I pray
That she may sink the rocks, that they be drowned
Within her own dark region underground
Where Pluto dwells, for while they are above
I cannot hope to win my lady-love.

'Barefoot to Delphi will I go and seek
Thy temple! See the tears upon my cheek,
Lord Phoebus, have compassion, grant my boon!'
And on the word he fell into a swoon
And long he lay upon the ground in trance.

His brother who had heard of his mischance
Found him and caught him up, and off to bed
He carried him. With torment in his head
I leave this woeful creature, if to die
In desperation he must choose, not I.

Meanwhile Arveragus in health and power
Came honorably home, the very flower
Of chivalry, with other noble men.
How art thou blissful now, my Dorigen!
Thou hast a lusty husband to thy charms,
Thine own fresh knight, thy honored man-at-arms,
That loves thee as his life, in whom there springs
No inclination to imagine things

Or ask if anyone while he was out
Has talked to thee of love. But not a doubt
Entered his head; he had no thought in life
Except to dance and joust and cheer his wife
In blissful joy; and so I leave him thus
And turn again to sick Aurelius.

In furious torment, languishing away,
Two years and more wretched Aurelius lay
Scarce with the strength to put his foot to ground.
No comfort during all that time he found
Save in his brother, who was a learned man
And privy to his grief since it began,
For to no other could Aurelius dare
Ever to say a word of his affair.
More secretly he guarded his idea
Than ever did Pamphilus for Galatea.*
To all appearances his breast was whole,
But a keen arrow stuck within his soul.
A wound that's only surface-healed can be
A perilous thing, you know, in surgery,
Unless the arrow-head be taken out.

His brother wept for him and fell in doubt
Of his recovery until by chance
It came to him that when he was in France
At Orleans – he was a student then –
He lusted in his heart like all young men
To study things prohibited, to read
In curious arts of magic, and indeed
Search every hole and corner with defiance
To learn the nature of that special science.
And he remembered how he took a look
One morning, in his study, at a book
On natural magic which it chanced he saw
Because a friend, then bachelor-at-law
Though destined later to another trade,
Had hidden it in his desk. This book displayed
Much about magic science, with expansions
Relative to the eight-and-twenty mansions

Belonging to the moon – an ancient folly
Such as to-day is hardly worth poor Polly,
Since holy church has managed to retrieve us
And suffers no illusions now to grieve us.

And so, remembering this book by chance
His heart as suddenly began to dance
Within him; feeling secretly assured
He said, 'My brother shall be quickly cured
For I am certain that there must be sciences
By which illusions can be made, appliances
Such as these subtle jugglers use in play
At banquets. Very often, people say,
These conjurors can bring into a large
And lofty hall fresh water and a barge
And there they seem to row it up and down;
Sometimes a lion, grim and tawny-brown,
Sometimes a meadow full of flowery shapes,
Sometimes a vine with white and purple grapes,
Sometimes a castle which by some device,
Though stone and lime, will vanish in a trice
Or seem at least to vanish out of sight.

'So I conclude that if I only might
Discover some old fellow of the kind
Who has these moony mansions in his mind
At Orleans, or has some power above
All this, my brother might enjoy his love.
A learned man could hoodwink all beholders
With the illusion that the rocks and boulders
Of Brittany had vanished one and all
And ships along the brink could safely call,
Coming and going; if it but endured
A day or two my brother could be cured.
She will be forced to recognize his claim
Or, at the least, she will be put to shame.'

Why draw my story out? What need be said?
He went to where his brother lay in bed
And brought him so much comfort with his plot
To visit Orleans that up he got

And started off at once upon the road
High in the hope of lightening his load.

They neared the city; when it seemed to be
About two furlongs off, or maybe three,
They met a youngish scholar all alone
Who greeted them in Latin, in a tone
Of friendly welcome; and he struck them dumb
In wonder with 'I know why you have come.'
And ere they went a step upon their way
He told them all they had in mind to say.

This Breton scholar wanted to be told
About the friends that they had known of old
And he replied that they were all now dead;
He spoke with feeling, many tears were shed.

Down from his horse Aurelius soon alighted
To follow this magician, who invited
Him and his brother home, set them at ease
And served them victuals; nothing that could please
Was lacking and Aurelius soon decided
He'd never seen a house so well provided.

And the magician caused there to appear,
Before their supper, parks of forest deer,
And he saw stags among them, antlered high,
The greatest ever seen by human eye.
He saw a hundred of them killed by hounds,
And others, arrow-wounded, lay in mounds.
Next, when the deer had vanished, he was shown
A river bank and there a hawk was flown
By falconers; they saw a heron slain.

Then he saw knights at joust upon a plain
And after that Aurelius was entranced
At seeing his beloved as she danced
And he, it seemed, was dancing with her too.
And when the master of this magic view
Saw it was time he clapped his hands and banished
The figures, and farewell! our revels vanished.
Yet all the time they had not left the house
While being shown these sights so marvelous,

But sat within his study where there lay
His books about them; there were none but they.

   The master called the squire who was to set
Their meal, and said, 'Is supper ready yet?
It's very near an hour I could swear,'
He added, 'since I told you to prepare,
When these two gentlemen came in with me
To see my study and my library.'

    'Sir,' said the squire, 'it's ready, and you may
Begin, if it so please you, right away.'
'Then let us eat,' he said; 'that will be best;
These amorous people sometimes need a rest.'

   After they'd eaten bargaining began;
What payment should this master-artisan
Have to remove the rocks of Brittany
From the Gironde to where the Seine meets sea?
He made it difficult and roundly swore
He'd take a thousand pounds for it or more,
He wasn't too eager even at that price.
Aurelius with his heart in paradise
Readily answered, 'Fie on a thousand pound!
I'd give the world, which people say is round,
The whole wide world if it belonged to me;
Call it a bargain then, for I agree.
You shall be truly paid it, on my oath.
But look, let's have no negligence or sloth
Beyond to-morrow in what we would be at.'
'No,' said the scholar, 'I can pledge you that.'

   Aurelius went to bed in high delight
And rested soundly pretty well all night.
Tired by his journey and with hope retrieved
He slept, the troubles of his heart relieved.

   And morning came; as soon as it was day
They made for Brittany by the nearest way,
The brothers with the wizard at their side,
And there dismounted having done their ride.
It was – so say the books, if I remember –
The cold and frosty season of December.

Phoebus grew old, his coppered face was duller
Than it had been in *Cancer* when his color
Shone with the burnished gold of streaming morn;
Now, as he entered into *Capricorn*
His face was very pale, I dare maintain.
The bitter frosts, the driving sleet and rain
Had killed the gardens; greens had disappeared.
Now Janus by the fire with double beard,
His bugle-horn in hand, sits drinking wine;
Before him stands a brawn of tusky swine,
And *'Sing Noël!'* cries every lusty man.

Aurelius, using all the means he can,
Gives welcome to the master, shows respect
And begs his diligence, that no neglect
Or sloth delay the healing of his smart,
Lest he should kill himself, plunge sword in heart.

This subtle sage had pity on the man
And night and day went forward with his plan
Watching the hour to favor the conclusion
Of his experiment, that by illusion
Or apparition – call it jugglery,
I lack the jargon of astrology –
She and the world at large might think and say
The rocks had all been spirited away
From Brittany or sunk under the ground.

And so at last the favoring hour was found
To do his tricks and wretched exhibition
Of that abominable superstition.
His calculating tables were brought out
Newly corrected, he made sure about
The years in series and the single years
To fix the points the planets in their spheres
Were due to reach and so assessed their 'root'
In longitude, and other things to suit,
Such as his astrolabe, and argument
From arc and angle, and was provident
Of fit proportionals for the minor motion
Of planets, and he studied with devotion

The measurement from the point where Alnath* swam
In the eighth sphere to where the head of the *Ram*
Stood in the ninth, in its eternal station
As we suppose, and made his calculation.
And finding the first mansion of the moon,
He calculated all the rest in tune
With that. He worked proportionally, knowing
How she would rise and whither she was going
Relative to which planets and their place,
Equal or not, upon the zodiac face.
And thus according to his calculations
He knew the moon in all her operations
And all the relevant arithmetic
For his illusion, for the wretched trick
He meant to play, as in those heathen days
People would do. There were no more delays
And by his magic for a week or more
It seemed the rocks were gone; he'd cleared the shore.

Aurelius, still despairing of the plot,
Nor knowing whether he'd get his love or not,
Waited for miracles by night and day
And when he saw the rocks were cleared away,
All obstacles removed, the plot complete,
He fell in rapture at his master's feet.
'Wretch as I am, for what has passed between us
To you, my lord, and to my lady Venus
I offer thanks,' he said, 'for by your care,
As poor Aurelius is well aware,
He has been rescued from a long dismay.'

And to the temple then he took his way
Where, as he knew, his lady was to be,
And when he saw his opportunity
With terror in his heart, and humbled face,
He made obeisance to her sovereign grace.

'My truest lady,' said this woeful man,
'Whom most I dread and love – as best I can –
Last in the world of those I would displease,
Had I not suffered many miseries

448

For love of you, so many I repeat
That I am like to perish at your feet,
I would not dare approach you, or go on
To tell you how forlorn and woebegone
I am for you; but I must speak or die.
You kill me with your torture; guiltless, I.
Yet if my death could never so have stirred
Your pity, think before you break your word.
Repent, relent, remember God above you
Before you murder me because I love you.
You know what you have promised to requite
– Not that I challenge anything of right,
My sovereign lady, only of your grace –
Yet in a garden yonder, at such a place
You made a promise which you know must stand
And gave your plighted truth into my hand
To love me best, you said, as God above
Knows, though I be unworthy of your love.
It is your honor, madam, I am seeking;
It's not to save my life that I am speaking.
I have performed what you commanded me
As, if you deign to look, you soon will see.
Do as you please but think of what you said
For you will find me here, alive or dead.
It lies in you to save me or to slay –
But well I know the rocks are all away!'
He took his leave of her and left the place.
  Without a drop of color in her face
She stood as thunderstruck by her mishap.
'Alas,' she said, 'to fall in such a trap!
I never had thought the possibility
Of such a monstrous miracle could be,
It goes against the processes of nature.'
And home she went, a very sorrowful creature
In deadly fear, and she had much to do
Even to walk. She wept a day or two,
Wailing and swooning, pitiful to see,
But why she did so not a word said she,

For her Arveragus was out of town.
But to herself she spoke and flinging down
In pitiable pallor on her bed
She voiced her lamentation and she said:
    'Alas, of thee, O Fortune, I complain,
That unawares hast wrapped me in thy chain,
Which to escape two ways alone disclose
Themselves, death or dishonor, one of those,
And I must choose between them as a wife.
Yet I would rather render up my life
Than to be faithless or endure a shame
Upon my body, or to lose my name.
My death will quit me of a foolish vow;
And has not many a noble wife ere now
And many a virgin slain herself to win
Her body from pollution and from sin?
    'Yes, surely, many a story we may trust
Bears witness; thirty tyrants full of lust
Slew Phido the Athenian* like a beast,
Then had his daughters carried to their feast,
And they were brought before them in despite,
Stark naked, to fulfill their foul delight,
And there they made them dance upon the floor
God send them sorrow, in their father's gore.
And these unhappy maidens, full of dread,
Rather than they be robbed of maidenhead,
Broke from their guard and leapt into a well
And there were drowned, so ancient authors tell
    'The people of Messina also sought
Some fifty maidens out of Sparta, brought
Only that they might work their lechery
Upon them, but in all that company
Not one that was not slain; they were content
To suffer death rather than to consent
To being forced in their virginity;
What then's the fear of death, I say, to me?
    'Consider Aristoclides for this,
A tyrant lusting after Stymphalis

Who, when her father had been slain one night,
Fled for protection to Diana's might
Into her temple, clung to her effigy
With both her hands and from it could not be
Dragged off, they could not tear her hands away
Till they had killed her. If a virgin may
Be seen to have so loath an appetite
To be defiled by filthy man's delight,
Surely a wife should kill herself ere she
Were so defiled, or so it seems to me.

'And what of Hasdrubal? Had he not a wife
At Carthage who had rather take her life?
For as she watched the Romans win the town
She took her children with her and leapt down
Into the fire; there she chose to burn
Rather than let them do their evil turn.

'Did not Lucrece choose death for her escape
In Rome of old when she had suffered rape
For Tarquin's lust? Did not she think it shame
To live a life that had been robbed of name?

'The seven virgins of Miletus too
Took their own lives – were they not bound to do? –
Lest they be ravished by their Gaulish foes.
More than a thousand stories I suppose
Touching this theme were easy now to tell.

'Did not his wife, when Abradates fell,
Take her own life and let the purple flood
Glide from her veins to mingle with his blood,
Saying, "My body shall at least not be
Defiled by man, so far as lies in me"?

'Since there are found so many, if one delves,
That gladly have preferred to kill themselves
Rather than be defiled, need more be sought
For my example? Better were the thought
To kill myself at once than suffer thus.
I will be faithful to Arveragus
Or slay myself as these examples bid,
As the dear daughter of Demotion did

Who chose to die rather than be defiled.

  'O Skedasus, thou also hadst a child
That slew herself, and sad it is to read
How she preferred her death to such a deed.

  'As pitiable or even more, I say,
The Theban maid who gave her life away
To foil Nichanor and a like disgrace.

  'Another virgin at that very place
Raped by a Macedonian, it is said,
Died to repay her loss of maidenhead.

  'What shall I say of Niceratus' wife
Who being thus dishonored took her life?

  'And O how true to Alcibiades
His lover was! She died no less than these
For seeking to give burial to her dead.

  'See what a wife Alcestis was,' she said,
'And what says Homer of Penelope?
All Greece can celebrate her chastity.

  'Laodamia, robbed of all her joy,
Protesilaus being killed at Troy,
Would live no longer, seeing that he was slain.

  'Of noble Portia let me think again;
She could not live on being forced to part
From Brutus whom she loved with all her heart.

  'And Artemisia, faithful to her man,
Is honored, even by the barbarian.

  'O Teuta, queen! Thy wifely chastity
Should be a mirror for all wives to see;
I say the same of Bilia and as soon
Of chaste Valeria and Rhodogoun.'

  Thus for a day or two she spent her breath,
Poor Dorigen, and ever purposed death.

  On the third day, however, of her plight,
Home came Arveragus, that excellent knight,
And questioned her; what was she crying for?
But she continued weeping all the more.
'Alas,' she said, 'that ever I was born!
'Thus have I said,' she answered, 'thus have sworn –'

She told him all as you have heard before.
It need not be repeated any more.

Her husband smiled at her with friendly eyes
And countenance, and answered in this wise:
'And is there nothing, Dorigen, but this?'
'No, no, so help me God!' with emphasis
She answered. 'Is it not enough, too much?'
'Well, wife,' he said, 'it's better not to touch
A sleeping dog, so I have often heard;
All may be well, but you must keep your word.
For, as may God be merciful to me,
I rather would be stabbed than live to see
You fail in truth. The very love I bear you
Bids you keep truth, in that it cannot spare you;
Truth is the highest thing in a man's keeping.'
And on the word he suddenly burst out weeping
And said, 'But I forbid on pain of death,
As long as you shall live or draw your breath,
That you should ever speak of this affair
To living soul; and what I have to bear
I'll bear as best I may; now wash your face,
Be cheerful. None must guess at this disgrace.'

He called a maidservant and squire then
And said, 'Go out with Lady Dorigen;
Attend upon her, whither she will say.'
They took their leave of him and went their way
Not knowing why their mistress was to go.
It was his settled purpose none should know.

Perhaps a heap of you will want to say,
'Lewd, foolish man to act in such a way,
Putting his wife into such jeopardy!'
Listen before you judge them, wait and see.
She may have better fortune, gentlemen,
Than you imagine; keep your judgments then
Till you have heard my story which now turns
To amorous Aurelius as he burns
For Dorigen; they happened soon to meet
Right in the town, in the most crowded street

Which she was bound to use, however loath,
To reach the garden and to keep her oath.
  Aurelius gardenwards was going too;
A faithful spy on all she used to do,
He kept close watch whenever she went out
And so by accident or luck no doubt
They met each other; he, his features glowing,
Saluted her and asked where she was going,
And she replied as one half driven mad,
'Why, to the garden, as my husband bade
To keep my plighted word, alas, alas!'
  Aurelius, stunned at what had come to pass,
Felt a great surge of pity that arose
At sight of Dorigen in all her woes,
And for Arveragus the noble knight
That bade her keep her word of honor white,
So loth he was that she should break her truth.
And such a rush of pity filled the youth
That he was moved to think the better course
Was to forgo his passion than to force
An act on her of such a churlish kind,
And against such nobility of mind;
So, in few words, the lad addressed her thus:
  'Madam, say to your lord Arveragus
That since I well perceive his nobleness
Towards yourself, and also your distress,
Knowing the shame that he would rather take
(And that were pity) than that you should break
Your plighted word, I'd rather suffer too
Than seek to come between his love and you.
  'So, Madam, I release into your hand
All bonds or deeds of covenant that stand
Between us, and suppose all treaties torn
You may have made with me since you were born.
I give my word never to chide or grieve you
For any promise given, and so I leave you,
Madam, the very best and truest wife
That ever yet I knew in all my life.

Let women keep their promises to men,
Or at the least remember Dorigen.
A squire can do a generous thing with grace
As well as can a knight, in any case.'

    And she went down and thanked him on her knees.
Home to her husband then with heart at ease
She went and told him all as I've recorded.
You may be sure he felt so well rewarded
No words of mine could possibly express
His feelings. Why then linger? You may guess.

    Arveragus and Dorigen his wife
In sovereign happiness pursued their life,
No discord in their love was ever seen,
He cherished her as though she were a queen,
And she stayed true as she had been before;
Of these two lovers you will get no more.

    Aurelius, all whose labor had been lost,
Cursing his birth, reflected on the cost.
'Alas,' he said, 'alas that I am bound
To pay in solid gold a thousand pound
To that philosopher. What shall I do?
All I can see is that I'm ruined too.
There's my inheritance; that I'll have to sell
And be a beggar. Then there's this as well;
I can't stay here a shame and a disgrace
To all my kindred; I must leave the place.
And yet he might prove lenient; I could pay
A yearly sum upon a certain day
And thank him gratefully, I can but try.
But I will keep my truth, I will not lie.'

    And sad at heart he went to search his coffer
And gathered up what gold he had to offer
His master, some five hundred pound I guess,
And begged him as a gentleman, no less,
To grant him time enough to pay the rest.

    'Sir, I can boast, in making this request,'
He said, 'I've never failed my word as yet,
And I will certainly repay this debt

I owe you, master, ill as I may fare,
Yes, though I turn to begging and go bare.
If you'd vouchsafe me, on security,
A little respite, say two years or three,
All would be fine. If not I'll have to sell
My patrimony; there's no more to tell.'

Then this philosopher in sober pride,
Having considered what he'd said, replied,
'Did I not keep my covenant with you?'
'You did indeed,' he said, 'and truly too.'
'And did you not enjoy your lady then?'
'No ... no ...' he sighed, and thought of Dorigen.
'What was the reason? Tell me if you can.'

Reluctantly Aurelius then began
To tell the story you have heard before,
There is no need to tell it you once more.
He said: 'Her husband, in his nobleness,
Would have preferred to die in his distress
Rather than that his wife should break her word.'
He told him of her grief and what occurred,
How loth she was to be a wicked wife
And how she would have rather lost her life;
'Her vow was made in innocent confusion,
She'd never heard of magical illusion.
So great a sense of pity rose in me,
I sent her back as freely then as he
Had sent her to me, let her go away.
That's the whole story, there's no more to say.'

Then the magician answered, 'My dear brother,
Each of you did as nobly as the other.
You are a squire, sir, and he a knight,
But God forbid in all His blissful might
That men of learning should not come as near
To nobleness as any, never fear.

'Sir, I release you of your thousand pound
No less than if you'd crept out of the ground
Just now, and never had had to do with me.
I will not take a penny, sir, in fee

For all my knowledge and my work to rid
The coast of rocks; I'm paid for what I did,
Well paid, and that's enough. Farewell, good-day!'
He mounted on his horse and rode away.

My lords, I'll put a question: tell me true,
Which seemed the finest gentleman to you?
Ere we ride onwards tell me, anyone!
I have no more to say, my tale is done.

[GROUP G]

The Second Nun's Tale

The Second Nun's Prologue

THAT nourisher and servant to our vices
Known in our English tongue as Idleness,
The portress at the gateway that entices
To self-abandonment, we should oppress
By her own contrary, a measureless
And lawful industry, with all our power,
Lest the fiend snatch us in an idle hour.

For he with many a cunning cord and bridle
Continually watches us to clap
All whomsoever of us that are idle
And easy to be taken in his trap.
Not till a man is tossed into his lap
Does he perceive the fiend; let us be loath
To slacken in our work and yield to sloth.

And though we dreaded not what is to be,
That is, our death, reason would teach us keep
From idleness that rots in sluggardry
From whence no harvest comes, which none can reap;
We see that sloth can leash us in a sleep,
To pass the time in sleeping, eating, drinking,
Devouring other people's work, unthinking.

So, to put all such idleness away,
The cause of so much ruin and stagnation,
I have, as diligently as I may,
Followed the legend in my own translation
Touching thy sufferings and exaltation,
Made of thy garlands, rose and lily-laden,
Cecilia, thine, O martyr, Saint and maiden!

Invocacio ad Mariam

AND thou that art the flower of virgins all,
    Of whom St Bernard had such skill to write,
To thee at my beginning first I call;
Comfort of sinners, teach me to indite
Thy maiden's death, who put the fiend to flight
And won by merit an eternal glory,
As all may find in following her story.

Thou maid and mother, daughter of thy Son,
Thou well of mercy, balm to sinful nature,
In whom God chose His dwelling as in one
Humblest and highest over every creature,
Who gav'st such nobleness to human feature
That God had no disdain to clothe and wind
His Son in flesh and blood of human kind.

Within the blissful cloister of thy womb
There took man's shape the eternal love and peace,
Lord and guide of the trinal circle, whom
Heaven and earth and sea shall never cease
To glorify, pure virgin, the increase
Of whose fair body, never by man mated,
Was the Creator of all things created.

In thee assembled are magnificence,
Mercy and goodness, with such clemency
That thou, who art the sun of excellence,

Not only helpest those that pray to thee,
But many a time in thy benignity
Thou goest before them freely ere they speak,
O leech of life, and grantest what they seek.

Help me then, fair and meek and blissful maid,
Me, banished in the desert, in the street
Of gall; remember who was not afraid
To say in Cana, 'Lo, the dogs may eat
The crumbs that fall about their masters' feet';
Though I be an unworthy son of Eve,
Accept me for my faith, for I believe.

Since faith is dead that does not live in works,
O therefore give me power to work apace.
Save me from darkness and the fiend that lurks
In darkness, O thou fair and full of grace!
Be thou my advocate in that high place
Where endlessly the angels sing 'Hosanna,'
Mother of Christ, dear daughter of St Anna!

Shed thou thy light upon my soul in prison,
Troubled by the contagion of the flesh,
Weighed down by lusts of earth that have arisen
Of false affection, tangled in their mesh;
Haven of refuge, O salvation fresh
And comforting to all by sorrow shaken,
Help me in that which I have undertaken!

And you, all you, that read what I shall write,
Forgive me if I show no diligence
To ornament my story or endite
A subtle style; I take the words and sense
From one who held in holiest reverence
The saint of whom he wrote, and tell her tale,
Begging you to amend it where I fail.

Interpretatio Nominis Ceciliae

FIRST let me tell you whence her name has sprung,
Cecilia, meaning, as the books agree,*
'Lily of Heaven' in our English tongue,
To signify her chaste virginity;
Or for the whiteness of her constancy,
The greenness of her conscience, of her fame
The scent and sweetness, 'lily' was her name.

Cecilia may betoken 'path to the blind'
From the example given in her story;
Or in Cecilia some would have us find
A union as it were of 'Heaven's glory'
And Leah, the Active Life, in allegory;
'Heaven' is set for thoughts of holiness
And 'Leah' for ceaseless labor and address.

Cecilia may be also said to mean
'Wanting in blindness,' as she had the light
Of sapience, and a bearing calm and clean;
Or, as the maiden was beloved and bright,
To say from 'Heaven' and 'leos' would be right
And mean 'a Heaven for people,' so to call
The good example of her works to all.

For 'leos' means 'people' in the English tongue,
And just as one may look to heaven and see
The sun and moon, and where the stars are hung,
So in this maiden, spiritually,
We see her faith and magnanimity
And the whole clarity of her wisdom thence
In many works of shining excellence.

And just as these philosophers will write
To prove that heaven is swift and round and burning,
Just so was fair Cecilia the White,

As swift and ceaseless, turning and returning
To works of mercy, and round in her discerning
And preserverance, burning with the flame
Of charity, and so I read her name.

The Second Nun's Tale

THIS maiden, bright Cecilia, so I read,
Was Roman born and came of noble kind,
And from her cradle fostered in the creed
Of Christ, and bore His gospel in her mind;
She never ceased in prayer, or so I find
It written of her, to God in love and dread,
Beseeching Him to guard her maidenhead.

And when this maid was given to a man
In wedlock – he was young and bore the name
(Her legend tells us) of Valerian –
Upon the day of marriage, when it came,
She was devout and humble, still the same;
For there, beneath her robe of golden mesh,
She wore a shirt of hair upon her flesh.

And while the organs made their melody,
To God alone within her heart there sounded
This prayer, 'Lord, keep my soul and body free
From all defilement, lest I be confounded.'
On Him who died upon a tree she grounded
Her faith in love, and every second day,
Or every third, she fasted and would pray.

Yet the night came and she must go to bed
Beside her husband, as is oft the way,
And turning to him privately she said,
'Sweet and beloved husband, if I may,
There is a thing I dearly wish to say
If you will hear, and yet I would conceal it;
Swear to me, then, you never will reveal it.'

Firmly Valerian on his honor swore
That for no cause, whatever it might be,
Would he betray her, he could say no more.
And she began to speak. 'I have,' said she,
'A guardian angel, one that tenders me
So great a love, that, whether awake or sleeping,
My body is committed to his keeping.

'Were he to feel – and O, believe it true –
That you had touched me either in love or lust
He instantly would bring your death on you;
Young as you are you would go down to dust.
But if you love me cleanly, as you must,
He will love you, even as he loves me,
And show the glory of his ecstasy.'

Valerian, corrected by God's grace,
Answered again, 'That I may trust in you,
Show me that angel, let me see his face,
And if indeed he be an angel true
Then I will do as you have begged me to,
But if you love another man, on oath
I say this sword of mine shall slay you both.'

Cecilia answered, 'You are well advised,
And you shall see the angel if you will,
But first believe in Christ and be baptized.
Go by the Appian way,' she said, 'until
You reach, some three miles hence upon a hill,
A village where the poorer people live.
Go up to them and speak the words I give.

'Tell them that I, Cecilia, sent you there
That they might show you Urban,* old and good,
For secret needs and say your thoughts are fair.
And when you meet Saint Urban, as you should,
Repeat my words; they will be understood
And when he has confessed and purged your heart
You then shall see the angel, ere you part.'

Valerian went out to seek the place
And just as she had told him there he found
Holy Saint Urban, met him face to face
At work upon a christian burial ground,
And told him on what errand he was bound.
And Urban, when his message had been given,
Was filled with joy and raised his hands to heaven.

And from his eyes the tears began to fall.
'Almighty Lord, O Jesu Christ,' said he,
'Sower of chaste thought, shepherd of us all,
Take thou the fruit, whose seed of chastity
Thou sowedst in Cecilia, unto Thee!
Lo, like a busy bee that knows no guile
Thy thrall Cecilia serves thee all the while!

'Her very spouse, that she but now has taken
Fierce as a lion, hither has she sent
Meek as a lamb, his violence forsaken
For Thee, dear Lord!' Now, as he spoke, there went
A man before them clad in white and bent
With age; a golden book was in his hand.
Before Valerian he took his stand.

Valerian fell down for very dread
On seeing him. He raised him from his fall,
Opened the golden book and thus he read:
'One Lord, one Faith, one God above us all,
One Christendom, and One that we may call
Father, supreme both here and everywhere.'
These were the words in golden letters there.

Thus having read, then said this ancient man,
'Believest thou these sayings? Yes or no?'
'All this I do believe,' Valerian
Replied. 'For nothing is more truly so
In Heaven above or in the earth below.'
The ancient vanished then, he knew not where;
Urban the Pope baptized him then and there.

Home to Cecilia then he went and found
Her standing with an angel in his room;
The angel held two coronals that were bound
With lily-flowers and roses in full bloom
And to Cecilia then he turned, to whom
He gave the first, the second with its weight
Of roses to Valerian, her mate.

'With a clean body and with spotless thought
Cherish these coronals forever. They,'
The angel said, 'from Paradise were brought
For you, and they shall never rot away
Or lose their savor, trust to what I say.
And they are such as none shall see, unless
His heart is chaste and hates all filthiness.

'And thou, Valerian, that wert so soon
Glad to pursue what good advice began,
Say what thou wouldest; thou shalt have thy boon.'
'I have a brother,' said Valerian,
'In all the world there is no other man
I love so well. I pray he may find grace
To know the truth as I do, in this place.'

The angel said, 'God liketh thy request;
You both shall bear the palm of martyrdom
And come hereafter to His blissful rest.'
Now while the angel spoke, Tiburce had come,
Valerian's brother, and aware of some
Sweet savor which the rose and lily cast
About the chamber, felt his heart beat fast,

And 'Where, I wonder, at this time of year
Can such a fragrance come from? Can you tell?
The scent,' he said, 'of rose and lily here –
Why, if I had them in my hands their smell
Could pierce no deeper, could not pierce so well.
I find a savor in my heart, and seeing
Nothing, I know that it has changed my being.'

Valerian said, 'Two coronals have we,
Snow-white and rosy-red and shining fair,
Such as your eye has never learnt to see;
As you have smelt their savor at my prayer
So, dearest brother, you shall see them there,
If without tardiness you will receive
The very truth, and knowing it, believe.'

Tiburce replied, 'Do you say this to me
In truth, or do I hear it in a dream?'
'Dreaming,' Valerian said, 'we used to be,
Till now we were in sleep, so it must seem,
But now awake, in truth.' 'Yet how to deem,'
Tiburce replied, 'whether we're dreaming now?'
Valerian answered, 'I will tell you how.

'The angel of God has taught me truth. Your eyes
Shall also see if you renounce the power
Of idols and be clean, not otherwise.'
(As to the miracle of these crowns of flower,
St Ambrose speaks of it to strengthen our
Belief, commends it solemnly indeed;
The noble Doctor's preface, if you read,

Says thus, "To gain the palm of martyrdom,
Cecilia, being filled with Heaven's grace,
Forsook the world, her chamber and her groom,
Witness Valerian and Tiburce, in face
Of whose conversion we may judge her case,
Which God in bounty honored with a crown
Of flowers for each, brought by an angel down.

"This maiden brought these men to bliss above;
The world well knows the worth, you may be sure,
Of a devoted chastity to Love.
This St Cecilia showed him, and secure
In faith he held all idols as impure,
Vain, dumb and deaf, even as those that make them;
And so it was she charged him to forsake them.")

'Who thinks not so is but a brute at best,'
Tiburce gave answer, 'if I do not lie.'
Cecilia turned and kissed him on the breast
In joy that he beheld with inward eye
And saw the truth. Said she, 'Though we should die
For it, let us ally ourselves to-day.'
Blissful and lovely she went on to say:

'Just as the love of Christ has fashioned me
To be your brother's wife, that love devised
A new alliance as for you and me,
And so I take you now that have despised
Your idols; therefore go and be baptized,
Make yourself clean and then you shall behold
The angel's face of which your brother told.'

Tiburce for answer turned and said, 'Dear brother,
First tell me whom I am to seek and where?'
'Whom you should seek? Be happy,' said the other.
'None but Pope Urban; I will take you there.'
'Urban, my brother?' He began to stare.
'Is that where you will take me, then?' said he.
'That would be very strange, it seems to me.

'You cannot mean that Urban,' he went on,
'That has so often been condemned to die
And lives in holes and corners, here and gone,
And daren't put forth his head if one goes by?
People would burn him, they would have him fry
If he were seen and caught. To seek him thus
Would surely make them do the same to us.

'So, in our search after the Deity
That Heaven in her secrecies may hide,
We shall be burnt on earth, most certainly.'
To which Cecilia valiantly replied:
'Men might fear death and would be justified
In seeking to preserve their lives, dear brother,
If there were only this life and no other.

466

'But there's a better in another place
That never shall be lost. Be not afraid;
God's Son has told us of it, by His grace,
The Father's Son, by whom all things were made;
Those creatures in whom reason is displayed
The Holy Ghost proceeding from the Father
Dowers with a living soul, believe it rather.

'By word and miracle the Son of God,
When in this world, declared and we have learned
There was an after-life for all who trod
The path He chose.' 'Dear sister,' he returned,
'Did you not say just now, in what concerned
The Being of God, there was but One, and He
Was Lord in truth? Yet now you speak of three.

'That too I shall explain,' she said, 'in season.
Just as the wisdom in a man is three,
Having invention, memory and reason,
So also in God's nature there can be
Three Persons that are One in Deity.'
And she began to preach in eager fashion
Of Christ's first coming and His pain and passion,

And all He underwent in our condition,
And how the Son of God had been withheld
On earth from making man a full remission,
Bound as he is in sinfulness and quelled
By many cares, and when she had dispelled
His lingering doubt, Tiburce in eager hope
Went with Valerian to seek the Pope.

Urban thanked God; with happy heart and light
He christened him and within little space
Perfected him in learning as God's knight;
And after that Tiburce was filled with grace
And every day thereafter saw the face
Of God's bright angel, and if he was stirred
To ask of God a boon, his prayer was heard.

It would be hard to tell in order due
How many wonders for them Jesus wrought,
But lastly, if I may be brief with you,
The officers of Rome went out and sought
These brothers. To the prefect they were brought,
Almachius named. He questioned them and strove
To search their will, and to the idol of Jove

He sent them. 'Make them sacrifice,' he said,
'Or strike their heads off; so my orders are.'
One Maximus, his officer, the head
Among the prefects and his registrar,
Took these two saints together, whom so far
I have described, and brought them through the city,
And as he led them forth he wept for pity.

When Maximus had listened to their teaching
He got the torturers to give him leave
To take them to his house, and by their preaching
He was converted ere the fall of eve.
Their faith was found sufficient to retrieve
The torturers too and bring them to disown
Their false beliefs and trust in God alone.

Cecilia came when evening drew to night
With priests who christened all with one accord,
And afterwards when morning had grown light
She gravely said, 'O you that are restored
In Christ and are the soldiers of the Lord,
Cast off the works of darkness and put on
The armor of righteousness, the night is gone.

'You have done battle greatly and prevail,
Your course is done, your faith has never swerved;
Go to the crown of life that cannot fail.
The righteous Judge and Saviour you have served
Shall give it you, for you have well deserved.'
And then they led them forth to sacrifice
As I have told you, or to pay the price.

But, taken to the temple, no advice
– To tell the matter briefly – could persuade
These men to offer incense, sacrifice
Or bow to Jove, but on their knees they prayed
To God with humble hearts and unafraid.
Their heads were severed in that very place;
Their souls went upward to the King of Grace.

And Maximus, who saw it, testified
With piteous tears that he had seen the sight;
High into Heaven he saw their spirits glide
With angels, full of clarity and light.
His words converted many before night.
And when Almachius heard what he had said
He had him scourged to death with whips of lead.

Cecilia buried him beside her own,
Beside Tiburce, beside Valerian,
In her own burial-place beneath a stone.
Almachius therefore hastily began
To issue orders; officer and man
Were sent to fetch Cecilia before him
To honor Jove with incense and adore him.

But they, converted by her holy teaching,
Wept bitterly, and cried with one consent
That they believed, continually preaching,
'Christ is God's Son, nor is He different
But very God, and this is evident
In that His servant is so good and fit;
And we believe her though we die for it.'

Almachius (for these doings made a stir)
Ordered her to be fetched that he might see
Cecilia for himself and question her.
'What sort of woman, then, are you?' said he.
'I am a gentlewoman born,' said she.
'I'm asking you,' he said, 'of your belief,
About your faith, though it may cause you grief.'

'You have begun your questions foolishly,'
Answered Cecilia, 'seeking to conclude
Two points in one, which shows stupidity.'
He, vexed at her rejoinder, then pursued,
'How is it that your answer is so rude?'
'How?' she replied on being thus arraigned,
'Of conscience and pure heart and faith unfeigned.'

Almachius answered, 'Do you take no heed
Of my authority?' And she returned,
'Your power is little to be feared indeed;
Power of mortal man is soon discerned
To be a bladder full of wind, and spurned;
For prick it with a needle when it's blown
And the inflated boast is overthrown.'

'Well, you began most contumaciously.'
He said, 'and you continue turbulent.
Do you not know the Principality
Has given ordinance to this intent
That every christian shall have punishment
Unless he will deny his christian creed,
And that denying it he shall be freed?'

'Your princes err, and so your nobles do,'
Cecilia said, 'and by some crazy law
Would make us guilty, but it is not true.
You know us innocent; because you saw
That we held Christ in reverence and awe
And bore the name of christians, down you sat
And put a crime upon us, just for that.

'But we that know the name for virtuous
Renounce it not, whatever be the price.'
Almachius answered her, 'The choice stands thus;
Abjure your Christendom or sacrifice.
There's no escaping; follow my advice.'
At this the beautiful and blessed maid
Began to laugh and answered, unafraid,

470

'O Judge, confused for all your subtlety,
Would you that I denied my innocence?
Is it your wish to make a sinner of me?
Look at him there upholding this pretense
In open court, a madman lost to sense
In his endeavors!' He answered, 'Sorry wretch,
Do you not know how far my power may stretch?

'Is there no force or power in my breath?
Have not our mighty princes given to me
Authority and power of life and death?
Why do you speak so proudly then?' said he.
'I do not speak in pride but steadfastly,'
She answered; 'I, and those upon my side,
Have deadly hatred for the sin of pride.

'If you are not afraid to hear the truth
I will be open and expose to view
Your monstrous lies. Authority forsooth!
You say your princes have bestowed on you
Power of life and death; but that's not true.
You can take life, have power to destroy,
But that's the only power you enjoy.

'But you may say your princes in their might
Made you death's minister. Say more than so
And you will lie. Your power is very slight.'
'Muzzle your boldness,' said Almachius, 'go!
And pay our gods the sacrifice you owe.
Your insults to myself can be endured,
I'm a philosopher and am inured.

'But there are insults that I will not swallow
That you have leveled at our gods,' said he.
Cecilia cried, 'Your sophistries are hollow,
There's not a word in what you've said to me
That did not publish your obliquity
And prove yourself, I say it without grudge,
An ignorant official, a vain judge.

'Nothing you lack to make your outward eye
Totally blind, for what is seen by all
To be a stone you seek to glorify,
A senseless piece of stone, that you would call
A god! Put out your hand and let it fall
Upon it, touch it, taste it! You will find
Your hand says "Stone!" although your eyes are blind.

'People will laugh at you to hear such stuff
As you have uttered, they will think you mad,
For it is known, and commonly enough,
That God Almighty is in Heaven, clad
In glory, and these idols – if you had
The eyes to see it – offer no delight
To you or to themselves; not worth a mite.'

All this she said and more it well may be,
Till he grew angry. 'Take her whence she came
Home to her house, and in her house,' said he,
'Burn her to ashes in a bath of flame.'
Thus he commanded and they did the same,
They shut her in a bath and set alight
A mighty fire beneath it. Day and night

They stoked it and from night to day again,
And yet in spite of all the flame and heat
She sat there cool and neither feeling pain
Nor sweating, not a drop from head to feet.
Yet it was in that bath she was to meet
Her death, for this Almachius in his wrath
Sent a man down to kill her in the bath.

Three grievous strokes upon her neck he smote,
This torturer, but by no circumstance
Could he succeed in cutting through her throat;
Now at that time there was an ordinance
Forbidding executioners to chance
Smiting a fourth stroke, whether soft or sore,
And so this torturer dared do no more.

Half dead with carven neck she perished there;
He left her lying and he went his way.
But all the Christian folk, or such as were
About her then, bound her with sheets to stay
The flow of blood, and she, to the third day,
Lingered in pain yet never ceased in teaching
The faith she fostered, and continued preaching.

Goods, movables, her rights in everything
She then bequeathed to Urban, saying, 'Lo,
There was a boon I asked of Heaven's King;
Three days of respite I desired, that so
I might commend these souls before I go
To you, that you may guide them in their search
And build my house for a perpetual church.'

St Urban and his deacons secretly
Fetched forth her body and buried it by night
Among his saints. Her mansion came to be
The Church of St Cecilia, hers by right;
St Urban hallowed it, as well he might.
And in that Church in every noble way
Christ and his saint are honored to this day.

The Canon's Yeoman's Tale

The Canon's Yeoman's Prologue

WHEN St Cecilia's life had reached the close,
Some five miles further on, as I suppose,
At Boughton-under-Blean we saw a hack
Come galloping up. Its rider was in black
And under that a dingy surplice lay.
The hackney horse he rode was dappled gray

And sweating hard, it was a sight to see;
It must have galloped miles it seemed to me.
His yeoman's horse was also puffed and blowing,
And sweated so it hardly could keep going.
The foam stood high upon its collar, flecked
Just like a magpie – that was the effect.

A wallet on the crupper, doubled tight,
Was fastened and it seemed he traveled light
To suit a summer day, this worthy man.
And as he came towards us I began
Wondering about him till I understood
His cloak was sewn together with his hood,
And pondering this it needed no research
To write him down a canon of the church.*

His hat hung down behind him on a lace
As he had ridden at more than trotting-pace,
In fact he had been galloping like mad.
To keep him cool and catch the sweat, he had
Beneath his hood a dock-leaf, dripping wet.
It was a joy to see that canon sweat!
His forehead dropped down moisture like a still
For plantain, pellitory-juice or squill.
When he came up with us he gave a hearty
Shout and he said, 'God bless this jolly party!
How fast I've spurred,' he said, 'all for your sake;
I was determined I would overtake
Your happy crowd and ride in company.'

His man was just as full of courtesy
And said, 'My lords, I saw the day begin
With your departure, when you left the inn,
And so I warned my lord and master, who
Is very eager, sir, to ride with you
Just for enjoyment; he is fond of fun.'

'God bless you, friend, for warning him. Well done!'
Our Host rejoined. 'And one may well suppose
Your lord is wise, he looks it, goodness knows;
I'll wager he's high-spirited as well.
D'you think he has a tale or two to tell

To brighten up our company this morning?'
   'Who? He? My lord? Rather! I give you warning
He's a great joker, all for jollity,
Not half he is, you can rely on me.
If you had studied him as well as I,
You'd be amazed how capable and sly
When he gets down to work my master is.
All sorts of enterprise! Those jobs of his
Are more than any of you here and now
Could bring about, unless he showed you how.
Homely as he may look among your crowd,
If you but knew him you would all be proud;
You wouldn't forgo acquaintance with my lord,
Not for a fortune; if I could afford
To bet, I'd wager all in my possession.
He is a man of very great discretion,
I warn you, sir, he's a superior being.'
'Well,' said our Host, 'while I'm not disagreeing,
What is he then? A clerical? Or what?'
   'Only a cleric? Him? I should say not!'
The Yeoman said. 'Much more, or else I'm daft.
Let me inform you briefly of his craft.

   'I say my master has such subtle powers
– Although I help him in this work of ours
I can't explain them all, he's so far on –
That all this blessed road we ride upon
From here as far as Canterbury town,
Why, he could turn it all clean upside down
And pave it all with silver and with gold!'
   The Yeoman paused as if his tale was told.
Our thoughtful Host said, *'Benedicite!*
All that you say sounds wonderful to me,
For if your lord is truly so sagacious,
So much to be respected, goodness gracious,
Why does he take his dignity so light?
That gabardine is hardly worth a mite
– Well, for a man like that; God bless my wits,
It isn't even clean, it's torn to bits!

Why is your lord so sluttish, may I say?
With all those magic powers can't he pay
For better cloth, if what you say is so?
Answer me that, that's what I'd like to know.'

   'Why?' said the Yeoman. 'Need you ask me that?
God help us all, the thing he's working at
Can never be successful – this remark
I can't make openly, so keep it dark –
He knows too much, I think. Easy to scoff,
But things when overdone just don't come off,
The learned tell us, it's a waste endeavor;
That's why he's such a fool – he's far too clever.
Often enough a man with too much brain
Is likely to misuse it. What's the gain?
I'm very sorry for it, but that's his way,
God help him! I have nothing more to say.'

   'Well, never mind, my man,' replied our Host,
'But what's this subtlety of his you boast,
If I may ask? What does he do all day,
If he's as sly and crafty as you say?
Where do you live now, if you don't mind telling?'
'In slums,' he answered, 'suburbs are our dwelling;
We lurk in holes and corners and blind alleys,
Places where every thief and robber rallies
By nature, fear-stricken and secret places
Where those reside who dare not show their faces;
That, to tell truth, is where we go a-walking.'

   'Now,' said the Host, 'if I may go on talking,
Why are you so discolored round the face?'
'God was unkind to it, that's about the case,'
He said; 'I'm used to blowing up the fire
And that's what changed my color. I don't inquire
Into complexions; mirrors leave me cold.
I work like mad at learning to make gold.
We're always blundering, spilling things in the fire,
But for all that we fail in our desire
For our experiments reach no conclusion;
Yet we keep plenty under that illusion

And borrow money, say a pound or two,
Or ten or twelve and even more, we do,
And make them think that at the very least
Their money will be doubled or increased.
Yet it's a lie, but still we live in hope
It might be managed somehow; on we grope.
But the whole science lies so far ahead
It can't be overtaken, though we said
On oath it could, it slides away so fast.
It will make beggars of us all at last.'
    Now while his Yeoman was enlarging thus
In came the Canon, hearing him discuss,
To listen closer; his suspicious head
Distrusted anything that people said.
Cato has said a guilty conscience delves;
The guilty think all talk is of themselves.
That was the cause the Canon drew in near
His Yeoman; he was very keen to hear,
And he addressed his Yeoman, having heard,
'You hold your tongue, don't speak another word
Or if you do you'll pay for it, d'you see?
You're slandering me before this company.
What's more, you're telling things that should be hidden.'
    'Yeah?' said our Host. 'Go on, don't be forbidden,
I wouldn't mind his threats if I were you,
They're not worth anything.' 'No more I do,'
He answered. When the Canon realized
That all his secrets were to be surprised
He fled away in very grief and shame.
'Ha!' said the Yeoman. 'Now we'll have a game,
Now I can talk, and I've a lot to tell.
He's gone, the foul fiend carry him off to Hell!
We'll never meet again, I'll tell you flat,
For pound or penny, I can promise that.
He was the one first brought me to the game,
Grief strike him down, before he dies, in shame!
For it's a serious thing to me I say,
As I am well aware, think as you may.

And yet for all my misery and grief,
Long hours and injuries without relief,
I never could leave the business, any price.
O that I had a brain that would suffice
To tell you all that's proper to that art!
Nevertheless I'll try to tell you part,
And since my master's gone I will not spare;
All that I know about it I'll declare.'

The Canon's Yeoman's Tale

PART I

I'VE served this canon seven years and more,
Yet am no nearer science than before.
All that I ever had I've lost thereby,
And so, God knows, have many more than I.
Time was when I was fresh and fond of cheer,
Liked decent clothes and other handsome gear;
Now I might wear my hose upon my head,
And where my color was a lively red
My face is wan and wears a leaden look;
If you try science you'll be brought to book.
My eyes are bleared with work on preparations,
That's all the good you get from transmutations.
That slippery science stripped me down so bare
That I'm worth nothing, here or anywhere.
Added to that I am so deep in debt
From borrowing money, you can lay a bet
Long as I live I'll never pay it, never!
    Let every man be warned by me forever;
Whoever tries his hand at such behavings,
If he goes on I say will lose his savings.
What's more, so help me God, his only gains
Are empty money-bags and addled brains.
And by the time the man's gone raging mad
And risked and lost whatever goods he had,

He then eggs others on and off they run
To lose their goods, as he himself has done.

A spiteful wretch takes pleasure when he sees
That others suffer from the same disease,
So I was told once by a learned man.
But what's the odds? I'll on as I began.

When we had fixed a place to exercise
Our esoteric craft, we all looked wise;
Our terms were highly technical and quaint.
I blew the fire up till fit to faint.

As for proportions, why should I rattle on
About the substances we worked upon,
The six or seven ounces it may be
Of silver, or some other quantity,
Or bother to name the things that we were piling
Like orpiment,* burnt bones and iron filing
Ground into finest powder, all the lot,
Or how we poured them in an earthen pot?
(You put in salt and paper, be it stated,
Before these powders I enumerated,
Securely covered by a sheet of glass,
And plenty of other things, but let them pass.)
And how the pot and glass were daubed with clay
For fear the gases might escape away,
And then the fire, whether slow or brisk,
We had to make! the trouble and the risk
We took to sublimate the preparation
Or in the amalgaming and calcination
Of quicksilver, crude mercury that is!

We always failed, for all those tricks of his.
Our orpiment, our mercury sublimate,
Our lead protoxide ground on a porphyry plate
And measured out in ounces, grain by grain,
Gave us no help. Our labor was in vain.
Neither the gas that rose as things grew hot
Nor solids at the bottom of the pot
Were the least use in what we tried to do,
Lost was our trouble, lost our labor too,

And all the money, in the name of Hell,
That we'd laid out on it was lost as well.

And there was also many another thing
Pertaining to the trade we had to bring,
Though I can't name them in an ordered plan
Because I'm an uneducated man;
Yet I will list them as they come to mind,
Though not distinguishing their class and kind:
Armenian clay, borax and verdigris,
Earthen and glass-ware vessels piece by piece,
Our urinals, our pots for oil-extraction,
Crucibles, pots for sublimative action,
Phial, alembic, beaker, gourd-retort,
And other useless nonsense of the sort
Not worth a leek, needless to name them all;
Water in rubefaction,* bullock's gall,
Arsenic, brimstone, sal ammoniac,
And herbs that I could mention by the sack,
Moonwort, valerian, agrimony and such,
Which I could number if it mattered much.
Our lamps – we had them burning day and night
To help us to succeed, if we but might!
Our furnace too for calcifying action,
Our waters in a state of albefaction,
Chalk, quicklime, ashes and the white of eggs,
Various powders, clay, piss, dung and dregs,
Waxed bags, saltpeter, vitriol and a whole
Variety of fires of wood and coal;
Alkali, tartar, salt in preparation,
Matters combust or in coagulation,
Clay mixed with horse-hair, sometimes with my own,
Crystallized alum, oil of tartar thrown
With tartar crude and unfermented beer,
Yeast and a dozen more than you shall hear,
Realgar,* various absorbent batters
And, I may add, incorporative matters;
Our silver in a state of citrination,*
Things sealed in wax and things in fermentation,

Our molds, our vessels for assaying metal
And many other things I learnt to settle
I'll tell as I was taught, if you want more.

    There were the bodies seven and spirits four
Which my instructor frequently rehearsed;
Among the spirits quicksilver came first
And orpiment came second, then he passed
To sal ammoniac and brimstone last.
As for the seven bodies that I mention
Here they all are, if they are worth attention:
Gold for the sun and silver for the moon,
Iron for Mars and quicksilver in tune
With Mercury, lead which prefigures Saturn
And tin for Jupiter. Copper takes the pattern
Of Venus if you please! This cursed trade
Robs one of all the money one has made,
And all one spends on it or round about it
Will certainly be lost, I cannot doubt it.

    If you would publish your infatuation
Come on and try your hand at transmutation;
If one of you has money in his fist
Step up and make yourself an alchemist.
Perhaps you think the trade is easy learnt?
Why then, come on and get your fingers burnt;
Monk, friar, priest, canon, let them come who may,
And study books and papers night and day
To learn the weird directions verse by verse,
They'll find it's all in vain, God knows, and worse.
And as for trying to teach a simpleton,
Pooh! No use talking of it; can't be done.
Whether you know your alphabet or not;
All's one for all the good that may be got.
Learned and simple, by my soul's salvation,
Achieve the same results from transmutation
Equally well, when all is said and done;
They all fail absolutely, every one.

    And still I have forgotten my intention
To speak of iron filings and to mention

Corrosive liquids, ways of mollifying
Or hardening substances, or of supplying
Oils and ablutions, stores of fusible metal,
And so on. It's beyond a book to settle
These matters, any book; it would be best
To give this catalogue and myself a rest,
For I imagine I have said enough
To raise the devil, be he never so rough.

Ah no, let be! For the Philosopher's Stone,
Called the Elixir, never can be known.
We seek and seek, and were it once discovered
We should be safe enough – expenses covered.
But there's no way; whatever paths we trod
The search was useless and I swear to God,
For all our cunning, when all's tried and done
That stone won't yield itself to anyone.
It's made us squander all we ever had,
Losses enough to drive us nearly mad
But for the hope that crept about our heart
Always supposing, when we felt the smart,
It would relieve us of our sad condition;
Sharp was the hope and hard the supposition.

I give fair warning you may search forever;
A golden future lures one on to sever
Oneself from all one ever had, and trust
An art for which one cannot lose the lust;
People will always find it bitter-sweet,
Or so it seems. With nothing but a sheet
To cover one at night, with no array
Other than some outlandish cloak by day,
One yet would sell them both and be bereft.
No one can stop until there's nothing left.

Go where they may a man can always tell
Such people by their pungent brimstone smell;
For all the world they stink as will a goat,
A hot and ram-like smell that seems to float
About them, and a man a mile away
Will catch the foul infection, I dare say.

See? By the smell and by the threadbare cloak
You're pretty sure to recognize these folk.

    If privately you ask them to confess
Why they go round in such a shabby dress,
They'll turn at once and whisper in your ear
That if they were discovered they must fear
Death for their learning, such is their pretense;
That's how these people trade on innocence.

    Well, pass on to the story you require;
Before the pot is placed upon the fire
My master takes a certain quantity
Of metals which he tempers, none but he
– I can speak boldly now he's gone away –
For he's a cunning worker as they say,
At any rate he's made himself a name;
He blundered very often just the same.
And how, d'you think? It happens, like as not,
There's an explosion and good-by the pot!
These metals are so violent when they split
Our very walls can scarce stand up to it.
Unless well-built and made of stone and lime,
Bang go the metals through them every time
And some are driven down into the ground
– That way we used to lose them by the pound –
And some are scattered all about the floor;
Some even jump into the roof, what's more.
Although the devil didn't show his face
I'm pretty sure he was about the place.
In Hell itself where he is lord and master
There couldn't be more rancor in disaster
Than when our pots exploded as I told you;
All think they've been let down and start to scold you

    Some said the way the fire was made was wrong;
Others said, 'No – the bellows. Blown too strong.'
That frightened me, I blew them as a rule.
'Stuff!' said a third. 'You're nothing but a fool,
It wasn't tempered as it ought to be.'
'No!' said a fourth. 'Shut up and listen to me;

I say it should have been a beech-wood fire
And that's the real cause, or I'm a liar.'
    I've no idea why the thing went wrong;
Recriminations though were hot and strong.
'Well,' said my lord, 'there's nothing more to do.
I'll note these dangers for another brew;
I'm pretty certain that the pot was cracked,
Be that as may, don't gape! We've got to act.
Don't be alarmed, help to sweep up the floor,
Just as we always do, and try once more.
Pluck up your hearts!' The muck was gathered up,
A canvas then was laid to form a cup
And all the muck was thrown into a sieve
And sifted out for what it yet might give.
    'By God,' says one, 'I saw some metal fall,
Some's saved although we haven't got it all.
If things went wrong just now and acted tough,
Another time they may go well enough.
We've got to risk our goods if we're to gain.
What about merchants? Lord! They don't maintain
A fixed prosperity, believe you me.
Sometimes their goods are swallowed by the sea,
And sometimes they come safely back to port.'
'Well, calm yourself,' my master would retort;
'Next time I shall have things in proper frame,
I'll see our ship comes home, or take the blame.
Something went wrong I know, I'll find out what.'
    Another said the fire was too hot.
But whether hot or cold you may depend
We always met with failure in the end.
Yet, though we never reached the wished conclusion
We still went raving on in our illusion,
Sitting together, arguing on and on,
And every one as wise as Solomon.
    However all that glitters is not gold,
And that's the truth as we're so often told.
It isn't every apple on the spray
Is good to eat, lament it how you may.

It's just the same with us. Though it may please us
To think we're wise, the wisest one, by Jesus,
Will prove the biggest fool, that's my belief,
And he that seems the honestest a thief.
That will be clear enough to you, my friends,
Before I leave you and my story ends.

PART II

THERE is a canon going up and down
Amongst us, one who could infect a town
As large as Nineveh and Rome spread flat
With Troy and three or four on top of that.
The endless tricks and cunning of this crook
Are more than could be written in a book
Though you sat down and wrote away forever,
There's none on earth so treacherously clever.
The terms he uses wriggle, wind and scuttle
In tones of voice so infinitely subtle,
A man engaged with him in conversation
Soon finds his brain is dizzy with rotation,
Unless the man's a devil like himself.
Many a man he's cozened of his pelf
And will again, if he should live awhile.
Yet there are men will travel mile on mile
To seek this Canon out and be acquainted,
Not knowing everything he does is tainted.
So if you care to listen to what I say
You shall hear all about it right away.

If, holy canons of the church, it rouses
The thought that I am slandering your houses,
Since it is of a canon I am speaking,
Reject the thought! God knows, there is some sneaking
Rascal in every house and God forbid
That all were judged by what one madman did.
Slandering you's no part of my intention,
But to set right the evils that I mention.

485

Nor is my tale aimed specially at you;
It will apply to many others too.
Among the twelve apostles our Creator
Found faith in all but one, who was a traitor.
Then why should the remainder be to blame
That stood in innocence? I say the same
Of you, except for this, if you will hear:
If any lurking Judas should appear
Among you, fling him out I say betimes,
Before you're shamed and beggared by his crimes.
And therefore take no umbrage, sirs, I pray
And in this instance listen to what I say.

There was a chantry priest, it would appear,
One who had lived in London many a year,
So pleasant in his manner and so able,
The lady in whose house he sat at table
Refused to take a farthing's worth of pay
For board and clothes, whatever his display,
And pocket-money was allowed as well.
No matter for that; I shall proceed to tell
My story of the canon, whose intrusion
Brought this unhappy priest to his confusion.
     This treacherous canon, then, came in one day,
Entered the priest's apartment where he lay
And begged him to advance a certain sum,
Which was to be repaid him, saying, 'Come,
Lend me a mark, it's only for three days,
I'll pay you on the nail – I'm one who pays.
And if I fail you when you come to check,
Another time just hang me by the neck!'
     This priest produced the money on the spot;
The canon, after thanking him a lot,
Took leave of him and went upon his way
And brought his money back the proper day.
When it had been paid back and matters righted
This foolish priest of course was quite delighted

And said, 'Trust me, I never take offense
If someone comes to borrow a few pence,
Or anything I have in my possession,
When he's an honest man of good profession
And doesn't break his day if he should owe;
To such a man I never can say no.'

   'What!' said the canon. 'I not pay when due?
That would be something altogether new!
My honor is a thing I hope to keep
Forever, till the moment when I creep
Into my grave. God send I do indeed;
You can trust that as surely as the creed.
And I thank God – in good hour be it spoken –
No one can say my word was ever broken
For any gold or silver I was lent;
I never stole a farthing with intent.

   'Now, sir,' he said, 'to speak of my concerns,
Since you are fond of doing kindly turns
And were particularly kind to me,
To pay you back the coin of charity
I'll tell you something, if you care to learn,
In simple language, how I came to turn
My talents towards alchemy and science.
Watch! You can place an absolute reliance
On seeing me work a miracle ere I go.'

   'What!' said the priest. 'Can that be really so?
Mother of God! I beg you to proceed!'

   'At your commandment, sir, I will indeed,'
He answered, 'God forbid that I should not.'
D'you see? This thief's kind service was a plot.
How true it is that proffered service stinks!
So say the wise, and anyone who thinks.
I'll verify that saying in a while
Upon this canon, root of fraud and guile.
He took a special pleasure and delight,
Such was his fiendish heart, and appetite
For bringing christian people to destruction;
God keep us from his treacherous seduction!

This priest had no idea with whom he dealt,
And what was coming to him never felt.
O foolish priest! O innocent in bliss,
Soon to be blinded, and by avarice!
O God-abandoned, blind in a complete
And thoughtless ignorance of the deceit
This wily fox is putting into shape!
You're in the snare, there will be no escape;
And therefore to press on to a conclusion
That only can refer to your confusion,
Unhappy man, I hurry on to volley
Anathemas upon your witless folly
And on the treachery of that other wretch,
As far as my abilities will stretch.

You think this canon was my master, eh?
Sir Host, by Mary of Heaven let me say
It was another canon and not he,
A hundred times more skilled in trickery.
His frauds have cozened people many a time;
It dulls my wits to speak of it in rhyme.
Whenever I think of them it brings a rush
Of blood for very shame, I have to blush
– At any rate my cheeks begin to glow
Though there's no color in them, well I know;
My face is tarnished, fumes of the diverse
Metals you heard me latterly rehearse
Have wasted and consumed and turned it yellow.
Now take account of this accursed fellow:

'Sir,' he addressed the priest, 'send out your man
For quicksilver, as quickly as you can;
Let him bring several ounces, two or three,
And when he's back I promise you shall see
A miracle you never saw before.'

'Certainly,' said the priest, 'he's at the door,
It shall be done at once.' The man was sent,
Ready to do his bidding; off he went
And, to tell truth, returned immediately
Bringing three ounces of the mercury,

And gave them to the canon for a start.
    The canon laid them carefully apart
And sent the servant out again for coal,
In order to start work towards his goal.
    The man came back and brought a scuttleful;
This canon then drew forth a crucible
Out of his bosom, showed it to his dupe,
'And now,' he said, 'be good enough to stoop
And measure out an ounce of mercury.
This is our instrument, as you can see.
Open your hand; now put the mercury in,
That's it ... and in the name of Christ begin
The study of science, be an alchemist!
    'Few, very few indeed, I would enlist
With those who share the secrets of my science.
But you shall watch me, using this appliance,
Do an experiment. I shall reduce
Or mortify this metal – no abuse
Of your good faith – before your very eyes.
Yes, you shall watch it as it mortifies
And changes into silver just as fine
And good as any in your purse or mine
Or anywhere else, and just as malleable.
It not, call me a liar and unable
To show my face, a subject for your mirth!
    'I have a powder here that cost the earth,
And it will make all good, for it's the basis
Of all my power – I'll show you – in these cases.
Send your man off, tell him to wait outside,
And shut the door on him. I won't be spied
Upon at work, for no one else must see
The way we set to work in alchemy.'
    He gave his orders and the thing was done,
The servant was sent packing at a run,
The chamber door was bolted with a jerk
And these philosophers got down to work.
    At the accursed canon's fell desire
The priest then set the thing upon the fire,

He grabbed the bellows busily and blew.
Into the crucible the canon threw
This powder. What it was I cannot tell
– Possibly chalk, or glass would do as well,
Or anything else indeed not worth a fly,
To hoodwink him, and urged him to look spry
And cover up the crucible with coal.

   'To demonstrate my love for you, dear soul,'
The canon said, 'in what we're going to do,
I'll leave the handling of it all to you.'

   'Oh, thank you!' said the priest, who was delighted,
And couched the coals just as he was invited.
And while he busied himself this fiendish wretch,
This treacherous canon, whom the devil fetch,
Produced a bit of beech-wood, charred to coal,
In which there had been subtly bored a hole
That held an ounce of silver filings, stopped
With wax securely, lest a filing dropped.

   Please understand this treacherous invention
Was not made then, but made of long intention;
The canon had devised it all before,
And other dodges too. I'll tell you more
Hereafter of those other things he brought,
For long before he came he had the thought
Of tricking him. So he did before they parted.
He couldn't wait to skin him, having started.
It dulls my wits I say to speak of him.
O, to take vengeance on this treacherous, trim
Liar! If only I knew how! But there,
He's slippery – here and there and everywhere.

   Now listen, gentlemen, for God's dear love.
He took this coal of which I spoke above
And palmed it dexterously, while the priest
Still busy as I said had nearly ceased
Poking, as I have told you, with a prong
Among the coals. 'You're doing it all wrong!'
The canon said, 'Here's how it ought to be,
Dear chap, I'll fix it; give the thing to me,

Just let me interfere a little. There!
St Giles, I'm sorry for you! I declare
You've got quite hot – why, man, you're pouring sweat,
Here, take this cloth and wipe yourself, you're wet.'

And while the priest was mopping up his face
The canon took his coal – the damned disgrace! –
And stuck it in the middle, somewhat higher
Than was the crucible, and blew the fire
Till up it flamed and all the coals were red.

'And now let's have a drink,' the canon said;
'All will be well quite soon, I'll undertake.
Sit down, let's cheer ourselves for goodness' sake.'

After a while this canon's beechen coal
Burnt up; out came the silver from the hole
Into the crucible and began to run
As you'd expect. What else could it have done?
Couched well above the flames it couldn't miss.
The priest, alas, knew nothing of all this,
Thinking the coals were all alike and good;
The trick of it he had not understood.

And when this alchemist saw all was ready
'Rise up,' he said, 'Sir priest, beside me – steady,
We haven't got a mold. Let's take a walk
For we shall need to buy ourselves some chalk
Which I can carve, if I may make so bold,
Into the shape required for a mold.
And you must get me out a bowl or pan
With water in it, for I tell you, man,
Our business here is just about to sprout.
And just to disabuse you of all doubt,
While you're away, to clear me of suspicion,
I shall go with you on your expedition
And stay with you till we return once more.'

And to be brief he then unlocked the door,
Went out and shut it, turning to re-lock it,
And off they went. The key was in his pocket.

Presently back they came with no delay.
Why should I drag my story out all day?

He took the chalk when they got back again
And made a mold of it. Let me explain:
Out of his sleeve I say he took a rod
Of silver – pour thy vengeance on him, God! –
Which weighed an ounce exactly; this he took
(Watch for the tricks of this accursed crook),
And carved his mold to make a perfect fit
For this same silver rod, depend on it,
So furtively the priest, you may believe,

Saw nothing. Then he tucked it up his sleeve,
Turned to the fire, took out the preparation
And poured it in the mold with great elation.
He cast the mold into the water-pan
When ready, saying to the priest, poor man,
'Look what we've got, put in your hand and grope
And you will find some silver there I hope.'

Hell's devils! What else could have been the stuff?
Silver filings are silver right enough.

The priest put in his hand and took a scoop
And out he brought the metal with a whoop,
Thrilled to the veins to see this silver rod.
'God's blessing on you, and the Mother of God
And all his saints preserve you, worthy master!'
He cried. 'And may they bring me to disaster
Unless you will vouchsafe your kind compliance
In teaching me this noble art and science.
I'll work for you with all my might and main!'

'Well,' said the canon, 'let me try again;
We'll have a second shot; pay careful heed
And you'll become an expert, and at need
Can try it in my absence, once you're in
The ways of scientific discipline.
Let's take another ounce of mercury,
This is no time for chattering,' said he,
'And do the same with it as we have done
Already with the first, our silver one.'

The priest then set to business and began
To do precisely what this cursed man

Commanded of him, puffing at the fire
In the mad hope of reaching his desire.
Meanwhile the canon, if I need explain,
Stood ready by to gull the priest again,
Dandling, to give him countenance in this,
A hollow stick – observe the artifice! –
Into the end of which an ounce, no more,
Of silver filings had been stuffed before,
As in the beech-wood coal, with wax no doubt,
To stop the silver filings falling out.

    And while the priest was busy at his job
The canon came and touched him with the knob
And with a flourish cast the powder in
Just as before – the devil scrape his skin,
Hear me, O God, and flay him for the trick! –
And stirred the crucible with this same stick
Primed in the treacherous way that you have heard;
He always was a crook in deed and word.

    He stirred the coals until the wax began
To melt over the flame, as any man
Except a fool of course would know it must.
Out of the stick slid all the silver dust
And down into the crucible it fell.

    What can be better, gentlemen, than well?
For when this priest had been deceived again
And taken it all for gospel, right as rain,
He was so happy that I can't express
In words his ecstasy of happiness.
He proffered to the canon on the spot
Body and soul. 'Eh,' said the canon. 'What?
I have some powers, though I seem poor to some,
But let me tell you there is more to come.
D'you happen to have some copper here?' said he.
'Yes,' said the priest, 'I think I have, maybe.'
'If not you'll have to buy some right away,
Be off with you, dear sir, be quick I say.'

    He went away and came back with the copper;
The canon took it from him as was proper

And carefully weighed out a measured ounce.
  My tongue is all too simple to pronounce
Words that could serve my thoughts or match my feelings
About his bloody-minded double-dealings.
Friendly he seemed to those he hadn't caught
But was a fiend in what he felt and thought.
It wearies me to say how false he was,
Yet I must try to speak of it because
It may help others to beware his treason
In time, and truly that's my only reason.
  Within the crucible the canon placed
His ounce of copper, set it then in haste
Among the flames and cast the powder in,
Telling the priest to stoop down and begin
Blowing the fire, and it was all a hoax;
He made a monkey of him with his jokes.
  He cast the molten copper in his mold
And put it in the water to get cold;
Leaning above it, in he put his hand.
Now in his sleeve – as you will understand,
You heard me say so – was a silver rod.
He took it slyly out, the filthy sod,
– The priest knew nothing of his treacherous plan –
And left it in the bottom of the pan.
He fumbled in the water, groped about
And with amazing sleight-of-hand took out
And hid the copper rod. With friendly charm
He took the unsuspecting victim's arm
And said to him, as if it were a joke,
'By God, you're much to blame! Stoop down and poke;
Help me as I helped you. That's only fair;
Come on, put in your hand and see what's there.'
  The priest took out the silver there and then.
The canon said, 'We must go out again
Taking these rods, all three, that we have made,
And ask some fellow in the goldsmith trade
Whether they're anything. I should be distressed
To find them less than silver of the best.

Well, it's a thing that can be proved forthwith.'
    So off they went to find a silversmith
And gave their metal to the man to try it
With fire and hammer; no one could deny it,
All were as should be, silver unalloyed.
    Was that besotted cleric overjoyed?
Never was bird gladder to greet the day,
Never was nightingale in depth of May
More joyful in her eagerness to sing,
Nor lady lustier in caroling
Or in her talk of love and womanhood,
Nor knightly soul more eager to do good
In deeds of arms to please his chosen lady
Than was the priest to learn that graceless, shady
Business; and he addressed the canon thus:
'For love of God who died for all of us,
And if I may deserve so much of you,
What will that powder cost me? Tell me, do!'
    'By our Lady,' said the canon, 'for a buyer
I warn you it's expensive; save one friar
And I myself there's no one who can make it,
Not in all England.' 'Never mind, I'll take it,'
The priest replied; 'for God's sake, what's the price?'
'It's dear,' he said, 'but at a sacrifice,
Since you're a friend and really want to bid.
God help me, it is yours for forty quid.
But for the kindness that you showed before
In lending me a mark it would be more.'
    This priest at once collected forty pound
In golden pieces and he took them round
To give the canon for his recipe,
Whose work in life was fraud and treachery.
    'Sir priest,' he said, 'I look for no renown
In this my art; in fact I play it down.
So, if you love me, keep the matter quiet;
If people knew my skill there'd be a riot.
By God, there'd be such envy and defiance
Against me for philosophy and science,

I should be killed; there'd be no other way.'
   'Why God forbid!' the priest said. 'Killed, you say?
Better to squander all the wealth I had
To save you – if I didn't, send me mad,
Dear God! – than see you suffer such an ill.'
'You have a solid reason for good will,'
The canon said. 'Good-by and many thanks!'
And off he went, this prince of mountebanks;
The priest never set eyes on him again
After that day. I hardly need explain
That when he tried experiments the priest
Had no success whatever, not the least.
The powder wouldn't work, it was a mock;
He had been tricked and made a laughing-stock.
That was the canon's way of introduction
When bringing down poor people to destruction.

   Gentlemen, think, there has been strife of old
In every class waged between men and gold,
So fierce there's hardly any to be had.
Alchemy has made many people mad
And on my word I think it well may be
The greatest reason for its scarcity.
   Their scientific jargon is so woolly
No one can hope to understand it fully,
Not as intelligence goes nowadays.
And they may go on chattering like jays
And take delight and trouble in their chatter,
But for all that they'll never solve the matter.
If you are rich it's easy to be taught
How to transmute and bring your wealth to naught.
   There's so much lucre in this fine affair
One's joy can be transmuted to despair.
It can impoverish the heaviest purses,
Yet all it does for one is buy the curses
Of those that lend their goods before they've learnt.
Oh fie, for shame! When people have been burnt

Cannot they learn, alas, to shun the fire?
And you that use it, master your desire
Lest you lose all; for better late than never.
Long is the ruin that can last forever!

  Prowl as you may the secret can't be found,
Though you're as bold as Dobbin blundering round;
Poor blind old horse, in dangers all unknown,
He's just as liable to hit a stone
As keep along the highway, and I hold
It's just the same transmuting into gold.

  Should, then, your outward eye see incorrectly
Let the mind's eye behold more circumspectly.
You may be wide awake, but though you stare
You will make nothing of that business there,
Rather will waste all you can grab or earn.
Slacken a fire that is quick to burn;
Meddle no more with alchemy I mean
For if you do all thrift will be swept clean.

  I should at once inform you if I may
What genuine philosophers would say.
Arnold* is one of those that make the quorum;
He wrote *Rosarium Philosophorum*
And came from Villa Nova. Thus says he:
  'There is no mortifying mercury
Without the use of sulfur, brother to it.'
The first of all philosophers that knew it
Was Hermes Trismegistus and he said:
  'Doubtless the dragon never can be dead
Or mortify, unless you also slay
His brother with him. Put another way,
The dragon stands for Mercury, none other,
And sulfur, known as brimstone, is his brother,
And these are drawn from *Luna* and from *Sol*.
Therefore,' he said, 'observe this protocol:
Let no man busy himself to seek this art
Unless he knows the language and the heart
Of science, both in aim and technical term,
For, without these, he is an ignorant worm.

This is a craft and science that is furled
As secret of the secrets of the world.'
   Plato had a disciple once, and he
Said to his master – if you care to see,
It is recorded in the *Chimica*
Senioris Zadith Tabula – *
'Tell me the name, sir, of the Secret Stone?'
And Plato said in answer, 'It is known
As Titan Stone upon the tongues of men.'
'And what is that?' said the disciple then.
'Magnesia,' answered Plato. 'Is it thus?
Then it's *ignotum per ignotius!**
What then may be Magnesia, master, pray?'
'Magnesia is the liquid, I would say,
Composed of the Four Elements,' he said.
'What's its root-principle or fountain-head?
Will you be pleased to indicate that fount?'
'No, no,' said Plato then, 'on no account.
Philosophers are under strict control
Never to tell that secret to a soul
Or write it in a book; it is unpriced,
Being a secret very dear to Christ.
It is His will that no discovery
Be made of it, save where His Deity
Wills to inspire His servants, else forbidden.
No more; from whom He wills He keeps it hidden.'
   So I conclude; since God will not allow
Philosophers to tell their pupils how
To find this stone, no doubt it's better so,
And my advice would be to let it go.
Make God your adversary for a whim
And work at what is contrary to Him
And to His will, and you will never thrive
Though you transmute as long as you're alive.
Aye, there's the point for which my tale began,
And may God prosper every honest man!
                      Amen.

[GROUP H]

The Manciple's Tale

The Manciple's Prologue

D on't you all know where stands a little town,
The one that people call Bob-up-and-down,
Near Blean Woods on the way to Canterbury?
Well, it was thereabouts our Host turned merry.
'Dun's in the mire!'* he said. 'Behold King Log;
For love or money drag him from his bog!
Will no one wake our friend asleep behind?
A thief could rob him and he wouldn't mind.
Look at him napping ... Forty winks? Cock's bones!
He'll tumble off his horse and hit the stones.
Is that the London Cook, the devil take him?
Make him come here, he knows the fine, we'll make him
Tell us a story, though I'm bound to say
It won't be worth a barrow-load of hay.
Wake up, you Cook!' he said. 'God give you sorrow,
What's up with you to sleep this sunny morrow?
Have you had fleas all night, or else got drunk,
Or spent the night in toiling with a punk,
And haven't got the strength to raise your head?'
    The Cook was drunk, pale-drunk, no touch of red,
And answered from a stupor, 'Bless my soul!
I feel all heavy, haven't got control;
I'd rather sleep,' he said, 'I don't know why,
Than drink a gallon of wine, the best you buy
In all Cheapside.' The Manciple said, 'Well,
If I can make things easier for a spell
For you, and not offend the company,
And if the Host extends his courtesy
To let me, I'll excuse you from your tale.
    'Upon my word, your face is pretty pale,

499

Your eyes are somewhat dazed, I can't help thinking;
As for your breath, I'm bound to say it's stinking,
Which shows you indisposed for such a matter.
Blunt words are best, I never was one to flatter.

'Look at him yawning there, the drunken sot!
You'd think he meant to swallow us on the spot.
Keep your mouth shut, man! Mercy, what a socket!
The devil of Hell's own hoof would hardly block it;
Your cursed breath may well infect us all.
You stinking swine, fie, how you gape and sprawl!
(Look out, take care, sir, he's a powerful man)
I'd like to see a punch-ball hit his pan!
He's about ripe for trouble in that line;
You'd think he had been drinking monkey-wine,
Far enough gone for playing with a straw!'

This speech annoyed the Cook who, turning raw,
Craned at the Manciple with so much force
For want of speech, he tumbled off his horse
And there he lay for all the care they took;
Fine cavalry performance for a cook!
Pity he couldn't have held on by his ladle.

They got him back at last into the cradle
After a deal of shoving to and fro
To lift him up, it was a sorry show,
Poor, pallid soul, unwieldier than most!

But to the Manciple at last our Host
Turned and remarked, 'Drink is in domination
Over the fellow; by my soul's salvation
I think he'd only tell a lousy tale.
Whether it's wine or maybe new-brewed ale
That's in him, he is talking through his nose;
Like someone with a cold, one would suppose,
Snuffling like that. I think he's going to spew.
It's just about as much as he can do
To keep his horse from falling in the ditch
And if his horse should fall, he'll follow, which
Gives us as much as we can do to strain
And lift his drunken body up again.

Carrying corpses would be just as grim.
Tell on your tale, I've had enough of him.
   'But, Manciple, it wasn't very nice
Of you to scold the fellow for his vice.
Another day those chickens you have loosed
May very likely all return to roost.
I mean he might allude to small amounts
That could be criticized in your accounts
As not quite honest, if it came to proof.'
   'That might be awkward; I shall keep aloof.
He easily could catch me in the snare,'
The other said, 'I'd rather buy the mare
Between his drunken legs than start a row,
I mustn't make him angry anyhow.
The things I said were only meant in jest.
   'Do you know what? I've something of the best
Here in this gourd, wine of the ripest grape;
Just watch and we shall have another jape.
I'll give the Cook some liquor if I may,
On pain of death he shall not say me nay!'
   And certainly, to tell you what occurred,
The Cook, alas, drank freely from the gourd.
What was the need? He'd had enough before,
Yet spluttered in the mug and drank some more,
Giving it back when he had had enough.
The Cook, who was delighted with the stuff,
Thanked him as best he could, for some time after.
   Our Host went off into a roar of laughter
And said, 'Well, now I see how necessary
It is to bring one's drink to keep us merry,
For it can turn all rancor and dissension
To love and harmony, and stop contention.
   'O Bacchus, thou! A blessing on thy name
That so convertest earnest into game;
Our thanks and worship to thy deity!
My prayers are done, you get no more of me.
   'Now, Manciple, on with your story, pray.'
'Well, sir,' he said, 'attend to what I say.'

The Manciple's Tale

W HEN Phoebus had his dwelling here on earth
As ancient books report, for what they're worth,
He was a paladin of lustiest marrow,
Better than anyone with bow and arrow.
He slew the serpent Python as it lay
Coiled in the sunshine and asleep one day,
And many a noble and distinguished deed
His bow performed for him, as you can read.

And every instrument of minstrelsy
He well knew how to play, while melody
Poured from his throat, clear joy to hear him sing.
Even Amphion, famous Theban King
Who built the town's defenses by his singing,
Was not so skilled in setting echoes ringing.

Added to that he was the handsomest man
That ever was heard of since the world began.
Why should I make description of his features?
He was the fairest living of earthly creatures.
And therewithal he was of noblest bearing,
Filled with high honor, excellence and daring.

This Phoebus, flower in the camp of youth,
Renowned for bounty, chivalry and truth,
To please himself and signalize his glory
In having vanquished Python, says my story,
Was wont to carry in his hand a bow.

Now in his house this Phoebus kept a crow
Lodged in a cage, and there for many a day
He taught it speech, as one can teach a jay,
And fostered it with care. This crow was white,
White as a snowy swan; it could recite
With perfect mimicry of tone and word
What any man had uttered, and the bird
Would use this talent when it told a tale.
In all the world there was no nightingale,

Moreover, with a hundred thousandth part
Of what it had in merriness and art.

Now in his house this Phoebus had a wife
Who lived with him; he loved her more than life
And night and day he gave his diligence
To pleasing her and showing reverence,
Except for this, if it's the truth they tell us,
I have to say he was extremely jealous
And wished to guard her (lest an exhibition
Be made of him) as those in his condition
Commonly do – in vain, it can't succeed.
A good wife who is pure in thought and deed
Should not be checked and spied on, that is plain,
And truly it is labor all in vain
To check a wicked one; it can't be done.
It's imbecility, say I for one,
For men to waste their labor checking wives,
And so the ancients say who wrote their lives.

But to my purpose, as I first began;
This excellent Phoebus does the best he can
To please her, thinking by his kind address
And by his management and manliness
That no one could extrude him from her graces.
But God knows, none can compass in such cases
The power to restrain a thing which nature
Has naturally implanted in a creature.

Take any bird and put it in a cage
And let your heart's intention then engage
To foster it tenderly with food and drink,
With every dainty mess that thought can think,
And keep it clean as nearly as you may,
Caged in a cage of gold however gay,
That bird would rather twenty thousand fold
Be in a forest which is rough and cold,
Feeding on worms and other wretched trash.
It's on the watch, and ready in a flash
To escape out of the cage and to be gone.
Freedom is what it sets its heart upon.

Or take a cat, nourish it well with milk
And tender meat, make it a couch of silk,
But let it see a mouse along the wall
And it abandons milk and meat and all
And every other dainty in the house,
Such as its appetite to eat a mouse.
You see, a natural lust is in possession
And appetite has banished its discretion.
She-wolves are also of this baser kind;
They choose the lowest wolf that they can find,
The least in reputation, to be mated,
When the time comes to have their passion sated.

These parallels are all produced to show
The faithlessness of men, they do not go
For women, not at all. The foul delight
Of men is wreaking lecherous appetite
On lower things than wives however fair,
However true, however debonair;
Flesh pines for the new-fangled, curse upon it,
And nothing with the stamp of virtue on it
Will pleasure us for more than a short while.

This Phoebus who was innocent of guile
Was well deceived, for all his excellent features.
She had a man, one of the lowest creatures,
Far beneath him, of little reputation;
Worth nothing next a man of Phoebus' station.
And, more's the harm, it happens often so
And is a common source of human woe.

It chanced his wife, when Phoebus was away,
Sent for her bully – bully, did I say?
Tut-tut, that was a very knavish speech!
Your pardon, lords and ladies, I beseech.

Wise Plato says, as those who can may read,
Words should be in accordance with the deed;
In tales told properly a word should bring
The sense of being cousin to the thing.
I'm a blunt, boisterous man and tell you all
There is no real difference at all

Between a lady-wife of high degree
Dishonest of her body, if she be,
And some poor wench, no difference but this
— That's if so be they both should go amiss —
That since the gentlewoman ranks above
She therefore will be called his lady-love,
Whereas that other woman, being poor,
Will be referred to as his wench or whore.
And as God knows, and so do you, dear brother,
One name is just as low as is the other.

Nor is there difference in my belief
Between a tyrant and an arrant thief
Or outlaw, when the tyrant has no claim.
They told great Alexander just the same,
That just because a tyrant has the might
By force of arms to murder men downright
And burn down house and home and leave all flat,
They call the man a captain, just for that.
But since an outlaw with his little band
Cannot bring half such mischief on a land
Or be the cause of so much harm and grief,
He only earns the title of a thief.

Well, I'm no scholar and you shan't be vexed
By hearing me enlarge on any text;
Back to the tale I started, but more fully.

When Phoebus' wife had notified her bully
They wrought their will in all its transient rage.
Now the white crow, still hanging in its cage,
Beheld their work and never said a word.
But once Lord Phoebus had returned, the bird
Unlocked its throat and sang, 'Cuckoo! Cuckoo!'

'What, bird!' said Phoebus. 'That's no song for you!
Were you not wont to sing your songs so gaily
That it rejoiced my heart to hear you daily
In tuneful voice? Alas, what song is this?'

'By God,' it said, 'I do not sing amiss.
Phoebus,' it said, 'in spite of all your worth,
Of all your beauty and your gentle birth,

Of all your minstrelsy and singing too,
And all your watching, someone's hoodwinked you,
Has bleared your eyes – a man whose reputation,
Compared with yours, has little estimation,
Not worth a gnat indeed; upon my life,
On your own bed I saw him plumb your wife.'

What more d'you want? The crow in his behoof
Boldly informed him, giving serious proof,
Of how his wife had done her lechery
And had put shame on him and villainy;
He swore he had seen it with his very eyes.

Phoebus fell backward at the crow's replies;
It seemed to him his sorrowful heart was breaking.
Setting an arrow to his bow and taking
Aim, as he bent it in his rage to slay,
He killed his wife; there is no more to say.

And all his instruments of minstrelsy
He broke in sorrow for it, psaltery,
Lute, harp, guitar, and then he broke his bow
And arrows, and he thus addressed the crow:

'Traitor,' he said, 'it was thy scorpion-tongue
Brought my confusion. Oh, my heart is wrung
With grief! Why was I born? Would I were dead!
O dearest wife, O gem of joy that shed
So grave, so true a light upon our love!
Now thou art dead and pale of face, O dove
Of innocence! That I can swear! O speed
Of hand too rash, to do so foul a deed!
O mind confused, O thoughtless rage surprised
That smote a guiltless creature, unadvised!
O fainting trust, O prompting to suspect,
Where was your thought and wisdom to direct?
O every man, beware how you are moved,
Never believe but what is strongly proved!
Strike not too soon, ere you can reason why,
Be soberly advised before you try
To execute your justice and assuage
Suspicion by the acting of your rage.

Alas, a thousand in their hasty ire
Have been undone and brought into the mire.
O sorrow! I shall kill myself for grief!'
    And to the crow he said, 'O wicked thief,
Now I shall pay you for your lying tale!
Once you sang sweetly like a nightingale,
But now, false thief, your liquid song is done
And all your snowy feathers, every one;
Never in all your life to utter word,
Vengeance shall fall upon you, traitor-bird.
You and your issue ever shall be black;
Their sweetest music, like your own, shall crack,
And you shall croak, foretelling storm and rain
In token that through you my wife was slain.'
    And up he started at the crow and tore
The fair white feathers out that once it bore;
He made it black, and took away its song
And power of speech, and flung it forth headlong
Down to the devil; nor do I wish it back.
And that's the reason why all crows are black.
    My lords, this is a parable conveying
A moral; pray take heed of what I'm saying.
Never tell anyone in all your life
That any other has enjoyed his wife,
For he will hate you mortally, believe it.
   Solomon said – the learned so receive it –
'Teach every man how to refrain his tongue.'
But as I said, you won't find me among
The scholars, but my mother long ago
Would say, 'My son, reflect upon the crow;
My son, you hold your tongue and hold your friends.
A wicked tongue but serves the devil's ends.
My son, the cross can save you from his net;
My son, God in His endless goodness set
A wall about the tongue of teeth and lip;
Take counsel ere you speak, let nothing slip.
My son, too often by some babbling speech
Many are blasted, so the scholars teach.

A little wisely spoken as a rule
Will save a man from being cursed for fool.
My son, restrain your tongue in self-denial
On all occasions, save in making trial
Of prayer or speaking in the honor of God.
The first of virtues, if you will kiss the rod,
My son, is to restrain and guard your tongue;
So teach your children this when they are young.
My son, superfluous, unthinking speech,
When to say less is still within your reach
And would suffice, will harm you, I was taught.
Much chatter is the food of sinful thought.
Are you aware what hasty tongues can do?
Just as a sword can cut an arm in two
Or slice it into bits, dear son, just so
A tongue can sever friendship at a blow.

'A chatterbox is hateful to the Lord;
Here Solomon the wise is in accord
With David in his psalms, and Seneca too.
My son, say nothing when a nod will do.
Feign to be deaf if you should hear the chatter
Of any fool that broaches dangerous matter.
And add this Flemish proverb to your diet
If you will learn it, "Little speech, much quiet."
My son, if you have said no wicked word
You need not fear to have been overheard,
Whereas a wicked word, I tell you plain,
Once said can never be recalled again.
What's said is said and goes upon its way,
Like it or not, repent it as you may.

'He is a slave to any that has heard
Him tell a tale, he'll suffer for that word.
My son, be cautious, fashion nothing new
By way of tidings, whether false or true;
Wherever you may be, with high or low,
Restrain your tongue and think upon the crow.

[GROUP I]

The Parson's Tale

The Parson's Prologue

THE story of the Manciple had ended.
From the south line the sun had now descended
So low, it stood – so far as I had sight –
At less than twenty-nine degrees in height.
Four o' the clock it was, to make a guess;
Eleven foot long, or little more or less,
My shadow was, as at that time and place,
Measuring feet by taking in this case
My height as six, divided in like pattern*
Proportionally; and the power of Saturn*
Began to rise with *Libra* just as we
Approached a little thorp. Our referee,
Our Host, that is, and trusted guide, who made
Decisions for our happy cavalcade,
Turned round and said, 'Matters, my lords, stand thus;
There's but one story lacking now to us.
We've carried out my sentence and decree.
We've heard a tale from each in his degree,
What I ordained is nearly done, I say.
God send the best of fortune, so I pray,
On whomsoever is last to pour the liquor.
Sir Priest,' he said, 'are you by chance a vicar?
Or else the parson? Tell the truth I say;
Don't spoil our sport though, be you what you may,
For every man but you has told his tale.
Unbuckle now and show what's in your bale,
For honestly, to judge you by your looks,
You could knit mighty matters out of books.
So up and tell a story, by cock's bones!'
The Parson said at once in level tones,

'You'll get no fable or romance from me,
For Paul in writing unto Timothy
Reproves all those who waive aside the truth
For fables that are wretched and uncouth.
And why unclench my fist on your behalf,
I that can scatter wheat, to give you chaff?
And therefore if you care to hear my preaching
I'll offer virtuous matter, moral teaching.
So if you'll hear me, granting that sufficed,
I would be glad in reverence of Christ
To give you lawful pleasure if I can.

'But trust me truly, I'm a southern man,
I can't romance with rum-ram-ruf by letter,*
And rhyme, God knows, I hold but little better;
I won't embellish things with tricks like those
If you'll excuse me, but I'll speak in prose,
A happy thing, to knit and make an end
Of all our feast. Jesu in mercy send
Me wit to guide your way one further stage
Upon that perfect, glorious pilgrimage
Called the celestial, to Jerusalem.
These are my thoughts; if you approve of them
I'll start my tale at once, so tell me pat
If you agree. I can't say more than that.

'Nevertheless I put this meditation
In full submission to the castigation
Of learned men. I am not skilled in texts,
I only take, as each of you expects,
The moral of it, and for your protection
As I protest, submit it to correction.'

These words had gained assent from everyone,
For that, we thought, was just what should be done,
To close upon a virtuous persuasion,
And give him both an audience and occasion;
Our Host was then requested to prevail
On our behalf with him to tell his tale.

Our Host was ready and found words for all,
And said, 'Now, master Parson, fair befall

Your reverent meditation! But I'm thinking
You'd better hurry, for the sun is sinking.
Be fructuous and brief in what you tell,
And may God send you grace to do it well!
Say what you please; you will be gladly heard.'
So he began this sermon, on the word.

The Parson's Tale

*The Parson's Tale is a prose sermon on the proper prepara-
tion for Confession and the true nature of the Seven Deadly
Sins. It seems therefore to lead naturally to Chaucer's Retractions which follow it. On the literal plane of meaning it
seems to be offered as an appropriate ending to a pilgrimage before the Saint's shrine is reached. On the allegorical
plane, referred to by the Parson when first called upon for a
story, it may be deemed a preparation for a last confession
to be made on 'that perfect, glorious pilgrimage' that is
called the celestial, to the Heavenly Jerusalem.*

A brief summary of the Parson's summary here follows:

God desires no man to perish and there are many spiritual ways to the celestial city. One noble way is Penitence,
the lamenting for sin and the will to sin no more. The root
of the tree of Penitence is contrition, the branches and the
leaves are confession, the fruit satisfaction, (that is, the performance of a penance), the seed grace and the heat in that
seed the Love of God.

Contrition is the heart's sorrow for sin. Sin may be venial
or deadly. Venial sin is for one to love Christ less than he
ought. Deadly sin is to love a creature more than the Creator. Venial sin may lead to deadly sin. There are seven
deadly sins of which the first is Pride.

Pride is shown in many forms: arrogance, impudence,
boasting, hypocrisy, joy in having done harm, etc. It may be
inward or outward. Outward pride is like a tavern sign that
shows there is wine in the cellar. It may show itself in too
many clothes or too few, or in the carriage of the body, as
when the buttocks jut as it were the hinder parts of a she-
ape in the full of the moon. One can show sinful pride in
retinue, in ostentatious hospitality, in one's strength, in

one's gentility. The remedy for Pride is Humility or true self-knowledge.

Envy *is sorrow at the prosperity of others and joy in their hurt. It is the worst of sins as it sets itself against all other virtues and goodness, and is flatly against the Holy Ghost, source of Bounty. Backbiting and grumbling are the Devil's* Paternoster.

The remedy for Envy is to love God, your neighbor and your enemy.

Anger *is the wicked will to vengeance. Anger against wickedness, however, is good, wrath without bitterness. Wicked anger is either sudden or premeditated; the latter is the worse. Malice aforethought chases the Holy Ghost out of the soul. It is the devil's furnace and heats hatred, manslaughter, treachery, lies, flattery, scorn, discord, menaces and curses. The remedy for Anger is Patience.*

Accidie *does all tasks with vexation, slackly and without joy, and is encumbered by doing good. It restrains one from prayer. It is the rotten-hearted sin of Sloth. It leads to despair. The remedy is Fortitude.*

Avarice *is a lecherous desire for earthly things, a kind of idolatry. Every florin in one's coffer is a mommet, an idol. It leads to feudal extortions by lords from their villeins, to fraud, to simony, gambling, theft, false-witness, sacrilege. The remedy is Mercy or 'pity largely taken.'*

Gluttony *is an immeasurable appetite to eat or drink. Drunkenness is the horrible sepulcher of man's reason. The remedy is Abstinence, Temperance and Sobriety.*

Lechery *is near cousin to Gluttony. It has many forms and is the greatest sin of theft there is, for it steals body and soul. The remedy is Chastity and Continence, and not to eat or drink too much. When the pot boils strongly the best remedy is to withdraw the fire.*

Confession *must be freely willed and made in full faith. A man must only confess his own sins, and truthfully with his own mouth, not paint them with subtle words. It must be a considered, not a hasty act, and frequent.*

Satisfaction *consists generally in alms-giving, penance, fasting and bodily pains. Its fruit is endless bliss in Heaven.*

Chaucer's Retractions

The Maker of this Book here takes his Leave

Now I beg all those that listen to this little treatise, or read it, that, if there be anything in it that pleases them, they thank our Lord Jesu Christ for it, from whom proceeds all understanding and goodness.

And if there be anything that displeases them, I beg them also to impute it to the fault of my want of ability, and not to my will, who would very gladly have said better if I had had the power. For our Book says 'all that is written is written for our doctrine'; and that is my intention. Wherefore I beseech you meekly for the mercy of God to pray for me, that Christ have mercy on me and forgive me my sins: and especially for my translations and inditings of worldly vanities, which I revoke in my retractions: as are the book of *Troilus*;* also the book of *Fame*; the book of *The Nineteen Ladies*; the book of *The Duchess*; the book of *St Valentine's Day of the Parliament of Fowls*; *The Tales of Canterbury*, those that tend towards sin; the book of *The Lion*; and many another book, if they were in my memory; and many a song and many a lecherous lay; that Christ in his great mercy forgive me the sin.

But the translation of Boethius *De Consolatione*, and other books of Saints' legends, of homilies, and morality and devotion, for them I thank our Lord Jesu Christ and His blissful Mother, and all the Saints of Heaven; beseeching them that they henceforth, to my life's end, send me grace to bewail my sins and to study the salvation of my soul; and grant me the grace of true penitence, confession and satisfaction, that I may perform them in this present life, through the benign grace of Him that is King of kings and Priest over all priests, who bought us with the precious blood of His heart; so that I may be one of those that at the Day of Judgment shall be saved. *Qui cum Patre,* etc.

Here ends the book of the *Tales of Canterbury* compiled by Geoffrey Chaucer, on whose soul Jesu Christ have mercy.
                                                                Amen.

NOTES

IN preparing this translation I have used the texts as they appear in the standard editions by W. W. Skeat in seven volumes (Oxford 1894–7) and by F. N. Robinson in one volume (Cambridge, Mass., 1933; also Oxford). The texts in these two editions are naturally not identical. I have generally referred to both, and where there seemed to be a discrepancy that could affect a translation I have made my own choice. I have followed the order of the tales as it is given by Skeat rather than that given by Robinson.

The notes which follow derive very largely from both these authorities and from other works of reference I have from time to time consulted. They correspond to the asterisks in the text.

25 *Martyr.* St Thomas à Becket of Canterbury.
26 *The Knight's campaigning.*
   Alexandria. Taken and immediately after abandoned by Pierre de Lusignan, King of Cyprus, in 1365.
   Algeciras. Besieged and taken from the Moorish King of Granada in 1344.
   Ayas in Armenia, taken from the Turks by Pierre de Lusignan in about the year 1367.
   Attalia, on the south coast of Asia Minor, taken by Pierre de Lusignan soon after 1352.
   Tramissene, now called Tlemcen or Tremessen in western Algeria.
   Balat is a conjecture for the original *Palatye* and occupies the former site of Miletus.
29 *Gaudies.* Every eleventh bead stands for a *paternoster* and is called a 'gaudy.'
31 *A Limiter.* A begging friar who was granted a district to beg in, to limit his activities.
   Four Orders. The four Orders of mendicant friars, the Dominicans, the Franciscans, the Carmelites and the Austin Friars.
33 *St Paul's.* Lawyers used to meet for consultation at the portico of St Paul's cathedral.
34 *A Franklin.* A class of land-owner, a freeholder, who is also free by birth, but not noble. It is noteworthy that his self-conscious chatter about gentility when he politely interrupts the Squire is rudely interrupted by the Host.
36 *Dry, cold, moist or hot.* A man's body was conceived as being

515

composed of the four elements, earth, water, air and fire in due proportions. *Earth* was thought to be cold and dry, *water* cold and moist, *air* hot and moist, *fire* hot and dry. Diseases were thought to be due to an imbalance in one or more of these qualities. A man's character could be roughly defined by reference to them, and their proportion decided his 'humor', e.g. a *sanguine* man (like the Franklin) was held to be hot and moist, which gave him the character of being a laughing, amorous, high-colored, fleshy, good-natured fellow, with many desires and capacities. A *choleric* man (like the Reeve) was thought to be hot and dry. There were also *melancholy* men (cold and dry) and *phlegmatic* men, cold and moist.

37 *Aesculapius* and the other medical authorities.

Aesculapius, mythical son of Apollo and Coronis, who learnt the art of medicine from Cheiron the Centaur, and whom Zeus struck by lightning for having restored too many people to life. He had a daughter called Hygieia and a temple was built to him, when after death he was deified as the god of medicine, at Epidaurus.

Hippocrates, the most famous physician of antiquity, born at Cos about 460 B.C.

Dioscorides, a Greek physician who lived in Cilicia in the first century A.D., with some of whose opinions Chaucer appears in the *Nun's Priest's Tale* and elsewhere to have been familiar.

Galen, a physician and a voluminous author on medical subjects, born at Pergamus in Mysia, who studied at Smyrna, Corinth and Alexandria and practiced in Rome. Approximate dates A.D. 130–201.

Rhazes, a Spanish Arab doctor of the tenth century.

Hali, Serapion and *Avicenna* were Arabian physicians and astronomers of the tenth and eleventh centuries.

Averroes, a Moorish medical author who lived in Morocco in the twelfth century.

Scotch Bernard. Bernard Gordon, professor of medicine at Montpellier about the year 1300.

John of Gaddesden, a medical authority educated at Merton College, Oxford, who died in 1361.

Gilbertine, supposed to be Gilbertus Magnus, an Englishman who flourished towards the middle of the thirteenth century, wrote books about medicine and is said to have been Chancellor at Montpellier.

41 *A Reeve.* A steward or minor official on an estate, generally an intermediary between a lord and his serfs.

Notes

42 *A Summoner.* One paid to summon sinners to trial before an ecclesiastical court. For further details of his profession see the opening of the *Friar's Tale.*

Cherubinny. In medieval art the Cherubin are generally depicted with flame-colored faces.

Questio quid juris. 'The question is, what is the point in law?'

43 *A Pardoner.* As the name implies, one who has authority (from the Pope) to sell pardons and indulgences, though not necessarily in holy orders.

80 *Dana,* a modernization of the name *Danè* as it is here found in Chaucer. He meant Daphne of course, who, being so inhuman as to flee the embraces of Apollo, was turned into a laurel. Her preserved virginity qualifies her for representation in Diana's temple.

87 *By the three forms:* in Heaven, *Luna.* On earth, *Diana.* In Hell, *Proserpina.* As in Keats' sonnet on *Homer:*
Such seeing hadst thou as it once befell
To Dian, Queen of earth and heaven and hell.

99 *Could not be expelled.* Chaucer is here airing his technical knowledge of contemporary physiology. Three forces or 'virtues' were believed to control the life in a human body: the 'animal' virtues in the brain, the 'natural' in the liver, and the 'vital' in the heart. The 'animal' controlled all muscles, and therefore should have been able to expel the poison from Arcita's liver. But he was too far gone.

109 *A voice like Pilate's.* Miracle plays represented Herod and Pilate as huffing roarers and braggarts. Their lines generally carry heavy alliteration.

116 *Money.* More useful in a town than in the country, where there are fewer things to buy.

119 *Him that harrowed Hell.* When Christ descended into Hell He led away therefrom Adam, Eve, the Patriarchs, St John the Baptist and others, redeemed and at last released. This act was commonly called 'The harrowing of Hell' in the middle ages and was the subject of several miracle-plays. The original story comes from the *Gospel of Nicodemus* in the Apocryphal New Testament.

132 *Solar Hall.* So called because of its large sunny windows. Its official name was King's Hall, having been founded by Edward III. Later it was merged in what is now called Trinity College.

133 *And how's your canny daughter?* In Chaucer's original the two young northerners from Strother, Alan and John, are made to talk in northern dialect and idiom, for instance,

the forms *swa* for *so, bathe* for *both, raa* for a *roe* are used by them. So far as I know this is the first time dialect occurs for comic effect in English fiction. As a page to the Duchess of Clarence, Chaucer would have spent time in Yorkshire (at Hatfield), and he may have picked up the peculiarities of northern speech there and then. I have attempted to reproduce this peculiarity with the help of Mr H. S. Taylor of Exeter College, Oxford, and Mr J. D. O'Connor, of the Department of Phonetics, University College, London, who have been so kind as to suggest such northern forms as I have used, e.g. *wor* for *our. Canny* here represents *faire* in the original. I am told that in Durham they say *canny* when they mean fair, pretty or attractive.

140 *Bromeholme*. A piece of wood, said to be of the true cross, known as the Rood of Bromeholme, much venerated in Norfolk.

142 *Jack of Dover*. The authorities disagree as to what this expression means. Some think it is a fish, others that it is a pie that has been cooked, allowed to cool, and then has been cooked again to freshen it up when rather stale.

144 *Led with minstrelsy to jail*. Skeat notes that in those days when disorderly persons were carried to prison they were preceded *by minstrels,* in order to call public attention to their disgrace.

145 *Artificial day,* that is, from dawn to sunset, as opposed to the 'natural day' of twenty-four hours.

146 *Ceix and Halcyon*. Their story occurs in Chaucer's first long original poem, *The Book of the Duchess,* c. 1369.

The Legend of Cupid's Saints. Better known as *The Legend of Good Women,* composed towards 1386 by Chaucer at the command of the Queen in expiation for his supposed defamation of women in the person of *Criseyde* in *Troilus and Criseyde*. The list of these tender creatures as given by the Man of Law does not precisely tally with those whose tales are told in the *Legend,* but is near enough for the Man of Law.

147 *Apollonius*. This horror, whether real or pretended on Chaucer's part, is supposed to be a dig at his friend the poet John Gower, who relates this tale in his *Confessio Amantis*.

Metamorphoses. There is an account in this work of Ovid, Bk. v., where the daughters of Pierus vied with the Muses and were transformed into pies for their presumption.

148 *Double Aces*. There was a game called *Hazard* in which dice

Notes

were thrown. Double-aces was the lowest throw, fives and sixes a high one.

153 *First cause of motion,* etc. Skeat notes that the old, Ptolemaic astronomy supposed the earth stationary and central with nine spheres revolving about it. The seven innermost each carried a planet with it (Moon, Venus, Mercury, Sun, Mars, Jupiter, Saturn). The eighth sphere contained the fixed stars and was believed to have a slow motion from west to east. The ninth and outermost sphere was called the *primum mobile* or sphere of first motion, which was held to make a diurnal revolution from east to west that carried all else with it in the same direction, which is opposite to the 'natural' motion of the sun, which advances along the signs of the zodiac.

154 *Scorpio.* These contrary motions are suggested by Chaucer as the cause of the failure of Constance's marriage because of the evil influence of Mars in *Scorpio,* which is the house of death, battle, travail and harm.

155 *O serpent masked in femininity.* Medieval poets and illuminators constantly represent Satan in Eden as a snake with a woman's face.

159 *St Mary the Egyptian.* It is said that this St Mary, whose day is April 9th, was in early life loose in her morals, but being converted, fled into the desert and lived forty-seven years there, beyond Jordan. She belongs to the fifth century.

179 *Johnny.* Sir John was a common name for a priest; *Lollards* were the strict but heretical followers of Wycliffe.

Phislyas. This word or, as it appears in some MSS., *phillyas,* is thought by Skeat to be a corruption of some technical word in philosophy. It may be so, but perhaps the word is a deliberate piece of nonsense to underline the unlearnedness of the Skipper.

180 *He has to clothe us.* It is obvious that this passage was meant for a woman speaker, presumably the Wife of Bath. It is likely that Chaucer had at first designed the tale for her, then changed his mind (having found one that suited her even better) and unloaded this one on the Skipper without remembering these tell-tale lines.

185 *Ganelon of France.* The villain of the *Chanson de Roland* that betrayed Roland and Oliver who, with Archbishop Turpin, formed Charlemagne's rearguard at Roncesvalles against the Moors. Ganelon was torn asunder by four horses.

186 *Two in twelve.* The MSS. differ as to the proportion; some say ten in twelve, some twelve in twenty.

Notes

191 *Tally*. Paying by tally was a common though often unreliable
method of buying on credit in the middle ages. A stick
was notched with notches to the amount owed and then
split. Vendor and purchaser each retained half. When pay-
day came the sticks were compared to see if they 'tallied.'
If they did the sum due was clear.

192 *Corpus Dominus*. The Host was no Latinist. He meant
corpus Domini, the body of our Lord. He makes the same
blunder later on.

221 *Zenobia* flourished A.D. 264 as Queen of Palmyra and was
married to Odenathus, a Bedouin. Recognized by the
Emperor Gallienus, she was attacked and defeated and led
in triumph by the Emperor Aurelian, but survived to live
in comfort.

225 *King Peter of Spain*. Skeat notes: 'He reigned over Castille
and Leon from 1350 to 1362 and his conduct was marked
by numerous acts of unprincipled atrocity.' There was a
quarrel with his brother Enrique who stabbed him to the
heart. This is the murder here lamented, though, if Skeat's
view be accepted, it was no great loss. Chaucer takes his
part because the Black Prince fought on his side against
Enrique at the battle of Najera, 1367.

Upon an argent field. The second stanza of this 'tragedy' is
written as a sort of heraldic riddle intermixed with puns.
The arms described (argent, a double-headed eagle sable,
displayed, debruised by a bend gules) are those of Bertrand
Du Guesclin who 'brewed' the treason by luring King
Peter into his brother's tent. The 'wicked nest' is a pun
on the name of Sir Oliver Mauny (*Mau* is Old French for
wicked, *nid* for *nest*), who was an accomplice, according to
Chaucer. Chaucer continues that this was not such an
Oliver as that in the *Chanson de Roland*, loyal soldier of
Charlemagne, but much more like Ganelon (the villain of
the *Chanson*).

I suppose this emblematic way of expressing what occurred would have been easily intelligible to Chaucer's
first audiences, but can see no way of translating it so as to
seem so to the modern reader without adding this long
note.

King Peter of Cyprus. Pierre de Lusignan, ascended to the
throne of Cyprus in 1352 and was assassinated in 1369.
Chaucer's Knight seems to have seen service with him.

Bernabo Visconti, Duke of Milan, was deposed and died in
prison in 1385. Chaucer knew him personally, though this
does not show from what the Monk has to say. He went

Notes

on the King's business to treat with him in 1378. The death of Bernabo is the most recent historical event mentioned in the *Canterbury Tales*.

227 *Dante*. See *Inferno* xxxii–xxxiii.

230–231 *Holofernes* and *Antiochus*. For both of these see the *Book of Judith* and *2 Maccabees* ix in the *Apocrypha*.

232 *Alexander of Macedon*, the Great, 356–323 B.C. His dazzling career, high intelligence and astounding magnanimity made him a legendary ideal of knightly soldiership in the middle ages.

233 *Aces*. The lowest possible throw of the dice in the game of *Hazard*.

234 *Brutus Cassius*. Chaucer supposed these two famous assassins to be one and the same.

239 *The equinoctial wheel*. I quote from Professor Robinson: 'A great circle of the heavens in the plane of the equator. According to the old astronomy it made a complete daily revolution so that 15 degrees would "ascend" every hour.' It was a popular belief in the time of Chaucer that cocks crew punctually on the hour.

240 *My Love is far from land*. The original, probably the refrain of a popular song, reads 'my lief is faren in londe' and means 'my love has gone away into foreign parts' but I could not resist the allusion to a song of our own, 'She is far from the land where her young hero sleeps.'

249 *Greek Sinon*. The Greek who tricked King Priam into admitting the Trojan Horse to Troy.

Bishop Bradwardine, a famous contemporary theologian. Proctor of Oxford University in 1325, and later Professor of Divinity and Chancellor.

Boethius, author of *De Consolatione Philosophiae* which Chaucer translated, was esteemed not only as a philosopher but also as a musician. In the fifth book of his great work there is a long argument on the subject of Predestination and Free Will on which Chaucer many times pondered and drew as a writer. He was a very learned poet, but carried his learning lightly. Boethius lived c. A.D. 470–525.

250 *Physiologus*. I quote from Tyrwhitt, 'a book in Latin metre entitled *Physiologus de Naturis xii Animalium*, by one Theobaldus, whose age is not known. The Chapter *De Sirenis* begins thus:

Sirenae sunt monstra maris resonantia magnis vocibus, etc.'

251 *Burnel the Ass*. A poem by Nigel Wireker of the twelfth cen-

Notes

tury. The tale alluded to is that of a priest's son who broke a rooster's leg by throwing a stone at it. In revenge the bird declined to crow in the morning on the day when the priest was to be ordained and receive a benefice, so the priest failed to wake up in time and being late for the ceremony lost his preferment.

252 *Geoffrey* is Geoffrey de Vinsauf, an author on the art of Rhetoric who flourished in the twelfth century. In his work *De Nova Poetria* there is an intricate passage about the death of Richard Cœur de Lion to exhibit the art of apostrophe and playing upon words. Fridays come in for ingenious abuse. Chaucer, who derived a great deal of his stylistic manner from a sane use of the rules of rhetoric as laid down by his 'dear and sovereign master,' is here poking gentle fun at him. It may be observed that the whole of the *Nun's Priest's Tale* is a farrago of rhetorical fireworks which must have made the poem far funnier to the fourteenth century, trained in such matters, than it is to us. I suppose a fair comparison would be between the delight taken in Pope's *Rape of the Lock* by a reader who knew the *Aeneid* and the delight taken in it by one who did not. The penalties of barbarism are heavy.

253 *Jack Straw* was one of the leaders of the riots in London during the Peasants' Revolt of 1381, according to Walsingham's Chronicle. He and his gang massacred a number of Flemings in the Vintry, and he was later captured and decapitated.

271 *In neighboring regions.* There were regulations against the mixture of wines. Lepé wine is light by nature, but may have been fortified with spirit for export. He is ironically suggesting that – as one cannot, of course, suspect an honest Fish Street vintner of deliberately mixing his wines – one can only suppose the mixture to occur spontaneously, thanks to the geographical proximity of Spain and France! I am told by Mr Warner Allen that this seems the first mention of the practice of fortifying wines that he has come upon in his researches.

273 *Hailes.* In Gloucestershire; the abbey ruins can still be seen. It formerly possessed a phial of Christ's blood; later publicly destroyed at St Paul's Cross by order of Henry VIII.

280 *Avicenna.* An Arabian physician (A.D. 980–1037) who wrote a work on medicines that includes a chapter on poisons.

287 *Ptolemy.* Claudius Ptolemaeus, an astronomer of the second

Notes

century whose chief work was known as his *Almagest,* an Arabic corruption of its title in Greek. His astronomical theories are those on which all medieval astronomy was based. His general wisdom also was proverbial.

288 *Dunmow.* The prize of a flitch of bacon for the married pair that have had fewest disputes during the previous year is still annually offered at Dunmow.

292 *Three misfortunes.* She is alluding to Proverbs xxx, 21–3. 'For three things the earth is disquieted, and for four which it cannot bear; for a servant when he reigneth; and a fool when he is filled with meat; for an odious woman when she is married; and an handmaid that is heir to her mistress.'

300 *Theophrastus and Valerius.* A work attributed to Walter Map, a wit and cynic who flourished about A.D. 1200. The subject of the work here referred to is *De non ducenda uxore,* a satire on matrimony.

301 *Children of Mercury.* Learning was held to be under the protection of Mercury; his 'children' are scholars, who in those days were generally celibate.

302 *Pasiphaë.* Wife of Minos, King of Crete. She fell in love with a white bull and became the mother of the Minotaur, half-man, half-bull.

310 *Sovereignty.* To realize the full force of the Knight's answer it may help to glance at the Introduction, p. 10–11.

329 *Trentals.* An office of thirty masses for the souls of those in Purgatory. The gibe about their being 'very quickly sung' a few lines later refers to the official view that the soul in question could not be released until the whole thirty had been sung. Thus it was held reasonable and charitable to sing them one after another, all on the same day if possible, so as not to keep the soul lingering in Purgatory longer than was necessary. Those who sang these masses were naturally paid for their work.

Qui cum Patre. The conventional close of a sermon, 'Who with the Father,' etc.

332 *Jubilee.* After serving fifty years in a Convent friars were permitted to go about alone.

334 *Cor meum eructavit.* The opening words of Psalm xlv, 'My heart is inditing of a good matter,' which less poetically rendered could mean, 'My heart is belching a good matter.'

345 *Petrarch.* Francesco Petrarca (1304–74), the Italian poet and humanist, crowned poet laureate at Rome in 1341. Among many other more famous literary works he translated the

Notes

story of Griselda into Latin from Boccaccio's *Decameron*, and it is from this translation that Chaucer seems to have taken his matter for the *Clerk's Tale*. Some have thought that this passage is autobiographical and that Chaucer himself met Petrarch in Italy in 1372, and got the story from him then. More recent scholarship has cast grave doubt on this.

Lynian. Giovanni di Legnano, Professor of Law at Bologna, 1363, died 1383. Wrote tractates on war and on astrology.

378 *Chaucer's Envoy*. This send-off to the tale of Griselda is in Chaucer's most mature vein of playful irony. It is also one of his trickiest miracles of rhyming. It is conjectured that the tale of Griselda was written long before he ever thought of the *Canterbury Tales* as such; stylistically it seems to me more skillful than the *Second Nun's Tale* (perhaps his first effort at telling a story) and less skillful than the *Man of Law's*. All three are of a pious or moral cast, and all three are in 'rhyme royal' stanza form. *Troilus and Criseyde* is also in this stanza form, but is far more mature in style. It would seem that in later life Chaucer, while wishing to include his earlier tale of Griselda among the *Canterbury Tales*, felt it needed a touch of irony to mitigate its doormat morality for wives. In four manuscripts the *Clerk's Tale* ends two stanzas before Chaucer's *Envoy*, and it is followed by a genuine, but ultimately rejected stanza that may be rendered as follows:

Now when this worthy clerk had told his tale
Our Host swore heartily, 'God's bones, that's good!
It would be better than a barrel of ale
To have had my wife to hear that tale, it would.
Well, it was noble and there's much I could
Have got from it if you but knew, say I.
What can't be done, however, best not try.'

On consideration, however, Chaucer seems to have transferred the Host's comment about his wife and the barrel of ale to the colloquy after Chaucer's *Tale of Melibee*, and to have indulged an ironical flight of his maturer fancy by adding the *Envoy* which follows the *Clerk's Tale*, and the two preceding verses which (in this version) begin:

But one word more, my lords, before I go.

These and the *Envoy* are in his most skillful and experienced manner; there isn't a line of padding in them and the dexterity of his rhymes is a miracle. I have attempted

PAGE

to reproduce it, but if I may again quote from my version of the *Clerk's Tale,*

> This world of ours, it has to be confessed,
> Is not so sturdy as it was of old.

379 *Chichevache.* In an old French fable there were two cows called Chichevache and Bicorne. Bicorne was fat because she made her diet on patient husbands who were in plentiful supply. But the monster Chichevache was thin, for her diet was only patient wives, poor cow.

385 *The Boat of Wade.* Wade was a hero of Anglo-Saxon antiquity to whom there are several scattered references outside Chaucer, but nothing is now known about this subtle boat of his except that its name was *Guingelot.*

407 *Jesus son of Sirach.* The supposed author of *Ecclesiasticus.*

413 *Cambuskan.* I have adopted Milton's spelling for this name from his famous praise of the tale in *Il Penseroso.* Skeat notes that the name in Chaucer (Cambinskan) was intended by him for the name more familiar to us of Genghis Khan, though the account here given of him suits his grandson Kublai Khan better.

415 *Gawain.* A knight of the Round Table, distinguished, though not specially so in Malory, for his extreme courtesy. A noble alliterative romance, contemporary with Chaucer, describes his adventures with a Green Knight of magical powers in whose castle Gawain was staying. The Green Knight's lady makes love to Gawain and he is in a cleft stick, for it would seem as discourteous to refuse her as to cuckold his host. Gawain's perfect manners, however, are equal to the occasion and he offends neither.

419 *Alhazen and Witelo.* Alhazen was an Arabian astronomer who died A.D. 1039. Witelo was a Polish mathematician of the thirteenth century.

420 *Aldiran.* The name of a star in the constellation of *Leo,* identified by Skeat as the star θ Hydrae.

426 *A pup.* The proverb here referred to is 'Beat the dog before the lion,' meaning that if you chastise a smaller creature in sight of a larger, the larger will take warning. One can see the application of this in the political field. Repress a minor rebel and a greater enemy may think twice before attacking.

A tercelet. The technical term for a male falcon or hawk.

430 *Velvet blue.* Blue for Chaucer's age was the color of constancy in love and green of lightness in love. This is echoed in *'Greensleeves is my delight'* and elsewhere. The fickle

birds were depicted on the outside to imply that such could never enter *within* the mew, where all was constancy. So in the *Roman de la Rose,* the walls of the garden of love are decorated *on the outside* with the figures of poverty, old age, hypocrisy, etc., which are never to be admitted in the land of true love.

433 *Cithero.* He means Cicero, of course, famous for all the 'figures' and 'colors' of rhetoric. These are technical names for various known devices of style, such as those referred to towards the end of the *Nun's Priest's Tale.*

438 *Without cup.* The sense of this proverbial phrase is that he drank misery straight from the cask and not in small portions, cup by cup.

443 *Pamphilus for Galatea.* This is not an error for Pygmalion and Galatea but refers according to Skeat to a long poem in barbarous Latin by one Pamphilus, declaring his love.

448 *Alnath.* The name still of a star of first magnitude known to astronomers as α Arietis. Chaucer was himself a considerable astronomer and wrote a treatise on the Astrolabe. The whole of this passage about the magician's calculations is highly technical and exact. Being no astronomer myself I have translated it with as much understanding as I could bring to bear on it, with frequent recourse to the full notes on pages 393–5 of the fifth volume of Skeat's large edition of Chaucer's works. Those interested in medieval science may there learn the astounding complexity of detail which underlies the bland verses of Chaucer, though he appears to assume that his readers will take it all for granted. The Franklin has just said that he 'lacks the jargon of astrology' ('I can no termes of astrologye') but all the same he makes no blunders, it seems. I hope I have been able to follow his example.

450 *Phido.* The whole of this speech is a set piece of medieval rhetoric in spite of the Franklin's disclaimer in his Prologue. It begins with the figure of *apostrophe* and passes to a long *digressio* built out of *exempla* from ancient history. All the instances of female fidelity that sprang to Dorigen's mind rose from authentic sources in Chaucer's reading which can be found in the notes to Skeat's or Robinson's edition of his works. On consideration I have thought it would be tedious to repeat them here.

460 The interpretations of the name *Cecilia:* (1) *coeli lilia,* lily of heaven; (2) *caecis via,* the way for the blind; (3) *coelum* (contemplation of Heaven) and Leah (type of the Active Life); (4) *quasi caecitate carens,* 'as if lacking in blindness';

Notes

(5) *coelum* and λεώς, heaven in Latin and people in Greek. Hence a heaven for people to gaze at.

462 *Urban*. Pope Urban I, martyred by beheading 25 May, A.D. 230.

474 *A canon of the church*. I do not know why Chaucer could so certainly infer the man was a canon because his hood and cloak were sewn together. Before the Reformation there were two types of canon, regular canons who lived under one roof, cloistered after the manner of monks, and secular canons who could roam about, after the manner of friars. This canon appears to have been a secular.

479 *Orpiment*. Trisulphide of arsenic. I understand from the historians of medieval science that all the details of alchemical technique described by Chaucer are accurate and reliable in so far as they can be checked. Some have thought they indicate a first-hand knowledge and that the indignation of the canon's yeoman against the frauds practiced in this business reflects a personal indignation of Chaucer's at having been fleeced himself. It may be so, but personally I should have thought he was too fly for any alchemist.

480 *Water in rubefaction*. Two mysterious processes – the rubefaction and albefaction of waters, i.e. reddening and whitening or clarifying a liquid – appear to be an important part in such experiments and are referred to in medieval textbooks of alchemy. For instance there is what Skeat calls 'a long and unintelligible passage about *rubrificatio*' in the *Theatrum Chemicum* printed in 1659. Alchemy dragged on into the eighteenth century.

Realgar. Disulphide of arsenic.

Citrination. Turning yellow. It was part of the theory that when the ingredients began to turn yellow they were on the verge of becoming the Philosopher's Stone, by which all could be turned to gold. The Philosopher's Stone was held to be heavy, sweet-smelling, constant and pink, and to exist in powder form as well; as in this tale.

497 *Arnold*. Arnoldus de Villa Nova, a French physician, theologian, astrologer, and alchemist who lived between 1235 and 1314. He wrote the treatise on alchemy mentioned in the next line. I cannot pretend to explain more of what is said of 'the dragon and his brother' than appears in the text.

498 *Chimica Senioris Zadith Tabula*. Printed in the *Theatrum Chemicum* (1659). The anecdote here attributed to Plato appears there attributed to Solomon.

Notes

Ignotum per ignotius. Literally 'an unknown thing (explained by) a more unknown thing.'

499 *Dun's in the mire.* An allusion to a parlor game. A large log is brought into the parlor, and placed centrally. The cry goes up 'Dun's in the mire!' (i.e. the dun horse is stuck in the mud). Two of the company then try to drag it out; if they fail, others join them one by one. This makes for agreeable scrimmages.

509 *Divided in like pattern proportionally.* In the original the phrase seems also somewhat roundabout. What Chaucer means is that his height is to his shadow as six is to eleven.

Saturn. According to Skeat's note the original, which names the exaltation of the moon as identified with *Libra,* is a mistake on the part of Chaucer or one of his scribes for the exaltation of Saturn. I have therefore followed Skeat rather than Chaucer at this point.

510 *Rum-ram-ruf by letter.* The Parson disclaims the power to tell a romance in the alliterative style of composition common at the time. *Sir Gawain and the Green Knight,* already mentioned in these notes (page 415), would be an example of one.

513 *Troilus.* For a brief account of most of the works here mentioned by Chaucer see the Introduction (page 9). The book of *The Lion* has been lost, but it is conjectured to be a translation from the French of Machault, a work called *Le Dit du Lion,* composed in 1342.

THE PENGUIN CLASSICS
(*Continued from back cover*)